ROAD WORK AHEAD

ONE FAMILY'S JOURNEY THROUGH TRAUMATIC BRAIN INJURY

BY
IRA R. ADLER

Copyright © 2014 by Adler, Ira R.

All rights reserved. No part of this publication may be reproduced, distributed or transmitted in any form or by any means (electronically or mechanically), or stored in a database or retrieval system, without the prior written permission of the author.

ISBN: 978-0-692-25009-9

Printed in the United States of America

Contact Information

The author may be reached by email at
adlerir.az@gmail.com.

For Michael, with love.

Contents

Acknowledgments

This book would not have been written without the encouragement and support of the many friends who helped our family through the experiences and events described herein. I will never be able to adequately express the gratitude I feel toward the doctors, nurses, and therapists of Denver Health Medical Center and Craig Hospital as well as the emergency technicians of the Denver Fire Department whose dedication and skills not only saved my son's life but also gave me great comfort in the darkest times.

I am particularly grateful to Judy Lefton and Lanie Constable for their comments and advice on an early manuscript and continual interest in this project. I also thank my friends, classmates and professors in the Psychology and Philosophy departments of the University of Arizona who have imbued me with a greatly expanded understanding of how our brains work, what makes up our cognitive processes and how we come to be who we are.

My deepest gratitude goes to Dana, Michael and Darcy, without whom I could not have endured this journey and whose love is my greatest motivation every day.

ROAD WORK AHEAD
ONE FAMILY'S JOURNEY THROUGH TBI

Preface

On June 2, 2006, my wife and I were awakened by a phone call informing us that our son had been in a serious car accident. The voice on the other end of the line told us that Michael was in the Emergency Department of Denver Health Medical Center with a life-threatening injury to his head.

We are not the first parents to receive such horrific news nor will we be the last. The events which transpired following that fateful call have taken, and are still taking, our family on a journey which contains all the elements of good drama – an emotional roller coaster of fear and hope, an exploration of science and medicine, occasional comic relief, and an inward expedition testing the strength of our long-held beliefs and faiths.

Each of us has suffered our own consequences. While Michael was the primary patient and lead character in this drama, my wife Dana, our daughter Darcy, and I experienced pain, rehabilitation and recovery as well. But the effects were not limited to family members. Many of Michael's friends were also affected. Each of us has part of ourselves in this accident but, more importantly, each of us has uncovered new strengths which lay dormant before they were summoned up to help us face the challenges of Michael's prolonged hospitalization and recuperation.

Our story... what happened and how we were affected... is meant to be shared with families who may be facing similar circumstances and with others who believe, perhaps naively, that this will never happen to their family. The specifics of our story are unique to us, but the lessons we have learned are applicable to people faced first with the surreal horror, and then with the reality, of Traumatic Brain Injury (TBI).

Our family's story, which continues today, comes out well. Not all do. We sincerely believe that, if you find yourself confronted by similar challenges, which seem unfathomable and insurmountable, you will discover that your inner strength to overcome those challenges is deeper and stronger than you ever could have imagined. May you also discover that your own strength is reinforced by the support of your extended families and communities.

Book One
Trauma

Prologue

We are all familiar with the old saying: *In an instant, life can change forever*. But, in fact, life changes with each moment lived. We move forward, never to return to experience how things were before. Each day of our existence is filled with new events, new observations, and new feelings. Like the quantum physicist who insists that a particle's movement is affected by the simple fact that it has been observed, each of our moments is affected by the simple fact that it is a ***new*** moment, which follows from the immediately ***prior*** moment linking us inevitably to the ***next*** moment. But each new moment comes with a new memory and a newly revised expectation of the future.

Before the accident, life was going very well indeed. Before the accident, I awoke to each day with the expectation of well-being. I had worked to become financially secure, succeeded just enough to retire at an early age and was satisfied with my role as husband, father and provider. My relationship with my wife was strong and loving. We were happy "empty nesters"... our children had departed our home to go to college, were on the verge of adulthood and moving past their childhood dependencies. We didn't deliberately think each day about the state of our children's health nor did we harbor any anxieties that they would not be in good health, safe and secure, as they had been the day before. Their futures looked to be well-assured. This seemed like a safe assumption.

Following the accident, when I wake up each morning, after first shaking out the cobwebs to experience yet another day, one of my very first conscious thoughts is, "I hope that both of our children are going to be safe today." The fear that another accident might bring harm to them is still palpable. Now my days never start without at least a hint of sadness. I still feel some anxiety, too. I worry about the worst. And my hopes and dreams for their futures are colored by the events which have transpired since the accident. Today, the ground beneath my feet is not quite as firm as it once was. Each day I try to cope with the consequences of that one event, that one day, June 2, 2006, and all that has followed.

Most of us maneuver and pick our way through life, the ever-changing landscape of experience. Whether events are pre-ordained or chance occurrences, we ride along our lives, like driving down a superhighway with many curves and bends. Which road will take us to our destination we can't know in advance.

Our lives are filled with obstacles, twists and turns. There is always road work ahead. We react to the small events of our days like insignificant bumps in the road. As we ride along, we may experience inconsequential, unnoticed cracks in the pavement, imperfections to which we respond with almost imperceptible course adjustments. Our cognitive responses to the familiar are like shock absorbers, smoothing our ride. And, then, without warning, we may hit a pothole or speed bump which throws us out of our seats and fills us with an unexpected adrenaline rush. Our equilibrium, like a car's suspension, may be thrown out of alignment. If the road is filled with large impediments, anticipated or not, we may bemoan the state of the roadway and ask: *When will they ever clear these rocks? When will the necessary road work here be completed? Will this road ever be paved smooth again?* We experience detours and delays caused by events or people like flagmen holding up traffic for what seems like an interminable amount of time and we try to maneuver around these obstacles.

But what if the pothole is really a sinkhole? What if the road ahead is not under construction, but closed to all traffic permanently? Can the vehicle be righted? Will the car function properly after repairs are made? Will it retain its value despite spending extended time in the shop? Will we ever reach our intended destination?

Faced with the challenges life throws in our path, we learn that not all movement or experience is necessarily progress. Our personal lives are affected by changes in course every minute of every day and we chart new directions at every turn. Sometimes we awaken to new obstacles and challenges which seem insurmountable. Yet we find that we still continue forward. And, sometimes, just sometimes, we find ways to overcome even the most formidable of obstacles which come between us and our life's purpose.

In that first moment, when we received the call from Denver, my wife and I didn't know that our lives had been irrevocably altered. Our long-enjoyed sense of well-being ended abruptly at that moment; life's journey took us on a sharp detour onto a very dark and bumpy road littered with many unforeseen obstacles.

Some say that the purpose of life "...is not the destination, but the journey itself." What they don't say is that the journey is neither always easy nor the destination always happy. Sometimes shit does happen ... and sometimes shit happens to you, and not just to the other guy.

This time it happened to our son, Michael.

Michael Alan Adler was born to Dana and Ira Adler in Denver, Colorado, on November 15, 1983.

Michael, as his mother likes to call him, arrived at St. Luke's Hospital in the early morning hours. He was delivered by caesarean delivery, some 22 hours after Dana's first signs of labor. Twenty hours after we arrived at the hospital, the doctors finally conceded that a natural birth was not likely. Sedated and sleeping, worn out from the extended labor, Dana gave birth to our son. Initially, Michael's shoulders were perpendicular to the incision in Dana's abdomen. As the doctors lifted his head, stretching his neck so that he looked like a newly born nestling reaching for his first feeding, his body refused to emerge. After being rotated *in utero* and lifted from Dana's womb, I heard the doctor declare, "It's a boy!" I stood looking through the glass window pane between me and the interior of the operating room. Seeing our son for the first time, I almost swooned to the floor with joyous excitement. Yet, only a minute or two later, the doctor handed Michael to me. Then, as I carried our new son in my hands from the delivery room to the neonatal nursery, I performed a superficial audit. Counting all ten of his fingers and all ten of his toes, two ears and two eyes, I declared to myself, "He's perfect." Never before had I felt quite as elated as when I looked down into his blue eyes and saw those glowing jewels looking up at me. I will always remember that feeling ... of floating down the hallway with the greatest joy and excitement. At that moment, all things were possible and his potential infinite.

Two days later, we brought Mike, which is what I like to call him, to our home in Arvada, Colorado. Our family was now complete. Dana, Darcy, our first child, who was four years old at the time, Mike and me. In accordance with our religious custom, we held a Brit Milah to formally name our son Moshe ben Yitzhak, Mike's Jewish name, at our home eight days following his birth. As is customary, many family and friends traveled to Denver to share in this celebration despite a driving snowstorm.

Baby Michael had wispy strands of blond hair which hung in his clear blue eyes. He enjoyed the adoration of his sister, his mother and me. He was a good baby with the normal amount of giggles, coos and some tears, and rarely got sick.

There was little exceptional about the child-rearing years which followed. Dana cared for Darcy and Michael while I focused on my career. Back then, in 1983, I was a typical, aspiring-to-management financial analyst at US WEST, the soon-to-be incorporated "Baby Bell." My days were occupied with analyzing business plans and projecting financial statements for the many new ventures which were formed as US WEST subsidiaries following the company's court-ordered divestiture from AT&T. Never satisfied to be just a member of the team, I was driven to take on more responsibility and visibility as I hoped to climb up the corporate ladder. Yes, in the days of the early 1980's, the brass ring always seemed to be at the top of the corporate ladder.

To be closer to my office, our family moved to a new home in the Highlands Ranch development on the south side of the Denver Metro area. Our new home was a multi-level affair, with separate bedrooms for each of our kids at the top of the second story landing. Darcy's room was pink and frilly; Mike's baby blue with clouds and balloons adorning his papered walls. Despite being consumed with the work of the newly formed telecom company, I have only happy memories of our young family while we lived in that home in Highlands Ranch.

Our children are separated in age by almost five years, and, as a result, they often had very different activities growing up. Our daughter Darcy attended the Highlands Ranch Elementary School and joined her first swim team – a five year old butterflier. She loved playing with the neighbors' kids and often explored the green belt behind their homes on her bike. Darcy also joined an Olympics of the Mind team, an after-school activity designed to foster intelligence and imagination. She became a cute singing penguin as a result. She loved school and teachers loved her.

As a toddler, Mike was at home with Dana or on play dates with the other children from the neighborhood. One activity stands out in my memory. Mike loved to play with plastic Tupperware, pots and pans in the kitchen cabinets. He was normally curious and looked into every drawer and cabinet he could open, removing their contents, putting them in size order and then crashing them onto the floor, only to rebuild them again.

During the winter months, playtime in Denver was often in snow. Brother and sister would lay on their backs in fresh snow in our front yard. Their little bodies were encased in their bulky snow suits. They waved their arms and opened and closed their legs, making snow angels. If it had snowed enough, they would ride a plastic toboggan, careening down the soft slopes around the back of the home and down the street, and, sometimes, when in a more adventurous mood, down the hills into the common area leading to the Highlands Ranch Recreational Center.

During the summer months, while Darcy was dedicated to swimming, Mike liked to splash about in his wading pool in our back yard. In this otherwise completely normal time, Mike provided a memorable moment. While playing in that shallow pool, he suddenly looked up at Dana, opened his eyes wide, stood up, totally naked, and proceeded to proudly pee on the lawn. He giggled at first, and then the giggle grew to laughter. So hard did he laugh that he had both Dana and me laughing uncontrollably along with him. Mike was gleeful at this unexpected outdoor bodily function.

Mike celebrated his second birthday in this home. I remember his birthday party for the unique glimpse Mike gave us into his own way of thinking. As he sat in his high chair at the kitchen table, he was surrounded by family and neighborhood friends, both children and adults. Suddenly, he stopped laughing and chattering. Instead, he stared ahead vacantly as if hypnotized by his own thoughts. All of us gathered around him with very concerned looks on our faces. Cagily, he just kept staring; the only movement was his little body breathing in and out. Finally, after several long minutes of keeping everyone transfixed on him, he shook himself out of his apparent trance, shouted "Happy Buh-thday, Happy Buh-thday" and, delighted by everyone's surprise, laughed gleefully. He loved that he could capture everyone's attention in this way and shouted his joy. I wondered where he had gone during his brief séance within himself. I noticed that he often got lost in his own thoughts as he investigated the world around him.

Then, when Mike was two years and six months old, I took a new job in Tucson, Arizona. I moved from Denver in June and the family joined me in August. Our first home in Tucson was a rented home and, after six months in Tucson, we decided to build our own small home just down the street from the rental unit.

Both Michael and Darcy thrived in this home... with a climbing fort out back, a basketball hoop in the driveway and a family pet, a golden retriever named Rusty. Darcy (and Dana) would host Brownie and then Girl Scout meetings in our family room, while Michael played on bunk beds in his room. These walls were decorated with murals of painted dinosaurs.

Tucson was ideal for Darcy to pursue competitive swimming. She was a star swimmer, one of the fastest swimmers in her age group not only in Tucson, but the entire United States! There was never a time growing up when she wasn't involved with a competitive swim team. Indeed, my memories of her childhood years are mostly of watching her in the pool. She was among the fastest "under 12" swimmers in the country! The sport carried her through her teenage and young adult (college) years. Dana, too, was deeply involved with Darcy's swimming: learning to be a stroke and turn judge and, as a parent volunteer, helping to run

Michael at Disneyland

the local swim club. I was proud to be known as "Darcy's Dad" in swimming circles. Darcy went on to excel on her high school and college swim teams, culminating in her participation in the U.S. Olympic trials held in Indianapolis in 2000.

As a youngster, Michael also tried swimming... then soccer, then baseball, then tennis, then golf, but he never really connected with any one sport. He did, however, play tennis and ran cross-country for St. Gregory's Middle School. Perhaps he just wasn't meant to be a team sport player. He was more contemplative than physical, skilled but not competitive by nature.

Perhaps he never fully got over a unique episode of ill health which befell him at a young age. When Mike was about eight years old, he started to feel sharp pains in his legs when he walked. As a result, he was unable to run like other children. He hobbled

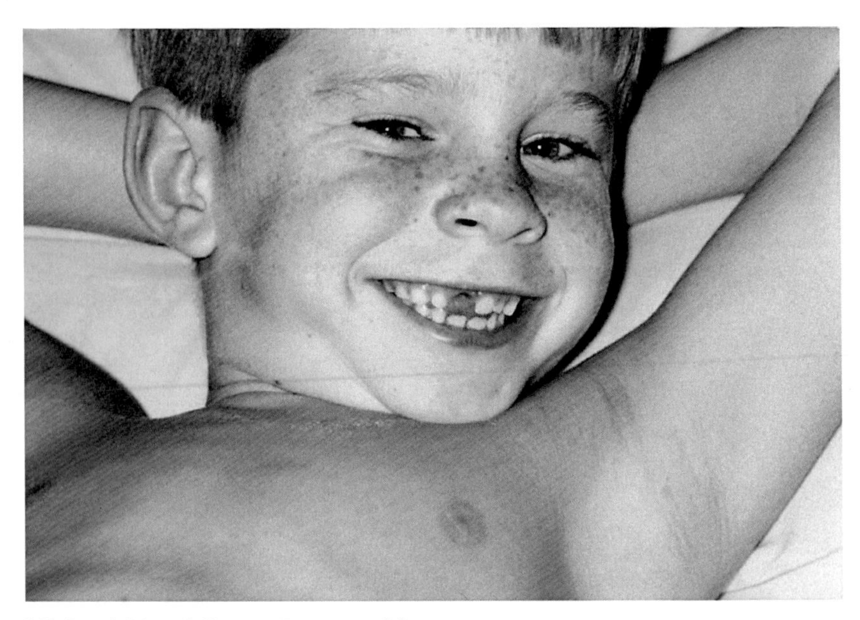

Michael Alan Adler at 5 years old.

unevenly about as if he had some sort of muscular ailment... like multiple sclerosis. But, thank goodness, it turned out not to be some terrible chronic disease. He was diagnosed with Osgood-Schlatter syndrome, an inflammation of the growth plate in the tibia. This condition most often affects active boys 10-14 years old, causing pain in the knee joints. As is often the case with Osgood-Schlatter's, he outgrew the problem within a few months and his motor skills were unaffected. But I sometimes wonder what it must have been like for Michael to be so young and unable to run about with his peers.

My paternal instincts were challenged by the effect of this syndrome on my son. Before he overcame its effects, I feared that Mike would be crippled with this exotic leg ailment permanently. My parental pride couldn't accept that our son's life might be so difficult, so unfair; "After all," I thought, "those afflictions only happened to other families." But, strangely, 16 years later, I had forgotten all about this episode, when I was surprised to learn that Mike hadn't forgotten about it at all. He remembered not only the name of this unusual condition, but also the pain it caused him, both physically and emotionally.

Michael was more interested in activities such as photography and learning. Always a bright child, he liked to learn but not to study. He liked being in school, but not being schooled. He was often "antsy" in class, distracted by others and inattentive to the lessons. Today, one might suggest that he had a learning disability, but, I think, he was just an active boy with an active mind. Quicker on the uptake than others, he easily became bored by the pace of class. As a result, he was, in fact, a bright student who brought home average grades.

For the first four years of our marriage, Darcy was our only child. Then for the next 14 years, our family unit consisted of Dana and me and both Darcy and Michael. Dana gravitated to Darcy's school and athletic activities, while I gravitated to Michael's interests. Then, in 1997, Darcy graduated high school and left home to attend the University of Illinois in Champaign. (During college, she continued to swim competitively and made Dana and me intensely proud parents when she participated in the 2000 Olympic Swimming Trials in Indianapolis and was named female athlete of the year at the University of Illinois. She graduated in 2002 with a degree in Leisure Management.) For the next five

Michael and Darcy sharing a laugh – circa 1988.

Michael, 1996: At age13, Michael read from the Torah on the occasion of his Bar Mitzvah.

years, finishing middle school and high school, Michael would be the "only" child. During this period, Michael and I grew closer as we "men" ganged up on the sole female at home, Dana.

While attending middle school, Michael's intellectual interests were especially stimulated by his Latin class. He became fascinated by classical history and travel. In fact, from his classical language experiences, he adopted a personal theme which has carried over for many years: ***Carpe Diem – Seize the Day***. For a long time, he used this as his identifier on the internet, choosing "CarpeD" as his sign-on.

Also, although he would complain about his English classes, in truth he enjoyed language and literature more than he would admit. Combining English with classical language, he developed a strong vocabulary and often surprised many people with multisyllabic and obscure words sprinkled throughout his daily speech. In high school, Michael participated in theater productions, both as an actor and stage hand, and worked on the high school yearbook as a page designer. He wasn't a joiner of clubs and, thus, had a fairly limited high school extracurricular resume.

Michael possessed a special sensitivity to the world around him and to other people. His sensitivity showed through in his photography. His talent was reflected in his subject matter, the story being told by, not the technical art of, the photo. He would photograph street scenes of people and old buildings. Also, he showed an appreciation for the beauty of nature through close-up photos of the desert vegetation around Tucson. One special photo of our second family pet, a yellow Labrador retriever named MJ (for "Monterey Jack"), won a Tucson photography club contest and Mike was awarded $50 in prize money!

But as much as what Michael liked to do reflected his intelligence, his personality was evidenced more through his relationships. Throughout grade, middle and high schools, Michael was extremely selective in his friendships. His closest friends numbered only two or three at a time, but those that made the cut were always important to him. A loyalist, he tended to stay close to those few friends rather than surround himself with groups or cliques. His first real love relationship with a young lady continued for two years. During his last few years of high school, he also met and became friends with Eric, a wonderfully creative, bright and sensitive young man. Mike and Eric were best buddies and hung out often together. Eric would later play a role in Mike's life following college as well.

As graduation from high school approached, after deciding to eliminate every college and university west of Arizona and most schools east of Arizona, Michael narrowed his search and looked north to the city of his birth, Denver. He applied to and was accepted at the University of Denver, where in 2001, he matriculated as one of about 800 freshmen. DU, as it is called, was a very good fit.

His college experience was filled with new, yet still selective, friendships. After living part of the first year in the requisite freshman dorm with a roommate with whom he was at first pleased to be matched, but then learned to despise for a variety of in-room transgressions (smoking, drinking, sleeping, etc), he moved on to a second dorm. His second roommate's only fault was that he used drugs... a lot. In his sophomore year, Michael moved into the Chi Phi fraternity house, where he hung out with his "brothers". As is common in the Greek scene, the members of the fraternity often drank to excess. They were, in fact, so often drunk out of their minds that Mike, who was relatively conservative, became disenchanted by their tiresome behavior. He moved again, this time to an on-campus apartment for his junior year. His roommate in this living situation reportedly didn't know how to wash dishes or vacuum the floors. Having grown up with Dana and me, Michael preferred orderliness and cleanliness. Then, as a senior, he moved to an off-campus apartment near Kennedy Golf Course, by Parker Road and Hampden in southeast Denver. He roomed with Ashley, a female DU student, and, maintaining a platonic relationship, they got along well for the first six months. However, her even-worse-than-the-prior-roommate's slovenly living habits finally got to him, driving him up the proverbial wall.

Do you discern a pattern here? Mike was a bright young man, thoughtful and caring in many ways, but he always had a low tolerance when it came to others' individual quirks and/or shortcomings. This is meant to be both a compliment (at least he recognized bad behavior for what it is) and a criticism (he was quick to judge and was rarely conciliatory). But, for better or worse, that was who Michael was.

During the first quarter of his junior year, Michael travelled to the University of Bologna (Italy) to study. Dana and I took advantage of his semester abroad and joined him in Bologna at the end of his formal term. We travelled to Cinque Terre, where Michael joined us to celebrate his 21st birthday. We hiked the trails between the five coastal towns and feted his coming of age with dinner at a small bistro in the heart of Verranazza. This was a uniquely happy time for us. After a few days, Dana and I left Italy to return home and Mike climbed aboard a train in Milan for a solo tour of Southern Europe which took him from Switzerland to France and Spain.

Back at the University of Denver, Michael had been drawn to his English classes and decided to major in Creative Writing. He also continued to pursue his love of history, an outgrowth of his interest in Latin back in middle school, earning a History minor. As June 2006 approached, Michael was set to graduate from DU on time (i.e., the four year plan). He intended to take a year off following graduation to work in order to build up some of his own financial resources. Then, he would attend graduate school in 2007 to obtain his Master's degree in English and his teaching certificate. That was the plan!

Along with school, Michael worked during his senior year as a part-time server at the Washington (Wash) Park Grille in order to earn some extra money. It was there that he developed his closest friendships during that last year of school. And, in January of 2006, he moved to his own condominium near the Lowry Town Centre in Denver, Mike's first experience as a homeowner. We, that is, Mike and I, purchased the condo, co-signing the loan. Dave, his best friend, who was also a graduate of DU and a server at the Grille, moved in as his roommate.

The condominium became Mike's and Dave's shared private retreat. They lived and worked closely together for five months as graduation from DU approached. Most of the time, they were inseparable, enjoying the same friends and activities around the restaurant's social scene. They talked about starting up their own restaurant and bar in partnership some day.

At 22 years old, Mike had grown from an adorable, yet impish, small child into a good-looking young man with an engaging, yet still impish, smile and manner. He was successfully completing college, making money working at the Grille, and, in general, was pretty carefree and independent...as were we, his parents. He looked forward to his emancipation from school, from his parents and from all of the encumbrances of childhood. He, like all young adults, anticipated a busy future and solid friendships to help along the way. He had a good job, a nice home to live in and was enjoying a relationship with a new girlfriend. Everything seemed in place for a great year ahead. Indeed, all ***was*** right with his world.

Mike had survived adolescence, high school and, now, the rigors of college. On June 1, 2006, Mike was about to leave the ivy covered haven of his college campus to chart his own course through adulthood. Dana and I were very proud of the man Michael was evolving into. He was very much his own person.

Chapter 1
Commencement

The sun shone brilliantly the morning of June 1, 2006.

Denver was known for its brown cloud caused by auto and other pollutants in the air. But in late spring, Denver's air can be so clear. On those clear days, the sky is always deeply blue, like looking into the waters of a deep and pure lake. The blueness of the sky is partly because of the city's altitude. Mile-high, of course. And, it is partly due to the semi-arid climate, which leaves the air dry, free of water vapors which grey other urban skies.

The air was warm and dry. The summer season seemed to have arrived early this year. On the morning of June 1, Michael Adler awoke from his sleep, instantly alert. His four years of college were almost over. Freedom from the routine of school was finally at hand.

He wouldn't have to wake up early anymore to go to class. In fact, on this night he was going to attend his last seminar class, a graduate level course, ending his four years as an undergraduate at the University of Denver. They had been a good four years, but enough was enough. It was time to move on. To what, when and how were not decided.

Mike had studied diligently in a variety of topics. His degree was going to be a Bachelor of Arts in English, with a History minor. But, in truth, he simply took classes that interested him. Some of these classes may have prepared him for a career, some not. The *History of Rock and Roll* had been a waste of time, but his creative writing classes had been fun. Core classes were just required curricula meant to be endured and attended... to simply get through. Writing was where his attention had been most focused. He loved to write short stories of a personal nature. These tales were not fully autobiographical, but were always strongly influenced by his life experiences. The stories were fiction, often with dark themes... fear, threatening situations, unknown threats lurking just around the next corner or down the next alley. He rarely wrote about having fun, happiness or the beauty of the world around him... unless he was describing a place or time of special memories... like the Greek Islands or Rome, Italy.

But on this day, Thursday, June 1, none of that mattered. Today, all of the studying, test taking and school work would be over and the only thing left to do to obtain his diploma was to complete a few short papers for a couple of graduate level seminars and to walk across the stage at the Commencement ceremony at the end of the following week.

Mike looked forward to Commencement. His parents, grandparents and sister were all planning to come to Denver to share in celebrating his accomplishment and transition from school boy to young adult. He was excited about their visit and, even more so, about his prospects. Mike was particularly looking forward to picking out his graduation present on this day. Dana and I had told him to go out and research the purchase of a new digital camera... his graduation present. He had hinted heavily that he wanted to have a new camera before the Commencement ceremony so that he could take it along to photograph his scheduled post-graduation trip to Panama, Dave's home, with Dave and their two girlfriends.

Mike had surfed about the internet and decided on a really cool Canon digital model which was just coming out. He had decided that a small camera, one which would fit easily in his hand and in the pocket of his cargo shorts, was a better choice than a more cumbersome SLR digital. He had a good eye for photographing people but didn't want to carry around all those extra bulky lenses. He found that he could buy the desired model at Wolf's Camera on Colorado Boulevard. He would travel there today, first thing, to make the purchase.

Then, thinking ahead to later in the day, he was reminded that he had one more seminar class to attend. Afterwards, he would be free to go out and celebrate with his friends. Dave, of course, would join him. Helen, Mike's newest love interest, whom he had met while she worked at the Wash Park Grille as a lounge server, would also be there, as would the two Julia's, and Tim and Liz, whom he had known since his first day on DU's campus, and a host of others. He wanted to have the new camera with him to record the celebration and maybe the last gathering of this group with all of its college camaraderie.

After checking out his email and grabbing a quick bite to eat, Mike, accompanied by Dave, left the third floor condo and walked down the three flights of stairs to the open parking lot. They jumped into Mike's silver 2001 RAV4 Toyota mini-SUV and headed south on Quebec toward Alameda Avenue. Alameda is a parkway lined by beautiful green trees and homes. The two way traffic was separated by a landscaped median, always a pleasant drive, especially in the Spring. After turning there and driving a couple of miles west, he turned south onto busy Colorado Boulevard. A few blocks further to the south and he would be at Wolf's Camera Emporium. Along the way, he and Dave chatted about work at the Grille, ideas for the trip to Panama, and cool cars.

Buying a new digital camera is a major purchase for a 22 year old. Mike had invited Dave along for moral support. They spent nearly every other moment outside of work together, cruising through the good life in Denver, a city made for young adults. Dave had graduated DU the year before with a degree in Hotel, Tourism and Restaurant Management and was then working full time at the restaurant.

They pulled up to Wolf's and jumped out of the car. After only a few minutes browsing the different models, Mike homed in on the targeted model and picked out a few accessories. He charged the purchase on his credit card knowing that the charges would be covered by Dana and me. Then, anxious to try the camera out, they hopped back into the Toyota mini-SUV and headed back to their shared apartment.

Reversing directions, they returned to their condo. They drove north on Colorado Boulevard, past the hotel where his parents, sister and grandparents were going to stay the next weekend when they arrived for Commencement. Mike turned right onto Alameda and headed east toward Quebec. They drove up the hill past the

Greek Orthodox Church on the right. They continued on past the Jewish Federation and the Lutheran Church, also on the right side, and then past the 1950 vintage residences.

Trees along the parkway created a porous canopy of freshly formed green leaves. On this glorious morning, the sun cast its rays through the leaves of the trees lining the street. The light created leopard-like spots on the shaded pavement before them. Having just passed the Orthodox Jewish Synagogue, they turned north onto Quebec and headed towards the Mayfair condominiums next to the Lowry Town Center.

Mike and Dave climbed the three flights of stairs to their condo and entered through the door at the end of the short, but dark hallway. As they looked around their home and at each other, they nodded knowingly. *There's no place like home... especially one made just for the two of them.* As if telepathically, they shared this simultaneous thought.

Michael had a full morning planned. He turned on some tunes from the radio and went to work learning how to best use the new Canon camera. He wanted to become familiar with all the intricacies of his newly acquired photo technology. *That last paper due for his class on the History of Drug Wars could wait until the weekend*, he thought as he downloaded the camera's software to his laptop. *After all, creative writing didn't take research, just creativity.*

The day passed quickly as they hung out in their condo, reading the camera's manual, charging up batteries, adding software to the computer for photo editing, and just chilling out in front of their other new technology purchase...a 32 inch plasma television! Very cool, indeed, for two guys in their early twenties!

By six o'clock that afternoon, Mike had packed up his computer, ready to head to the last class. He placed the new camera in the left pocket of his cargo pants in anticipation of snapping some memories later in the evening following the seminar session. In two hours, classroom time would all be over. College would be behind him. A summer of travelling and working at the Grille lay ahead. He would soon have to decide what to do for a career; but not tonight, not now. Right now he had reached his immediate goal and was about to enjoy the rewards of his efforts.

The class lasted the usual 90 minutes. Professor Arthur Gilbert thanked the class for an engaging evening discussing the drug wars of South America. Surely this was the kind of topic every college graduate could apply in their future endeavors, right? Dr. Gilbert ended the class by congratulating those going on to graduation. Although Professor Gilbert was one of Mike's favorite professors, Mike didn't linger in the classroom; instead he bolted out from Sturm Hall, for the last time as a student, never stopping to look back. He jumped in his small SUV and pulled out his cell phone to text Dave in order to learn which drinking establishment they would head to with the girls tonight. They weren't going to stay at the Grille and just hang out having a few drinks at the bar, not tonight. No, this was the time to celebrate. They deserved a more vibrant location! His phone beeped back and the screen read, "Sing Sing". He drove home, changed clothes, and, once again accompanied by Dave, headed toward Downtown Denver.

Fifteen minutes later he was parked and headed inside the friendly sports bar. Looking across the room, he saw 20 twenty-something's sitting around a couple of tables pushed together to accommodate the crowd. Helen was there. She still had two semesters to go before she got her degree in marketing. She was a naturally attractive young woman, with a great smile. Mike smiled back at her. They were just getting to know each other after only a few weeks of being "involved." Their relationship was nothing serious yet, just fun and flirtation.

Most were drinking beer, although some had wine and some were drinking shots of what Mike presumed was some savory, yet potent, liquor. He started his own celebration with a few shots of tequila and then, with Dave as sommelier, ordered some fine wines. He pulled out his new camera and began taking photos, showing everyone the cool features of this new model, like the digital image on the screen on back which rotated to right itself whenever he turned the camera from horizontal to vertical.

Michael was as comfortable with this group of people as he had ever felt around anyone. These were his kind of people: his roommate Dave, Dave S. from DU, Tim, Liz, Charla, Erin and

Julia B., aka Julia No. 1, from his fraternity days (or was it his fraternity daze?). They were joined by Helen and Julia N., aka Julia No. 2, and other co-workers at the Grille. This was now his post-college cohort and fellow DU alumni who understood the "real" Michael Adler: the sensitive, thoughtful, yet sometimes sharply sarcastically-witted Mike Adler. As he looked around the tables pushed together, he had the feeling that these people would stay his friends forever.

They partied at Sing Sing for an hour or so, and then, when the bar got too crowded, headed over to the Grille. There, they bought more wine and toasted their good fortune. But as the evening wore on, getting late, Mike and Dave decided to return to their condominium to finish the evening. They all had to work the next day, getting their shifts at the Grille in before they left for Panama ten days later.

They re-corked the last bottle of wine which still had a few glasses left. Taking the bottle with them, Mike and Dave left the lounge and got back in the RAV. Mike slid into the driver's seat, rolled down the window to let the cigarette smoke clear from the car, and started the engine. Dave climbed in on the passenger side and belted himself in, holding the wine on his lap. A dope pipe remained in the console, not needed just then after the night of drinking. They both had a pretty strong buzz going already.

Once again, as during the day, they drove over to Colorado Boulevard, and turned right onto Alameda. The time was 1:30 a.m. on Friday, June 2nd, when they passed the same Greek Orthodox Church and headed east up the hill. Dave later told us that, as they went up the hill, he had reminded Mike, who was looking down and searching the radio for some good tunes, to watch his speed as the police had been setting speed traps to catch drivers for some weeks now along this stretch of road.

The pavement, wet with water runoff from the sprinklers in the landscaped center median, reflected the street lights. Driving in the left lane near the Lutheran Church, Mike looked down to the middle console of the car for a pack of Camel cigarettes. The car drifted slightly to the left and bumped up against the south curb of the median. The bump startled Mike, who, trying to react quickly but feeling sluggish, jerked the steering wheel back to the right to correct the car's path. The car slid uncontrolled across the wet pavement. As the tires made contact with the dry asphalt, the car took off across the right lane heading for the south curb. The car jumped the curb on the southeast corner of Alameda and Fairfax, traveling sideways at 40 mph when it hit the tree. The trunk of the tree and an extended branch did not yield, crushing the driver's side door and roof, pushing and then collapsing the driver's seat against the center console.

The noise of the accident was so loud that neighbors up and down the street emerged from their homes to see what had happened. One neighbor was startled by the noise which was just outside his bedroom. Another, working in his garage early that morning, also came running. They called 911 and EMTs from a nearby fire station were dispatched to the scene.

Chapter 2
The Call

Dana and I live close to the foothills of the Santa Catalina Mountains on the north side of Tucson, Arizona. Our home is a small patio home at the end of a quiet cul de sac surrounded by desert arroyos. The front range of the Catalinas looks down on our home from the north, imposing rock spotted with green desert brush and saguaro cacti. There are no neighbors living within 100 yards of our home to the west, and, to the east, we have neighbors for less than six months of the year (November – April). Once they return to their homes "back east" or "up north," the street becomes our own private domain for the balance of the year.

During the day, the air is filled with the sounds of the many varieties of birds which live in the arroyos. There is an abundance of wildlife which is at home here: javelina, bobcats, snakes, lizards, rabbits, an occasional gila monster and a tarantula or two. They are the authentic desert dwellers; we are the intruders. At least, this is the common view expressed by Tucsonans.

The only regular human contacts on our street during the six warm months are the daily newspaper deliverers who swing by to drop the newspapers on our driveway at 5:00 a.m. and the weekly garbage pick-up trucks. At night, we are virtually alone. There is no noise but for the occasional but very soft rumble of cars passing over the cobblestone entrance to our gated community a short distance away. Our neighborhood is both peaceful and serene.

We live just two miles from the nearest grocery store and a fifteen minute drive to almost everything else we want to do in metro Tucson. For Dana, our home is the base from which she scoots about town to this or that meeting, to temple and to her Mom's home which is in an independent/assisted living residence.

For me, our little retreat in the foothills is less than a half hour's drive from being able to play my favorite game. Golf, of course! In fact, Tucson has an abundance of good golf courses and I have tried to avail myself of their green pastures at least twice a week.

In 2006, busy days in town were balanced perfectly with our private little retreat in the evenings. We were living the good life of empty nesters. We were free to come and go as we pleased, confident that our family was well cared for. We indulged in reading books just for pleasure, strolling about the neighborhood when we felt the urge, and visiting with our friends, whom we have come to know over our 20+ years in Tucson. In fact, May 31, 2006 marked the 20th anniversary of my arrival in Tucson to go to work for Tucson Electric Power Company, the local electric utility. I had now lived in Tucson longer than I had lived in any other location. It was, and is, home.

On the evening of June 1st, Dana and I were in no mood to cook for ourselves. We decided to visit a newly opened pizza restaurant down on Swan Road and Camp Lowell Drive. We had read in the newspaper that the restaurant was run by two local boys and we liked to support locally owned businesses. The restaurant was in a small store front in a nearby strip center. The food, thin crusted pizzas and house salads, was satisfying and tasty. We enjoyed a nice quiet dinner together.

We were feeling good about the two of us. We talked about retirement and about our family. As we ate our caprese salads and goat cheese pizzas, we discussed our plans for a family vacation in early July to celebrate Michael's graduation from college. We looked forward to leaving Tucson's intense summer heat to spend two weeks up in Lake Tahoe where we had rented a home. We anticipated the time away and the golfing, hiking and biking. We were to be accompanied at various times over the two weeks by some of our friends, my sister's family and, of course, Darcy and Michael. And, we had reservations to see "Much Ado About Nothing" at the Lake Tahoe Shakespearean Festival.

But more immediately, we were looking forward to travelling up to Denver for Mike's graduation from DU. The Commencement was scheduled nine days from this date, i.e., Saturday, June 10.

We were, indeed, very proud of Mike's accomplishments. Our son had successfully completed college. From a phone call with him earlier in the day, we knew he had his last scheduled class that same evening. He had the idea that he would teach at the college level someday. He had informed us that getting certified to teach would have to wait, however, because he had a good paying job at the Wash Park Grille, one of our favorite neighborhood restaurants. Mike wanted to take a year off from serious academic pursuits and life's obligations in order to earn some money, building up his financial reserves, while he generally kicked back. There would be a lifetime of career work ahead of him, so this short hiatus from serious pursuits was okay with us. Oh, to be 22 years old!

Far away, on the East coast, Darcy, then 27 year old, resided in Richmond, Virginia, and was gainfully employed at the local Jewish Community Center. When she had graduated college, she readily accepted the fact that, after college, she would be on her own financially, a fact that Mike was about to face head on in the coming months. Her independence was also an accomplishment worthy of recognition. After an illustrious student-athlete career at the University of Illinois and a first job in Mesa as a marketing manager for the East Valley Tribune, a local newspaper, she had moved back East to be near her then-boyfriend/soon-to-be-husband, James. She, too, was happy in her life, which, in turn, made us happy for her.

On this warm summer evening, Dana and I were also feeling sanguine about our own accomplishments: we had successfully funded Michael's entire $140,000 experience in education and "independent" living in Denver and we had invested in a condominium to provide him a home while he worked and considered graduate school. A year earlier, I had retired from a successful corporate financial management career, and we felt financially secure having more than sufficient funds to live a comfortable life together going forward. Dana had additional reasons to feel satisfied. A year earlier, she had completed a two year term as president of Temple Emanu El. After years of pursuing and being pursued for various volunteer positions on not-for-profit boards and fundraising committees, she planned to cut back on her commitments. Finally, we had downsized our housing to this special patio home we had purchased after several months of looking into properties east, west, north and south around Tucson. We had found our own little "slice of heaven," as Dana would put it.

On the night of June 1, 2006, we counted our blessings. Full of pizza and relaxed by the warm dry breezes of the summer-like evening, we returned home about 7:30 and went to bed around 10:00 p.m.

I was in bed, sound asleep, when I was stirred awake by the sound of Dana's voice. Through my sleep, I had heard a cell phone ringing in the kitchen, but had ignored it as just part of some dream. It was no dream. Dana was speaking to someone out in the kitchen. I struggled to wake up enough so I could catch some of what she was saying. The words weren't clear through the bedroom doorway, but I could hear panic rising in her voice.

"Can you tell me more, what happened?" I heard her say hurriedly. I couldn't make out exactly what she was saying as she asked more questions. In fact, I couldn't really believe my ears ... *Who could she be talking to at this ungodly hour?* The clock on the bed stand next to me read 1:15 a.m. (MST). It was early in the morning on Friday, June 2.

My first thought was*: I hope I can get back to sleep after she stops wandering the floors, talking to people in the middle of the night*. I was still not fully awake nor was I thinking very clearly. The fact that Dana was not in bed in the middle of the night was not that unusual of an occurrence. She often had something on her mind that she wanted to take care of which would keep her from her sleep until she dealt with it. But this was different... ***Who was she talking to?***

The conversation she was having seemed to stop. She suddenly materialized in the bedroom without the phone. She flipped the light switch lighting up the bedroom. *Uh oh! What now?* I knew that whatever the news was, it wasn't good if she was coming in to share it with me at 1:15 a.m.

"Michael's been in an accident."

Her words pierced through my sleep. I was instantly jolted awake, adrenaline flowing. "He's at Denver Health Medical Center in the Emergency Room. Oh God, what should we do?" she said, her voice trembling with fear. I sat up, still unsure that I had heard her correctly, trying to absorb what she had said. My heart raced.

"What happened?" I asked, seeking confirmation of what I thought I had heard; my first impressions were confused by the seemingly implausible string of words she had just spoken. *How could this be? This type of thing only happens to other families, doesn't it?* The thought raced through my mind but the moment felt like an eternity. Every sense was alert now; every feeling being recorded.

Dana repeated, now beginning to cry, "Mike's been in an accident and he is badly injured and at Denver Health. That was the Emergency Room calling on my cell phone. I heard the phone ring and didn't get up. But then I heard a voice message being left, so I got up to listen to it. Oh my God, what are we going do?" Her whole body started to quake. She was unable to catch her breath. Tears flowed down her cheeks.

I jumped up from the bed and reached out to hold her, trembling in my arms, still trying to absorb the news. *Our son? Are you sure? Are they sure?* I asked who we could call to get more information. Gasping for air through her sobs, she told me she had written down the number of a doctor from the Emergency Room in Denver. She had left the piece of paper in the kitchen.

Befuddled and still confused, I was awake enough to be fearful of hearing even worse news, but desperate for more details. I ran into the kitchen and dialed the number written above the doctor's name...Dr. Eberhard. He answered immediately. I identified myself as Michael Adler's father and asked about our son's condition. Now I felt myself beginning to tremble ... I feared hearing the worst. *Is he going to die? Or has he already died?*

Dr. Eberhard spoke clearly and calmly. He said Michael had just been admitted after a serious car accident. Mike had been brought to Denver Health by the Denver Fire Department paramedics. Our phone number had been located in Mike's cell phone under I.C.E. ("In Case of Emergency"). His condition was critical. They might need to perform surgery. He would call back in a few minutes when there was more news.

No, wait! Don't hang up yet! I pleaded inside myself. I couldn't comprehend all that he had said to me. I asked him to repeat some of the information as if that might change what I was hearing and somehow overcome my disbelief. Again, he spoke in measured tones. He told me that Mike had a crushed left skull, left temporal edema, a shattered pelvis, brain swelling and bleeding. I reached for a pen and some paper to record what I was being told. *How? Why*? He said that Mike was the driver. Alcohol was involved. The accident had been very bad. Although the one passenger was hurt slightly, he was okay. *Who was the passenger?* Dr. Eberhard told me that Mike had to be pulled free of the vehicle by the paramedics. *What about loss of blood*?

How does one fully absorb such news at 1:30 in the morning? A crushed left skull, left temporal edema, a shattered pelvis, brain swelling and bleeding ... I listened intently to his every word, trying to memorize as he spoke, jotting down the terminology of his injuries. He told me he had to go tend to Michael and that he would call back as soon as he was able to with more information.

I hung up the phone and turned to Dana, who was growing more hysterical, crying more loudly, shaking more violently. I held her again, trying desperately to control my own emotions and organize my own thoughts. But I was shaking also.

I hoped Dana would gain some control so we could try to begin to deal with this. We needed to spring into action. *How can we get up to Denver as soon as possible? Will Mike be alive when we arrive?* We had to keep close to the phone. And, we needed to find someone up in Denver to get to the hospital right away.

But what to do first? We decided to call Dana's dad, Wilbert, and his wife, Joanne, to get them to go down to the hospital immediately. They lived in the Southwest part of the Denver metro area, near Ft. Logan Military Cemetery, and were the closest relatives. Bert was the extreme optimist in the family, the one person you can count on for some positive statement of belief, despite all evidence to the contrary. My father-in-law was 85 years old and not as vibrant as in years past, but we knew he would race down to Michael's side as quickly as anyone could. Joanne, his wife, whom he had married a few years following his divorce from Dana's mother, was 18 years his junior and shared his rosy outlook on life. In fact, nothing negative could ever sway Joanne's reasoning that all can be right with the world if only we believed it so. We called, waking them both at 2:30 a.m. Denver time (MDT), and delivered the horrible news of Mike's accident. Bert said he would go down to the hospital immediately and call us later with whatever news he could get.

Not fully trusting his senior capacity to comprehend all that was likely to be said to him about Mike's condition by the doctors at Denver Health, we next called our dearest friends, Bill and Anne, who lived 20 miles southeast of Denver in newly constructed suburbs. Bill and Anne had introduced Dana to me at Bill's 30th birthday party, 26 years earlier, way back in 1979. They remained our closest friends. Our call woke them up around 3:00 a.m. and we relayed all that we knew about Mike's accident and condition. They have two sons who have, from time to time, challenged them with auto accidents and the like so we knew they would understand the situation despite the panic in our voices. Without hesitation, Anne said they would be on their way to the hospital.

Knowing that people we knew and trusted were going down to the hospital to be with Mike was of some comfort, but we knew we had to get to Denver as soon as possible. Michael needed us… NOW.

OK, what next do we do? Flight arrangements, car arrangements…the fastest way to Denver. Dana, now taking charge, jumped on her computer and saw that Frontier Airlines had a flight leaving at 6:30 a.m. Over the internet, we booked two one way seats. We had no idea when we would be coming back to Tucson, whether in a day or a week? Longer? Dana also called a rental car company and got a car for our morning arrival. I went to get suitcases and began to pack up a few articles of clothing.

Then the phone rang. The loud tone startled us both. We stopped moving about and stared at the phone. I shivered deep inside. All of the horrible "what ifs" raced through us, yet we wanted to know more about Mike's condition. *What news could come to us at 3:00 in the morning?*

"This is Dr. Yu and I am the on-call neurosurgeon tonight in the ED. Is this Mr. Adler?" the foreign sounding voice asked and then continued without waiting for a response, "I need to place a bolt in your son's head to monitor his brain pressure[1] and I need your permission to proceed with the surgery." The voice was difficult to understand, heavily accented.

Bolt? Brain pressure? Permission to perform surgery? What was he talking about? My mind struggled to comprehend what the doctor was saying. I could not fully grasp any of it. Focusing on Dana and the fear in her trembling body, I wanted to be provided more information.

The doctor continued, "He has multiple skull and facial fractures and there may be bleeding internally in his brain. We have to monitor the brain pressure immediately. This is surgery so I need your permission to proceed."

Permission? The request made no sense to me. *And if I say 'no', then what?* "Of course, go ahead and do what you have to do," I said, still not believing I was being asked to give my permission. "We're trying to get up there as soon as we can." The words spilled out as quickly as I could muster a response. There was no hesitation, only an overwhelming feeling of helplessness. *We were so far away from our son; what could we do to help him?* A new wave of adrenaline pumped into my body; I could feel my stomach tightening. The feeling we were not in control in any way sickened me. I could hardly breathe.

"Thank you," the surgeon said and the phone went dead. *Did that call really just happen? At 3:00 a.m.?* The whole morning

---

1 Swelling of the brain in the space confined by the skull can cause damage by pressing the brain tissue against the skull bone. Swelling can result in further compressing, shearing and/or stretching of the axons, key neuronal structures, and "starve" the brain of oxygen due to constriction of blood vessels serving the brain. Intracranial pressure is, therefore, important to monitor following a traumatic injury. A subarachnoid screw or "bolt" is placed just through the skull in the space beyond the dura mater (the outermost membrane which protects the brain) between the arachnoid membrane and the cerebral cortex, containing a sensor. If swelling is found, removal of parts of the skull – to make room for the expanding brain tissue – may be necessary.

was beginning to feel surreal. We had to find a way to accept the news, and we had to act quickly, keep our heads, and fly up to be with Michael. We didn't have time to stop and consider the situation. We had to keep on moving until we were by his side. *At least Mike was still alive!*

In silence, we rapidly packed a few random articles of clothing, three days' of clothing each. We packed just enough to get by and to not have to check our baggage when we got to the airport. Time would be valuable when we landed. It later turned out that we would wear these clothes for the next three weeks, rotating outfits every day in three day cycles. But, around 4:00 a.m. on June 2, we loaded up the car with a suitcase and a small duffel bag and were ready to leave for Tucson International Airport.

But before leaving our home for what turned out to be the next three months, we called the Emergency Department, the ED, in Denver once again to check on Michael's status.

"He is very seriously injured. He is stable for now, but very seriously hurt. He has a very serious head injury and he's unconscious, but that's all we can say for now," reported Dr. Eberhard, the first ED doctor we had spoken to. In other words, he had nothing new to tell us, no new information and no words of comfort. *But he is stable!* It had been just over two hours since that first call had awakened Dana.

I said, "Thank you, we'll be there as soon as we can." Hanging up the phone, feeling helpless, a flood of horrifying thoughts began to break through the wall of activity. We were still so far away. We would be traveling and out of touch with the hospital. *What if he died before we could get to the hospital? What if we were not by his side when he most needed us? What if he needed further surgery? Who would give permission? What if he never woke up again? How did this happen? Why?*

"Wait, where is Dave?" Dana asked. "I know Dave and Michael were together. Is he all right? Should we try and call Dave?" Without waiting for my answer, she grabbed her cell phone and made the call. She reached him in the hospital. "Dave, this is Dana. Were you with Michael tonight? Where are you? What happened?" Dave, stumbling over his words, trying to gather his thoughts proceeded to explain what he was able to recall. He said that he thought Michael was hurt but he didn't know where he was. Dave was in the hospital but he was okay, maybe having suffered a slight concussion. He remembered they had been at the Grille and they had corked a bottle of wine to go home and continue the graduation celebration. He knew they had been in an accident and Michael was bleeding and not responding to the EMTs who were trying to get him out of the car. Dave had been unconscious briefly but remembered throwing up and being put in an ambulance. With heaviness in his voice, Dave mustered the energy to ask, "Is Mikey okay?"

Chapter 3
Denver Health Medical Center
Surgical Intensive Care Unit

Tucson streets are almost empty at 4:00 a.m. The few cars and trucks on the road carry workers to their early morning duties... opening restaurants, getting their assignments for construction projects, travelling to their worksites. There is no University of Arizona traffic at this time of year. The students have left town following graduation and the end of the Spring semester in mid-May.

The rhythm of another June day was just starting to pick up its slow, laid back pace. Through the pre-dawn quiet, Dana and I drove to Tucson International Airport, hardly speaking to one another. We were deep in our own private thoughts. What words of comfort could be shared? "Oh, don't worry, Mike will be all right." "He's in good hands." "I'm sure he'll recover quickly." No, none of that was spoken. We just drove silently, unable to express our worst fears out loud. Our brief nervous glances at one another were just enough to disclose our uneasiness. A few times along the way, we would reach out to touch each other's hands.

The ride to the airport took about 25 minutes. We parked the car in the long-term parking lot and took the shuttle to the terminal. I don't remember checking in and, fortunately, the plane was on time so our wait on the concourse was short. We attempted to comfort each other; neither was successful. Dana stood up and walked away. Despite the early hour, she called her "sponsor." "Oh my God. Oh my God. I can't believe this has happened," her sponsor cried through the phone. "How long will you be in Denver? Who is picking you up from the airport? Where is Michael?

What can I do?" The answers Dana could provide were as concise as the questions. When she composed herself, Dana's sponsor did what all good sponsors do. She reminded Dana of the importance of her sobriety...now more than ever. "As soon as you are able, find a meeting. You will not believe the support you will receive in the rooms and you're going to need a lot of it!" With that bit of advice, Dana ended the conversation, thanking her.

We then boarded the plane with the other early morning travelers. Our seats, reserved only two hours before, were in the back of the small regional aircraft. In the row in front of ours and across the aisle, a man and a woman struggled to squeeze into their seats with their baby child and toddler. Without any provocation, both Dana and I teared up as we looked at them. *Who was with our baby? Will we ever be a happy family like that again?* We held each other's hands tightly now, but we looked away from each other's face. We were simply not able to look into the other's eyes without seeing the other's fear, the terror we ourselves felt. I spent a few minutes of the flight writing some notes in a notebook. They were questions to ask the doctors when we arrived. Note taking was busy work that helped fill the flight time. I made a list of issues/questions to ask when we arrived at the hospital:

RE: Mike's condition

Extent of injuries:
- Head – skull, jaw, teeth, ears, ENT
- Brain – motor skills, cognitive skills, communications
- Neck – spinal column, back-vertebrae and spinal cord
- Arms – broken? Arms, elbows, wrist, hands
- Thorax – any internal injuries? Bleeding?
- Skeletal – pelvis/spinal connection, urology?
- Legs/Feet-knees, femur

Process/priorities?
- What procedures? What doctors?
  - Brain surgery to remove damaged tissue or foreign objects

Plastic surgery/ENT surgery
Orthopedic surgery (pelvic)
Other? Maxo-facial surgery?
Where? Which hospitals? Where to recover?
Length of time
Insurance? Limitations/amount of coverage? Risk of cancellation?
Police Report
Attorney – call Adam (cousin)
Denver Health Medical Center
SICU 303-436-8355 Patient code 2789
Cancel Loew's reservations (graduation hotel)
Cancel Highland Garlands/Gardens (graduation restaurant)
Car rental
Call Eric (Mike's friend)
Email tree

The two hours in the air seemed interminable to us. We were like two thoroughbred horses loaded into the starting gate before being released to speed around the track. The starting gate had closed behind us, but we were trapped waiting for the front gate to open. But once we had landed and pulled up to the plane's assigned gate, the doors of the airplane had opened and we had instantly sprung into action. On the ground in Denver, outside of the airplane, we raced through the terminal. We walked -- no, trotted -- through the concourse, weaving past slower moving passengers on their own unhurried travels, to the train which took us to the main terminal. When the train doors opened, we hurried up the escalator from the train station, through the main terminal to the exit doors to the car rental shuttle bus. When the shuttle bus pulled into the Enterprise Rent-a-Car parking lot, we jumped out, located the rental car, loaded our bags in the trunk and, with as little delay as possible, sped away from the airport.

While I navigated through traffic, Dana contacted Anne. Expressing relief that we were in Denver, Anne cautiously reported that Michael was doing okay. Knowing our angst, she spoke comfortingly, "He's stable; he looks comfortable; he's in good hands." She and Bill, as well as Wilbert and Joanne, had been in to see him and an excellent staff of trained ICU nurses was caring for him. They were looking forward to seeing us. Tears ran down our cheeks when Dana shared Anne's words with me.

By 10:30 a.m., Denver time, we had travelled across I-70 and I-25, and wound our way through downtown Denver, having exited I-25 one exit too soon. We were lucky that we had knowledge of Denver's streets and, despite the crisis which waited ahead, we felt a strange sense of being home.

Dana and I knew about Denver Health Medical Center (DHMC). When we lived in Denver, it had been known as Denver General Hospital. Dana's mother had worked there for 10 years. Denver General was the large central county hospital, the place where victims of violent crimes like shootings and stabbings were brought by ambulances with their sirens screaming. Fire departments brought burn victims there for emergency treatment. The Emergency Department is the most accessible entrance on the corner of Speer Boulevard and Broadway; the Main Entrance is located in the "rear" of the building, off of a side street.

Trauma and medical care for the poor or displaced used to be DG's primary mission. Patients with adequate healthcare insurance coverage were few. The hallways were patrolled by policemen because of the violent nature of the people who were patients or visitors. Doctors and nurses who worked at DG used to need to be escorted to their cars by security guards to protect them from the violence and petty crime which lurked just outside of the hospital's doorways. It was not the surrounding neighborhood that made it dangerous. It was the population being served inside the hospital that threatened. If one was the victim of violence, DG was the place to come. On the other hand, if you had a sore throat, any other hospital was preferable to DG. Now, in 2006, we learned that it was the closest Level I Trauma hospital to where Mike's accident had occurred.

We pulled into the parking garage at DHMC around 11:00 a.m. We parked on the second tier of the garage and raced to the Main Entrance of the hospital. We stopped at the reception desk just beyond the automatically opening glass doors. "Where is Michael

Adler? Where is the ICU?" we demanded, out of breath. The woman at the main reception desk, Martha, whom we would get to know well over the next month, directed us down the hallway to the right of the desk, up the stairs to the second floor where the Surgical Intensive Care Unit ("SICU") was located.

We walked, trotted, and then ran through the hallway, accelerating as we passed doctors, nurses, patients wandering with their IV poles at their side, patients' families - mothers, fathers, sisters and brothers, aunts and uncles, cousins, and crying babies. We passed people sitting in the padded metal chairs which lined the walls of the waiting areas outside of the various clinics. *Welcome to Denver Health!*

Climbing the stairs, we reached the landing in the center of the second floor. We twirled around, searching for the entrance to the SICU. It was in the northeast corner of the floor. As we approached, I felt my sense of panic increase and the muscles within my gut tighten up.

As we approached the reception desk, in the waiting room to the right of the doorway, we found Bill, Anne, Bert and Joanne. We quickly hugged each of them and thanked them for being there for us. They told us Michael was stable, but warned us to be prepared for what we would see. *Thankfully, he's still alive!* But, without any further delay, having waited 8 hours since the fateful phone call and having travelled 800 miles, we turned and raced through the doors labeled Surgical Intensive Care. We hurried to go see Michael, who was in Room 15.

Walking through the steel doors of the SICU with their remotely controlled security locks, a boost of adrenaline kicked in. My mind was racing. Time seemed to slow down. My senses were bombarded with the sights and sounds of the hospital. I tried to fully absorb these first moments with our injured son. The glare of the bright fluorescent lights in the ceiling made me squint and the smell of the place, the odd mix of human odors and hospital antiseptic, etched into my memory.

I felt the *gravitas* of mortality as I approached Michael's SICU room. *People die in intensive care*. We were actually there, in that time and these strange surroundings, and we worried that he may be gone in a moment. Michael, Dana and I were bound to each other by genetic linkages, yet I felt at that moment that we are all separate and alone. Dana or I would have sacrificed our own happiness in a instant for some sort of supernatural intervention ... either for a rewind of the clock to before this horrible event or for some miraculous resolution of this moment. We rarely get what we most wish for but, somehow, we survive our worst nightmares and what life throws at us. We had no choice but to face up to what was waiting for us in that SICU room.

We came around the corner of the hallway, past the SICU nurses' stations and came face to face with Michael for the first time.

"Oh my God! Oh my God!" we both whispered at the unfathomable sight of our injured son. Our eyes were immediately drawn to his. Michael's eyes were swollen completely shut. His closed eyelids bulged from his eye sockets. His eyelids were so bruised that they were both dark black - not deep purple or red... they were as black as a room with no windows at midnight. There was no movement of his eyes behind his eyelids.

The skin on his forehead, torn by the bark of the tree, had already scabbed over in newly formed patches of dark red, dried blood. But his face and mouth were not lacerated. *Small relief*. His mouth was contorted by tubes emanating from his lips and taped to his cheeks, pulling his mouth to one side. There was no sign of moisture on his lips. His mouth was forced open by the tubes emerging from between his teeth. His lips were dry and cracked from the cold, arid air of the hospital. Another tube from his nostril ran down to a machine.

His hair was matted down on his head. A large area, about three inches square, above the left side of his forehead, was bald from being shaved for surgery. A long and narrow device in the shape of a pen stuck out vertically about five inches from the taped center of the bald spot where it entered his skull. It was connected to a wire cable leading to a monitoring device. This was the "bolt" implanted during the night by the neurosurgeon I had spoken to on the phone when I gave my permission to operate.

His color, but for the dark bruises and scarlet scabs, was pale;

he looked cold. Despite the intrusions of medical equipment, his face was relaxed as if he himself was dormant...with no expression of any kind.

He was dressed in a hospital gown which was open over his chest. A massive tangle of wires fell from his chest, twisting and turning, and reconnecting to a monitor standing on a pole just right of the head of his bed. His chest heaved and fell in time with the respirator machine's pump/click - pump/click - pump/click rhythm. The machine seemed to be keeping time, pacing his life like a slow metronome.

Over the next ten days, the sights and sounds of these machines were to become almost comforting as we learned about their functions, but, at this first encounter, they seemed oddly surreal to me. *Were these machines the only things keeping Michael alive?* The steady pattern of the electronic orange line against the black background of the monitor measured his heart's efforts.

Michael was lying on his back, tilted up slightly in bed. He looked larger now in that hospital bed than he had appeared the last time he had been home with us in Tucson. *Had he been working out? Or just gaining weight?* We didn't realize at the time that it was his swollen body which looked unnaturally large to us both. Immobile as he was, we could not see any outward evidence of his lower internal injuries. The doctor had informed us over the phone that his pelvis had been fractured, crushed really, by the force of the driver's door collapsing toward him as the car gave way to the tree.

We stepped forward and, instinctively, reached for his hands, one of us on each side of his bed. We both tentatively reached out also to touch his cheeks. His face was cold to our touch. Michael did not move; he did not talk; he did not moan. He didn't greet us or acknowledge our presence in any way. He didn't squeeze our hands back as we squeezed his. He didn't try to form "hello" with his mouth. He didn't open his eyes and look around at us when he heard our voices. He just lay there. Unconscious. As his body was still absorbing the shock of the previous evening's blunt force trauma, he was completely unaware of any of it as far as we could discern.

A young doctor, who must have followed us into Mike's room, went straight to the monitors taking a quick read of the data before he began to address us. He introduced himself, but I was oblivious to his name. He shook our hands and proceeded to explain Michael's condition. As we listened, Dana and I continued to stare down at Michael's eyes, swollen shut and black. We were mesmerized and could not look away.

The neurosurgical resident began speaking quietly to us, calmly and matter-of-factly, explaining Mike's condition. "Our CT Scan shows diffuse axonal injury and some intracranial bleeding. This is a Traumatic Brain Injury." The words, though spoken softly, screeched inside my head. Immediately, questions began to crowd out the sound of his voice.

What do those words mean? ***Would he live?*** *Would he be in a coma for the rest of his life? Would he ever wake up?* ***WOULD HE LIVE?***

I tried to listen carefully as the doctor described Mike's condition. But, poignantly and ominously, he volunteered no prognosis. He simply continued to review his vital signs for us. "We're waiting to see if he wakes up" was all that the doctor offered. He recited what he understood to have transpired in the early morning hours...a car skidding...hit a tree...Jaws of Life... transport to DHMC, the closest Level 1 Trauma hospital...the implantation of the bolt...the blood alcohol tests.

Diffuse Axonal Injury. Traumatic Brain Injury. Intracranial bleeding. I had never before believed I would hear these terms used in the context of one of my family members, let alone anyone else I knew. *What did they mean*? *How would we find out*? The only thing I knew for certain that Friday morning, June 2, 2006, was that I would never again forget those words or this moment. They hit me as if I myself had been careening down the highway at 90 mph and had hit a wall. The good news was that Mike was alive and being cared for. The bad news.... All the rest felt like bad news. *Was our Michael gone forever*? *Would our lives be forever altered*?

There we stood in SICU #15 by Michael's bed in stunned silence. We had just begun to absorb the whole scene before us. His bed was in the center of this room in the Surgical Intensive Care Unit of Denver Health Medical Center. The walls were blue; there was a window to the courtyard one floor below at ground level; a curtain could be pulled across the entire front of the room to give the patient and the doctors privacy; a sliding glass door opened to the nurse's stations. There were monitors behind Mike's bed for respiration, heart rate, temperature, brain pressure, and blood pressure connected to Michael by various wires and tubes. I had the fleeting thought: *This room must have looked empty in the days before digital medical technology.* The lighting was fluorescent, casting a clinical cold light throughout the room. The walls were crowded with cabinets and counters which held various medical supplies.

As we began to absorb what the doctors and nurses were saying to us, we tried to get straight answers to our most critical questions. The answers were not comforting. We were told that his x-rays and CT Scan showed that Michael had widespread contusions of the brain's white matter. He had multiple and extensive facial and cranial fractures. We were also told that his pelvis was fractured in the accident as was his left femur. (The first reports that his femur was broken proved later to be incorrect.) His thorax and internal organs were healthy and functioning and, miraculously, there were no spinal cord or spinal injuries. These last bits of information about his spine were our first pieces of good news; paralysis seemed less likely.

Mike moved a little, his reflexes stimulated by the irritation of a drainage tube or other external stimuli poking out of his nose or mouth. But we noticed that he hadn't really moved his left leg (below the broken pelvis and femur). In fact, he didn't respond at all when tested with pin-poking on his left wrist and lower left leg. *Will he be partially paralyzed on his left side?*

Swelling of the brain was a major concern. We didn't yet understand why or how swelling could affect his brain further, but the doctors made it clear to us that damage could result. The "bolt" in his head pointed straight up from the top front of his skull, just above his hairline, now receding into a shaved area. It looked like an alien antenna. It was the monitoring device that measured his intracranial pressure (ICP). It had registered in the 6-8 range all that first day. We later learned that pressures measured below a 10 were deemed acceptable in this situation.

There was nothing more to do than to stand next to Michael's bed, hold his hands, talk to him to let him know we were there by his side, and to wait until the next doctor or nurse would arrive and talk more about his condition and their plans for treatment. All the questions we had when we were driving to the airport in Tucson and which occupied us in the airplane were now crowded out by the terrible reality of what we were experiencing in the SICU.

As we talked with the neurosurgeons and the SICU nurses, we learned that it might be weeks before he awakened and the brain contusions healed. They referred us to a measurement for the recovery stages from brain injuries called the Rancho Los Amigos scale.[2] We would follow Mike's progress in relation to this scale throughout his stay at DHMC. But, at this point, Mike was in a Level 1 coma. And we wondered if Mike would ever move through any, let alone all, of these stages...and, even if he reached Level 8, what would his life be like? Standing there next to his bed on that first day, 100% recovery did not seem to be in the cards. At best, the road ahead of Michael seemed treacherous indeed.

We were not given a copy of the police report, but we heard from the nurses that Mike was driving intoxicated, perhaps a DUI (Driving Under the Influence felony) according to the police. The Denver Police had taken a blood sample at the scene and it was being evaluated for blood alcohol level at the police lab. As a result of the potentially criminal finding, there was a "hold" placed on all information about Mike, including what room he was in. Visitors, other than Dana and me, would have trouble finding him as a result of this bureaucratic procedure. The doctors told us, however, that his blood alcohol level (BAC) tested by the hospital was between

---

2 The Rancho Los Amigos scale is discussed in a variety of source locations. The summary contained herein is derived from the Traumatic Brain Injury Manual for Patients and Families published by Craig Hospital, 1999. See Appendix A.

.06 and .08, just below the DUI threshold in the State of Colorado.

Details of the night before began to emerge from various conversations. We were told by the doctors and nurses that he allegedly bumped the curb on Alameda and overcorrected his car's steering so that it skidded sideways across the right lane of the street, jumping the curb at Fairfax and hitting a tree sideways. The impact was to the driver's side door and to Michael. The driver's side window was down and it was likely that Michael's head hit the tree directly. The damage was so severe to the driver's side door that Michael had to be extricated through the roof of the car, torn away by the Jaws-of-Life used by the paramedics and EMTs.

I tried to imagine what it was like to be in an auto accident, hitting a tree at 45 mph. I imagined that it would be the equivalent of being hit by a wooden 2x4 on the side of the head, swung like a baseball bat. I intuitively knew that a trauma of this severity is not one that "resolves" or heals itself in just a day or two. I was just beginning to appreciate the full import of Mike's situation.

Questions continued to roll around in my head. *Will Mike ever talk normally again? Will he be able to think for himself, live on his own? And, if not, how do we provide for his future?* We still felt as if we had a million questions, yet no answers.

Standing by Michael's side, Dana had gathered her strength and, while weepy still, she had tried to calm herself. She told me she was determined to remain positive and hopeful, despite the horrific scene before her. As for me, I was scared right through to my core. I was afraid of what the future would hold for our son, and for Dana and me. Not just the immediate future here at Denver Health but the longer term. *How would Mike's life now be lived?* I admit that I acquiesced to my doubts and fears on this first day.

As we stood vigil by Michael's bedside, Dana stroked Mike's bare chest slowly back and forth. She needed to touch him, trying to feel his life force and adding her own to his. She held his hand. His fingers closed around her fingers tightly, clutching reflexively. Talking quietly, she repeated over and over to him the events of the day. "Michael, you were in a car accident. You are in the hospital. Mom and Dad are here with you." She shared with Mike the names of the people who had already responded and shown their concern by calling and of the family members who love him.

She stared at his closed blackened eyes; she wept, then gathered herself, but, again, she wept.

One or both of us stood or sat by his bed the entire day. We closed our eyes occasionally to try to focus our own thoughts as if to try to will his awakening from the coma and his return to us. We closed our eyes hoping that this nightmare would be over when we opened them again. But this was not a nightmare; this was the real world and it would not be over anytime soon.

Throughout the day, we took breaks in the waiting area and made contact by phone with what seemed like the entire population of Tucson. Everyone we spoke to was shocked to hear about the accident and everyone wanted to be kept informed on a real time basis. We spent what seemed like hours on our cell phones, repeating the events of the past day and what we understood of Michael's status. We talked to our mothers, fathers, sisters, brothers, cousins; we talked to our friends, many of whom had children very nearly the same age as Michael; we talked to strangers in order to cancel our appointments and dates back in Tucson. Each call required a recitation of the last 24 hours' events. Each call began the same way: "We got a call last night that Michael had been in a serious accident. He's in a coma here in Denver. We flew up this morning. We don't know if he will recover. It's a very bad injury to his brain." We re-lived the initial shock and nightmare of this first day over and over and over, as if rehearsing the lines of some dark script from a terrifying movie.

To make all these calls and to receive all the responses, Dana and I shuttled back and forth into the Waiting Room area. We walked down the hallway from Mike's room, through the security doors which required a key code to get back in, and out past the receptionist for the SICU. The Waiting Room was periodically filled to capacity with huge, extended families of other patients who had been admitted to the SICU. The families were often Hispanic or African-American. English seemed like a second language in the Waiting Room. Babies were either being fed or cried for attention. Young children ran about uncontrolled, looking for something to entertain themselves with during their lengthy waits for medical news about their loved ones. Grandparents slept in chairs, oblivious to the chaos around them. We sat along the row of chairs in the hallway, talking on our cell phones, entirely consumed by our own family's trauma and generally oblivious to theirs.

At six o'clock in the afternoon, the SICU nurse told us that we had to leave the Unit. To say the least, we were surprised. *Who would remove the parents of a young man in a coma, after they had travelled 800 miles to be by his side*? We were politely but firmly ushered out of the SICU to the Waiting Room. We learned that the nurses and doctors were shift-changing as they did every day in the SICU at this time of day. It is the time when they clean up patients from the day's activities, update records and pass along instructions for the next twelve hour shift's personnel. We were informed that we would not be allowed back in until 8:30 p.m., when visiting hours started back up. And, then, we would only be allowed to stay until 11:00 p.m.

Faced with no other choice and realizing that we hadn't eaten all day since arriving in Denver, Bert and Jo took Dana and me over to a nearby restaurant, Racine's, to eat dinner. We wouldn't go far from the hospital. We needed to be nearby so that we would somehow not miss a moment when we could be with Michael.

One of the hardest things to do is to return to something normal, like eating dinner, after a traumatic event such as we experienced this day. Sitting in the restaurant, among people who had just come from work and were gathering for some food and spirits, we felt out of place and out of time.

Should we be here while these other people are enjoying their evening out? Can they see that we are in deep pain and emotional turmoil? Don't they know that our son is only several blocks away, fighting for his life and trying to wake up from his coma? We ate enduring the smiling presence and pleasantries of the waiter, who had no idea of the turmoil which was boiling up inside of us, and, as quickly as possible, we returned to the hospital and the waiting room before 8:30. Even though we could not yet re-enter the SICU, at least we were nearby... just in case.

At precisely 8:30 p.m., we resumed our first day's vigil by Michael's bedside. The nurse for the night shift was measuring and recording Mike's vitals and making sure there are no signs of new, unexpected problems. We took our respective places by Mike's bed again, Dana on his right and me on his left, and returned to staring down at him as we had all day. We waited for a sign, any sign that he would wake up. There was none.

At 11:00 p.m., Denver time, we were told to leave the SICU and to get some rest, as we would need our strength for the long recovery period ahead. Leaning forward, Dana kissed Michael on the forehead and wished him a good night. "I love you, Michael," she whispered. I, too, kissed his cheek and told him we would return early the next morning. We reluctantly left for Bert's home, where, as it turned out, we would be residing for the next three weeks.

Thus, June 2 at Denver Health Medical Center came to an unsatisfying and uncertain end. We were exhausted and needed to rest. We had been awake since 2:30 a.m., MDT. But, despite our physical fatigue, sleep was still driven away by the suddenness of the shock and the depth of the fear which consumed our thoughts.

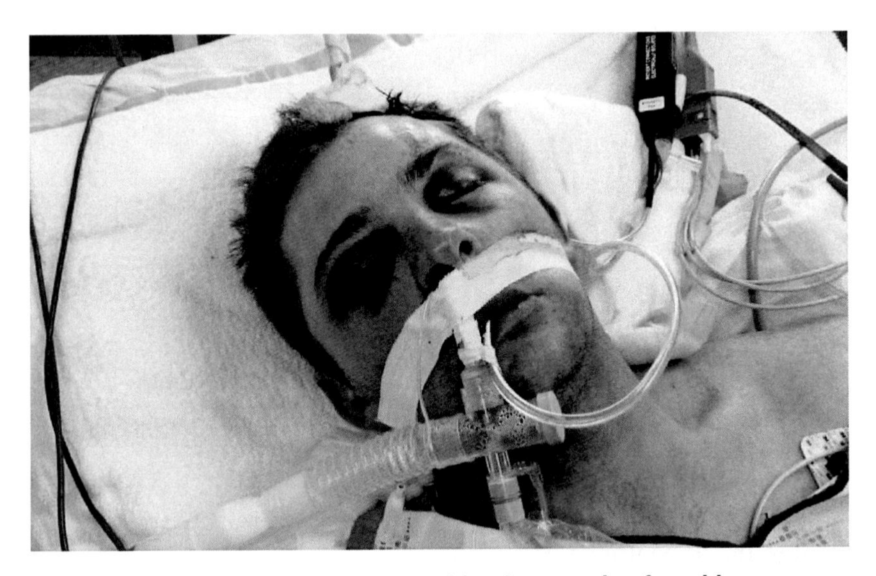

June 4, 2006: Michael lay in a coma with tubes running from his nose and mouth. The "bolt" measuring his intracranial pressure was inserted in surgery two nights before in the Emergency Department. The cranial swelling and bruising around his eyes had begun to subside.

Chapter 4
Inside TBI

What was this that had struck down our son? Traumatic Brain Injury and Diffuse Axonal Injury? Just after midnight the morning of June 3, back at Bert's and Jo's home, I sat down at their computer in their office/living room, to "Google" the topics. Just under a bazillion articles and references appear. I quickly learned that there is a Brain Injury Association of America (BIAA), which had an Arizona branch (BIAAZ) and a Tucson chapter. I made a mental note to return to that website at a later date for resource information in case Michael didn't recover as quickly or as completely as we naively hoped.

I tried to pick out articles which might describe TBI. As I scanned them, I became more and more horrified. Impossibly, I actually became more filled with fear and sadness than when the first call had come in the night before. Reading the articles, the reality of Michael's situation started to sink in.

A brief tutorial into the components of the brain was my starting point. I read that the brain is such a complex organ that the effects of a brain injury are difficult to appreciate at first. The brain is a jelly-like substance surrounded by a firm container, the skull. It is made up of billions of electrical connectors called neurons. Each neuron has receptor ends called dendrites and emitter ends called axons. Electrochemical impulses sent from axons across a gap called the synapse are received by the next neuron's dendrites. The axons are covered in an insulating material called myelin, giving the appearance of "white matter."

When aggregated, the billions of neurons form several key components or sections of the brain, each of which normally performs specialized functions. The base of the brain connected to the Spinal Cord is the Brain Stem, the main transmission line to the rest of the body. Key functions like breathing, heart rate and blood pressure are controlled by the neurons making up the Brain Stem. Also, reflexes and wakefulness are controlled by the Pons, a part of the Brain Stem. Behind the brainstem is the Cerebellum. The Cerebellum controls the coordination of the body's physical movement, conditioning and speech muscles. Right above the Brain Stem is the Diencephalon, which bridges the Brain Stem to the higher functioning Cerebrum. The parts of the Diencephalon include the Thalamus and Hypothalamus. They direct the messages coming from the Brain Stem and other parts of the brain to the other areas of the brain, like the router on a computer system. These parts of the brain also control our urges: sexual feelings, appetite, and weariness, for example. The Limbic system connects the Diencephalon to the Cerebrum and controls our emotions and many of our thoughts. The chief executive, the master strategist and deep memory bank, is contained in the Cerebrum. All of our executive functions – decision making, memory, rational thought, planning and organization – are found in the Cerebrum.

In addition, I learned that these parts were political – having a left and right perspective, and a forward and back component. The Cerebrum is divided into a right hemisphere and a left hemisphere. The front portion is called the Frontal Lobe (executive functions, emotions, and motor movement), the side portion is the Parietal Lobe (sensation/perception and spatial orientation), the lower side portion is the Temporal Lobe (memory, language, and speech production), and the back of the Cerebrum is called the Occipital Lobe (vision).

Confused? So was I. But the fact remained that Mike's brain, this complex jelly-like organ with billions of electrical connections, had been effectively hit by a stationary object while it was moving at 45 mph. In an accident like a fall or a crash, the head is moving at a rapid rate of speed. Then the skull, the body's own crash helmet, suddenly stops against a stationary object... for example, a tree. The brain, however, floating in Cerebrospinal Fluid, continues to travel at a high rate of speed, colliding into the skull. As the brain compresses against the sharp edges of the interior of the front of the skull, the neurons get torn and the axons sheared by the jolt. Sometimes the neurons are cut by bone fragments from a shattered skull. After motion stops in the initial direction, the brain reverberates back against the opposite side of the skull, and a *coup-contrecoup* injury may occur as the side of the brain opposite the initial impact collides again with the skull's bone. More axons are compressed, twisted, stretched and torn.

Electrical impulses in the brain, which normally travel from neuron to neuron across the synapses, lubricated by the chemistry of the brain, are short-circuited. Where the neurons and other protective tissues tear, blood vessels are also torn. The blood from the tears leaves telltale signs of iron, which provides the magnetic scanner evidence of damage within the brain. Sometimes swelling of the brain's folds occurs, which can cause more injury by increasing the pressure of the brain tissue against the inflexible ridges of skull bone. With nowhere to go, the swollen tissue presses on the skull and may cause further damage.

This type of brain injury is called "traumatic" because it is caused by an external trauma, not an organic or internal event such as a stroke. A trauma is some sort of violence to the body. Trauma occurs when something hard and inflexible comes into contact with something moving rapidly, which is soft and flexible, like our bodies.

Michael's injury was a Traumatic Brain Injury with Diffuse Axonal Injuries. There was evidence of widespread bleeding, rips and tears of the axons throughout his brain. His injury was called a "closed head" injury because nothing internal seeped out or was exposed and nothing external (like a glass shard, sharp metal object of some sort or tree bark) had invaded the interior of the skull. The CT Scan, picking up on where the bleeds were most concentrated, showed that his head had first hit on his front left temporal lobe, shattering the skull bone which protected it as well as causing extensive facial bone cracks. Then, his brain had bounced back against the rear of his skull injuring his occipital lobe in the *contrecoup*.

TBI. It consumed my every thought, raised every fear, and made all other routine concerns dissolve into insignificance.

Reading about TBI that night had its own devastating impact on me. The initial turmoil of the day had begun to wear off and now I was left only with my feelings of loss, sadness and concern for Michael and our family.

Article after article pointed out that, when the brain gets injured, virtually every aspect of our lives may be affected. Every type of reflex, every autonomic action, every conscious thought, each type of memory (working, short term, long term), emotions, behavior, motor skills, hearing, eyesight, taste, sense of smell, touch, understanding of language, etc. You name it, and the brain controls it. The list of potentially affected functions is so long that it emphasizes the obvious: We take so much for granted in our daily lives. When we sprain a finger and realize that we can no long grip a pen or hold a fork, only then do we appreciate our hands and fingers. Still we know that the finger will heal and that our bodies, our minds, our very Self is not permanently affected. But, when our brain gets injured, our very existence may be threatened. The brain is tied to every organ, every type of thought and action, and, indeed, every aspect of who we are.

One particularly frightening article, co-authored about 10 years earlier by what appeared to be eight well-regarded neurological and neurosurgical specialists, referred to the likely outcomes for patients with neuron tears and damage widely spread throughout the brain. The article from the WebMD website was simply entitled "Diffuse Axonal Injury" and, according to the website, was last updated on February 24, 2004. Under the section "Mortality/ Morbidity", it stated:

> "DAI rarely results in death. As many as 90% of patients remain in a persistent vegetative state."

Holy Shit! I read these words several times over, trying to make sense of their meaning and their application to Mike's situation. Now I was ***really*** scared for Michael (as if I hadn't been before!). *What if he ends up in a "persistent vegetative state"?* I looked up the term "persistent vegetative state." On the Wikipedia site, I found this definition:

> "A **persistent vegetative state (PVS)** is a condition of patients with severe brain damage in whom coma has progressed to a state of wakefulness without detectable awareness. There is controversy in both the medical and legal fields as to whether this condition is irreversible."

As I read this, early in the morning of June 3, a deep sickening feeling spread throughout my body, tightening my stomach and chest. My own breathing became shallow and rapidly panting. My eyes darted back and forth across the computer screen as I read it over and over again. *"...wakefulness without detectable awareness..." No, not our son! Please don't let him lay there forever "without detectable awareness,"* I pleaded silently. I don't know who I was calling upon with this plaintive thought. All I know for sure is, that night, no one answered.

I went to bed in the basement of my in-laws' home knowing that the very first thing tomorrow when we returned to the hospital I would ask a doctor to read this article. I wanted someone to confirm, or correct, the article's prognosis. I got to bed well after midnight. Dana and I both tossed about all night, never really sleeping.

Awake, we talked through the night. We discussed whether or not Darcy should be there in Denver with us. When we had first arrived there in Denver, we thought that she should stay in Richmond until we found out more about Mike's condition. We had told her to stay put for the immediate future. We felt that seeing Mike in this state would be too difficult for her and we had wanted to protect her from that. But, as we talked more this night about Mike's condition and the seriousness of the accident's effects, we knew that the entire family would be better off knowing that she was here with us. How difficult it must have been for Darcy to be in Richmond and not know what we knew about Michael's status and his chances for recovery. We decided to call her in the morning and have her find a flight to Denver right away. We needed her there... with us and for us.

We got no rest that night. Each time that I dozed briefly, I needed a moment upon awakening to realize that the horrific dream which had started the night before was no dream at all. *It wasn't a nightmare; it was real. It was not going to go away.*

We stirred out of bed before dawn, about 5:00 a.m., on Saturday, June 3. Although it was immediately on my mind, I didn't show the WebMD article I had found the night before on the internet to Dana. I didn't want to needlessly scare her, risking throwing her back into the hysterical shock of the day before. *But the doctors were so noncommittal yesterday. "We'll just have to wait and see," was all that they had said. Now I had reason to fear the worst. Mike may have a life of unconscious existence being cared for by Dana and me until…forever?*

Chapter 5
Shifting Into Gear

When the sun came up, we gave up on sleep. We immediately called the SICU for an update on Mike's condition. The nurse reported that there was no change. After breakfast and showers, we left for the 15 minute drive up Santa Fe Drive to 6th Avenue, turning right toward downtown and DHMC. We arrived at the hospital at 8:30 sharp and went straight into Michael's room in the SICU.

Michael's appearance was not much different from the night before. Tubes hung from his body everywhere. The sounds of the respirator whooshed and clicked - pumping air in, and then out, of Michael's lungs, again and again. He did not respond when we talked to him.

On this morning, the hospital's cleaning lady, who came by to mop the floor, declared that Mike's black eyes were "real shiners." To us, they seemed to have lightened up just a little, turning more reddish purple than black as the blood had started to drain down his face. The swelling in his right eye, which was about the size of a small plum, also had gone down just a bit. Looking for any signs to be hopeful, we took this as the first indication that his healing had begun.

Dana stationed herself again by Michael's bedside, right where she left off the night before, holding Mike's hand in hers, speaking quietly to him. She repeated over and over, "Mike, you've been in a car accident and you're in the Intensive Care Unit at Denver Health Medical Center." Perhaps he could hear her.

But the prognosis of the internet article – *persistent vegetative state* - weighed heavily on my mind as I looked down on Michael's almost inert body. I wanted to ask the first person I could find, anyone wearing a white lab coat, to look at this article which was so ominous in its conclusions ("as many as 90%...").

The morning shift change in SICU personnel had already taken place and the night nurse was gone. Another new nurse was waiting for us. She went over Michael's vital signs. While we had wanted to talk to the attending doctor and the specialists brought in to review Mike's condition, both physical and neurological, they had already completed their rounds and there were few, if any doctors, in sight.

The only "doctor" I could find that morning was the Physician's Assistant to the Neurosurgical team. I gave him the article and asked him for his opinion of its accuracy. He glanced through the article, and, instead of answering me right then, he looked up and told me that he would have to read the article in more detail to determine whether or not he agreed with its content. Whether he was skeptical or just being cautious, I felt that he was dodging the questions the article posed. Perhaps he had to consult with the attending physician before he was allowed to opine on such matters. He took the article and left. He said nothing to alleviate my concerns.

We waited by Michael's bedside. After about an hour, the Physician's Assistant appeared in the doorway to Michael's room. He motioned to me to come outside of the room into the area by the nurse's station. When I had given him the article, I asked him to discuss this out of Dana's earshot, hoping not to alarm Dana any more than necessary. We stepped outside of the sliding glass doors and to one side, trying to hide behind the pulled curtain so Dana would not see us talking. He handed the article back to me. He was not smiling. "This is a pretty good article." His words were simple but poignant. *This real world nightmare seemed to be getting worse all the time. Oh, how I wish he had told me that, for some technical reason, the article I had found was not applicable to Mike's case, that it was hogwash and not worth the paper it was written on, or, at the very least, that the information was seriously outdated.* I again asked him to not share this information with Dana. I wanted to tell her about it when the time was right, when I might be able to explain more about its meaning or when it had become irrelevant by Michael's re-awakening.

Despite my well-intentioned efforts to conceal this information, Dana saw us talking in the hallway, and, wondering what was being said, came out to join us. I told her I had asked the physician's assistant to review an article I had found on the internet and that he thought it was pretty accurate. I did not speak to its contents. Cautiously, I offered the article to Dana for her reading. My offer was immediately rejected. She was in full denial that Michael would or could not recover or that his condition could be compared to what the article described. "No way! Read all you want but I don't want to be dragged down like that," she rebuked. She went back into the room, stroking Mike's forehead and soothing him with her soft and comforting voice.

During this second day, Mike was moved from his bed by the nurse and her assistants. He was positioned sitting up for a portion of the day (no, he was not sitting up of his own accord). Removed from the respirator, he breathed on his own for a short while. His respiration rate was 32 breaths per minute (normal breathing rate is closer to 12-15 per minute). As his body struggled to breathe without mechanical assistance, his pulse became elevated – 125 beats per minute– and the volume of air registered by the respirator monitor had decreased. We were told that these signs indicated how hard Michael's body was working to survive. To ease his physical effort, Mike was put back on the respirator and back to bed after about an hour of being in the chair beside his bed. Then, the respiratory therapist changed the respirator tube from going up Mike's nose to entering through his mouth. Not only did this change make him look a lot better, but it also reduced the possibility of infection in his sinuses.

His state of consciousness was the same. He was in a Level 1 coma. There was no responsiveness, no awareness, just a constant quiet sleep. All we heard was the sound of the respirator sending air into his lungs to assist his breathing.

However, it was not really quiet in Mike's room. Throughout the day people came in and out of the room, checking in, poking and prodding Mike with their instruments and needles. His lab tech was a Nicole look-alike (the spitting image, in fact, of one of Michael's high school friends) who took blood samples several times each day from his fingertips.

On this second day, we met the DHMC Trauma Coordinator, a friendly and sympathetic-looking woman, who explained her role as providing patient and family assistance. She offered us as much assistance as we required. Despite our unanswered questions about Mike's condition, his treatment, his prognosis, we never saw her again.

Later in the day, I talked with the Neurosurgical resident and the Neurosurgical Attending doctor about Mike's injuries and prognosis. They offered more detailed and descriptive information about his injuries (frontal lobe this, occipital lobe that, good ICPs) but still no prognosis. They were waiting and watching just as we were.

We did learn that the ENT (Ear, nose and throat) doctors had decided that Mike would not need facial surgery to repair his facial bone and skull fractures. This news came from the SICU nurse as we had not yet met either the ENT or Orthopedic specialists. It was ironic that the doctors see the patients, but not at times when we, the patient's representatives/next-to-kin, were present or available. These phantom experts were, however, charged with keeping our son alive. Dana and I were frustrated by our lack of first-hand information with which we could form some sort of opinion or expectations about the outcome so that we might begin to develop plans for Michael's immediate future. We just watched and waited, and wondered what we should be doing and what we were *not* being told.

Despite the lack of medical information, we felt that we had much to be thankful for. It is difficult to describe the magnitude and multitude of the outpouring of love and concern for Michael, Dana and myself during this second day. The initial news of Mike's accident had been widely distributed over the internet and by word-of-mouth and shared throughout the Tucson community. We had been contacted by family and many close and caring friends and acquaintances. The news spread to many people beyond our immediate circle as well. Email, phone calls and written notes streamed in and, while accepted for their kind intent, often overwhelmed us.

The rabbi from Congregation Emanuel in Denver came by and offered up a *Mi Shebeirach* healing prayer for Michael at his bedside – on this Saturday which was both Shavuot and Shabbat, no less. Congregation Emanuel had been contacted by our rabbi in Tucson and their clergy and administrator had immediately joined our support group. Janet Bronitzsky, the executive director at Congregation Emanuel, and the daughter of members of our own congregation in Tucson, and her husband Mark, came to DHMC and sat in the SICU waiting room with us. Mike's cousin Adam and his young son, Sam, visited. Friends of Mike's, the two Daves, came by with Julia and Helen. They offered that the Wash Park Grille would send food over anytime we needed it. Of course, Wilbert and Joanne as well as Bill and Anne were often there in the waiting room, lending their support.

The attention and many expressions of caring astounded me. While we were scared and emotional, we were both trying to be hopeful, even optimistic. All of the caring and love expressed to us for Michael by so many people overwhelmed me, an ex-corporate finance guy who had never before experienced this kind of human outpouring. Although it was exhausting to relay the news of the day over and over again, we were happy for the contacts from all of these wonderful caring people.

But our emotions were starting to take their toll on us. This was a difficult day for Dana and me; a day when the initial shock began to wear off and reality had begun to sink in; a day when all we could do was watch, wait, and try to comfort Michael with our presence. At Michael's bedside, Dana and I held each other. We cried copious tears, welling up frequently. We reminisced together about Mike's birthday parties, about a picnic outing years ago when Darcy, Michael and I went to Buffalo Park, south of Denver, about Little League baseball and soccer, about Halloween and vacations.

Dana spent long minutes with Michael, talking softly to him, encouraging him and simply expressing her love to him. We lived this with you, Mike, and were trying to come to grips with your, and our, new futures.

Unable to see further ahead, we made plans only for the next day. We would be calling the insurance company for a rental car and, hopefully, meeting with all of the medical specialists assigned to Michael's case. We also would call our internist in Tucson for prescriptions - ours, not Michael's. We had left Tucson in such a hurry that we forgot our own medications.

After the day shift, required once again to leave Michael's side during the shift change, we rushed back to Bert and Jo's home for dinner. Our dinner breaks were rushed affairs, travelling home and back to the hospital. While there was not much to do in the hospital as we waited for Michael to awaken, *if he would*, we were always anxious to return, lest we not be there when he did come out of his coma. We thought Michael would probably be both confused and scared. We expected an awakening like we had seen on television and in the movies, where the patient opens his eyes and is happy and relieved to see everyone around his/her bedside, able to talk freely and clearly, remembering everything which had transpired. But we lacked the proper understanding of how consciousness returns, *when and if it does*.

Back at my in-laws' home, we sat down to dinner and, numb from the events of the past two days and nights, we ate. Between bites of food, we chatted about Mike. To appreciate the conversation, you need to know that Bert and Jo were the eternal optimists, cosmic souls reaching out for strength from as many spiritual sources as they could find. Logic, reason and scientific knowledge are subordinate to the "life force" from their perspective.

"Yes, he's a good kid, and a strong young man," we acknowledged again and again. They repeated over and over again their assurances that Mike would fully recover. As I listened to their comments which were meant to be consoling, I could not help but wonder how they could be so positive when Michael's doctors would not even attempt a prognosis of recovery. I could not share in their blind optimism. I felt that someone had to keep an eye on reality. I am not much for faith healing. Yes, we knew slightly more of the details of Mike's injuries than when we had first arrived, but there was nothing in those details which indicated anything about his chances for his recovery, full or otherwise.

Following dinner, Dana and I jumped onto the internet again... Dana at Jo's computer, me at Bert's ... to read our emails. We responded to as many as we could before we needed to return to the hospital for the evening visiting hours. After an hour of trying to answer each email individually, we realized that we would have to organize and coordinate our responses. Otherwise, we would be duplicating efforts and confusing many people.

At 8:00 p.m., we left the house again to travel back to the hospital. We arrived at the start of the night shift, meeting yet another SICU nurse. All of the SICU nurses who attended to Michael were great technicians and were kind, compassionate caregivers. Their professionalism gave us a strong confidence in their competence and a sense of calm inside this tornadic-like event. Now late into the evening, we stayed by Mike's side, holding his hand and encouraging him. He lay there not moving, still in a Level 1 coma. Reluctantly, we left at 11:00 p.m., the end to this second day.

We awakened at 5:00 a.m. on Sunday, June 4, after a second night of tossing and turning in our bed in the basement. Despite our physical and emotional exhaustion from the last two days, we could not turn off our worries and fears; they were like childhood monsters under the bed, coming alive when the lights were turned off.

I tried to read the newspaper while eating breakfast. Dana sat down at her father's computer and pulled up her emails and my emails. By now the news of Michael's accident had spread still further by phone calls and the internet to many of our friends and acquaintances in Tucson and elsewhere. There were over 20 emails waiting! This was to be the start of a tsunami of emails we received over the next few days. Each contained an expression of shock upon hearing of Mike's accident and heartfelt wishes for Michael's recovery. Many offered prayers for Michael, Dana and me to help us through these terrible times. Almost unanimously, the messages offered us assistance. Below is a very small sampling of the many notes we received in the just the first few days following the accident.

Emails dated June 4, 2006

> "[We] just want to let you know that you and Michael are in our prayers and our thoughts...I am confident that Michael's strength and spirit along with the care of his doctors and the love of his family and friends will lead him speedily back to recovery and health."
>
> "...What a shame. It is our sincerest hope that he comes through this ordeal a whole person..."
>
> "I am confident that the positive spirit, energy and strength he inherited from the two of you will get him through this trauma...I hope that you feel the strength of our love and concern and that it will help sustain you through this difficult time."

I made several calls that morning. The first was to Eric, Mike's best friend from Tucson, who had been planning to spend the next two months of the summer with his mom who coincidentally lived in Denver. Eric was stricken by the news of the accident. He didn't say very much on the phone. He just thanked me for letting him know and said he would be up in Denver the following week.

The second call was to John Purvis., Esq., an attorney referred to us by my graduate school roommate and college friend, Gary, a successful international business attorney residing in Boulder. Sometime during the day before, I had called Gary's office. We hadn't spoken for several years, but I knew he would be willing and able to provide legal assistance despite our relationship hiatus. Relationships with old roommates are often renewed as if there has never been any lapse of time. Gary expressed his dismay at the news of Michael's accident and told me to call an attorney who had a great deal of experience with auto accidents and claims. Purvis was not home so I left a message on his home phone. The following day, Monday, his secretary set up an appointment time for me to meet with him two days later, when he would be down at his Denver office. The purpose of the meeting, as I saw it, was to discuss the legal ramifications of Michael's accident, which involved alcohol impairment at some level, and the potential for liability claims against the City and County of Denver, Toyota, and Mike himself.

At 8:00 a.m., we traveled back up to the hospital. It had only been two days and two nights, but the trips back and forth to the hospital from Dana's father's house were already feeling like a terrible routine... as if we were caught inside the movie "Ground Hog Day" (without the humor). We would travel in the morning up Santa Fe Drive, past the Drive-in Starbucks, up to I-25 for a short distance, then onto 6th Avenue going east to the hospital, and, each evening, we would drive back - down Broadway, past the Mayan Theater, sometimes stopping at the Dairy Queen on Broadway to satisfy our need for summertime comfort food, then further south to Hampden Avenue, where we would turn west until we reached Sheridan Boulevard. When we returned for the evening, we retraced the same routes, to and fro. We were yoyos on a string, dropping down and being pulled back up, over and over, again and again ... and again.

When we arrived at Michael's room, we were fortunate to actually see one of Michael's doctors, the orthopedic surgical resident. He reviewed the x-rays of Michael's fractured pelvis with me. He said that Mike had fractured both columns of his acetabulum and the iliac wing of his pelvis. He explained that the acetabulum was the part of the pelvis that holds the ball of the femur in place. The femur itself was not broken, despite previous reports. I envisioned the force of Mike's femur being pushed sharply up into his pelvis in a jolting movement caused by the tree collapsing the door of his car while Michael's fragile body kept moving forward.

Orthopedic surgery to repair these injuries was scheduled for Tuesday, June 6. The surgical resident would hand off Mike's surgery to his boss, the attending orthopedic surgeon. As it was described to us, they intended to perform open anterior surgery; that is, they would cut Michael open by splaying his stomach horizontally beginning below his belly button, then cutting across to his left side and around to his left lower back. They said they intended to use both titanium plates and screws to repair the acetabulum but would probably allow the iliac wing to heal itself unless they saw more damage than the x-ray showed once inside. The surgeons cautioned that they might sever a nerve which crosses over the top of the thigh and, if cut, might leave Mike with some numbness across his leg.

I asked them how Michael would tolerate the general anesthetic if he were still in a coma when the surgery was performed. They explained that there would be no increased danger to Michael as a result. But I still wondered how the anesthetic might delay his return to consciousness, pressing the point with them. The doctors seemed to be unconcerned and dismissed my question so that I felt like I was just another foolish father.

Although we were preoccupied with Michael's medical issues, we still had to deal with the more mundane aspects of a prolonged stay in Denver. We called our auto insurance company to arrange for a rental car. Happily, this was covered under the auto policy. However, like all things mundane, this was no easy trick to arrange. Dana explained to the agent that we were from Tucson, but calling from Denver. Not the brightest bulb on the tree, the agent responded by continually asking us if we wanted to pick up the car at the Tucson International Airport.

"No," Dana said in measured tones, "We're in Denver." "Then you can pick up the car at the airport," the agent replied. "No, we can't go out there. We are here on a medical emergency. We want to pick it up at your office in Sheridan, Colorado, which is much closer," Dana explained. "Are you sure you don't want to pick it up at Tucson International? It's closer to your home," the agent went on. They went back and forth like this for several minutes like a well-rehearsed Laurel and Hardy routine until finally Dana got through to the agent. We picked up the car the next day.

Not much else had changed in the 24 hours which had just past. Mike's condition was just "stable," i.e., there was no improvement. Because he was still in a coma, we were not focused on cognitive issues at this point; only his physical condition and medical treatment seemed to occupy our thoughts. His physical body was showing signs of strain from the trauma as it tried to heal itself. His temperature had been rising and, as a result, he was sweating profusely. One of our fears was that, just being in the hospital, exposed Michael to iatrogenic illnesses. We were told that the fever was symptomatic of a blood infection which he was now fighting and for which he was receiving antibiotics. How he came to contract a blood infection was not clear. However, given that he had been bleeding in his car, in the ambulance, in the ER, and inside of his head, we were not really surprised by this.

His lungs had also become congested, perhaps a result of being kept on a respirator for several days. He had developed pneumonia. The nurses and respiratory techs cleared his lungs of phlegm periodically by suctioning out his breathing tubes. This procedure must have been painful because Michael's body reflexively fought the introduction of the suction tube into his lungs. He spasmodically choked and coughed, his chest heaving wildly, for the few seconds of the suction tube's intrusion into his lungs. Once the tube was removed, his chest convulsions subsided.

Dana and I didn't know what to react to the most: the soaring fever, the convulsions or the coma. Mike seemed to be getting worse – not better. And, yet, all we could do was watch and wait, wait and watch.

On a brighter note, during this day, Michael was visited by Cantor Regina Heit from Congregation Emanuel in Denver. She graced Michael by singing a special Mi Shebeirach prayer in the SICU room. Her beautiful voice, singing *a capella*, filled the halls with her soothing spirit and message of hope. This prayer is chanted in both Hebrew and English, and the melody enchants all who are within earshot.

Mi Shebeirach: A song of healing

Mi shebeirach avoteinu
M'kor hab'racha l'imoteinu

May the source of strength,
Who blessed the ones before us,
Help us find the courage to make our lives a blessing,
and let us say, Amen.

Mi shebeirach imoteinu
M'kor habrachah l'avoteinu
Bless those in need of healing with r'fuah sh'leimah,
The renewal of body, the renewal of spirit,
And let us say, Amen.

Lyrics by Debbie Friedman and Dvorah Setel

Cantor Heit left us with a compact disc of her singing various Jewish prayers, which included her rendition of this prayer. The playing of the Mi Shebeirach became a nighttime ritual for Michael, Dana and me and served to soothe his and our spirits before we retired for the evenings. We played the Mi Shebeirach on that CD every evening for the next three months.

Progress Report #1 – June 5, 2006

[We were inundated with requests from family and friends for information about Michael's condition and our status. In order to most efficiently share information about Michael and ourselves, we began to send out a broadcast email, which served as a periodic newsletter. We called these "Progress Reports" hoping to imply that Mike was moving forward and recovering. When this first letter was sent out, it was received by some as shocking news. The email was forwarded by the recipients to many others as well. In just hours, a large segment of the Tucson population was made aware of the accident and Michael's challenge to overcome its effects. We continued to compose these and send them out over the internet for the next 2-1/2 months.]

To all of our Friends and Family:

To catch everyone up, our son, Michael, had a serious car accident on Friday, June 2. We flew to Denver on the first available flight and Darcy joined us last night.

He is at Denver Health Medical Center which is a Level 1 Trauma Center. We are very blessed that he is alive and in this facility. The level of care and attention he is receiving is outstanding and we are grateful to his doctors and nurses. He has four specialty teams assigned to him; Neurology, Orthopedic, ENT and Pulmonary.

Michael's Diagnosis: Severe brain trauma, fractured pelvis, facial fractures. There is no reason to go into the details of the brain trauma. He has been unconscious since the accident. His spine and all internal organs are uninjured.

Current Status: Michael's movement has been purposeful – good. His ICP (intracranial pressure) is very low – good. He has been weaned from his ventilator three times (the last time was yesterday) meaning that he was breathing on his own. The first time was for 1 hour, second 1-1/2 hours, yesterday 8 hours – also good. BP – good. He has developed a fever and they are treating him for a blood infection and pneumonia. He is considered septic today - not good, but expected, we are told. He is having an angiogram on his head this morning [to make sure he was not developing blood clots which might be dislodged and enter his brain] and is scheduled for pelvis surgery this afternoon.

Needless to say we are overwhelmed and still in shock. The love and support of all of our friends and family is also overwhelming, but greatly appreciated.

Michael's address is: Michael Adler, Denver Health Medical Center, 777 Bannock Street, SICU #15, Denver, CO 80204

We love hearing from you and will try to keep you informed as soon as we know more. Our cell phones are on and sometimes we pick up and sometimes we don't, but we know you all understand.

Please keep him in your prayers and again, thank you for your love and caring.

Dana and Ira

The first days in SICU were full of a quiet tension. The hours dragged by as we sat by Michael, staring down at him, waiting for him to show us a sign of consciousness. There were few. His body would react to being poked or prodded by the nurses or techs. His chest would heave when his lungs reflexively tried to clear the phlegm which had settled in them or were being suctioned. His hand might clutch when we touched our hand to his. We wanted him to know we were there with him. Touching him was our only sure way of communicating.

We would talk with Michael. We did not know, but hoped, that he could hear our voices or could understand what was being said. We talked to him about all the people who had called us, who were concerned about him, and who were anxious for us. We would explain over and over again where he was in case he was conscious enough to feel the presence of the hospital despite the darkness surrounding him through his closed eyes. We explained that he was in an accident and that he was badly injured, although we have been told that he would have no memory of the event itself. But most importantly and most frequently, we told him that we loved him and that we knew he would be better soon.

We tried to hold our discussions of his condition out of his earshot, often in the hallway outside of his room. Just as his body was struggling to overcome the physical trauma, his mind was waiting to re-awaken all the thoughts and memories of his life. In those first moments in the SICU, he didn't need to hear the technical aspects of his treatment.

I didn't write any notes in my notebook at the end of June 4. I was simply too emotionally and intellectually drained at the end of the third day in Denver to write anything. But on the fourth day, I once again made some notes. Mike was still doing well physically, i.e., his vital signs were good. And he showed good purposeful movement (as opposed to paralysis or reflex movements). He was weaned from the respirator again, was repositioned to be sitting up, but, once again, his heart rate rose very quickly and his ICP increased. His respiration rate was again in the 30 breaths per minute range and so he was returned to bed and reconnected to the respirator.

We were told that the latest CT Scan confirmed the diagnosis: diffuse axonal injury – meaning that neuron/axon damage had indeed occurred throughout his brain, not just on his left side. This meant that there was a strong likelihood that Mike would have at least some continuing cognitive deficits, if and when he woke up. We always believed he would wake up; we always hoped for the maximum recovery, but we needed to prepare, at least emotionally, for something less than that.

Our nurse on this day was Mary, a sweet, young, but experienced, SICU nurse. She worked with Mike almost constantly throughout the day. Lindsay, the Nicole look-alike, was also there pricking Michael's fingers regularly for blood tests.

Given that Michael was stable, I planned to go down to DU later in the day. I wanted to ensure that the University was aware of Mike's accident and that he would still receive his diploma. I was afraid that, if we were to wait for Mike to regain consciousness and recover, he might never receive the diploma he had worked so hard for. We wanted to be able to congratulate him on his graduation when he awakened. In fact, I became obsessed with this mission. I thought that, if Michael never regained full consciousness or if he awoke with permanent deficits, he might never again have a chance to graduate. But he was only nine days away from graduating when the accident occurred. I would be damned if this was going to deprive him, and us, as his proud parents, of the sense of accomplishment which a diploma would give.

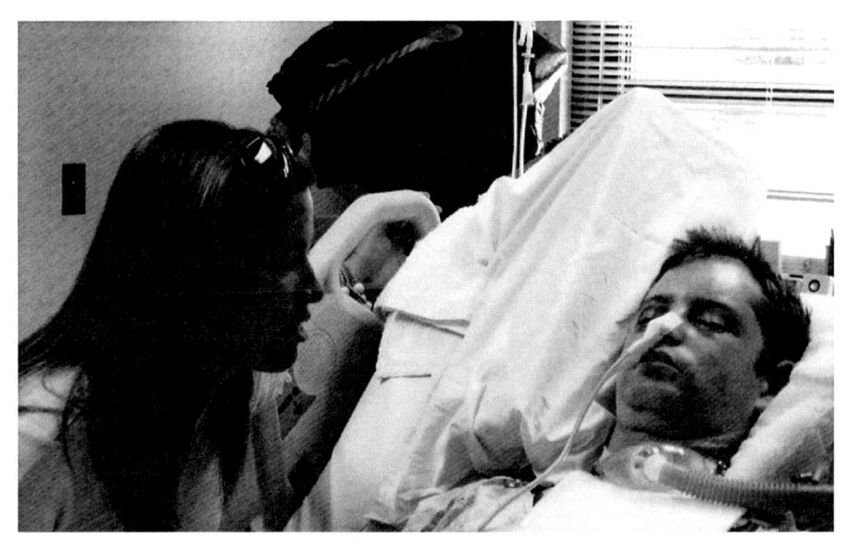

Debbie, Mike's cousin, came from California to visit Michael in the SICU during the first week at DHMC. Mike is connected to the respirator by a blue tube emanating from the tracheostomy in his throat. A N-G (nasal-gastro) tube is inserted in his nose and down to his stomach for feeding.

Chapter 6
Back to School

The University of Denver is a private university located in south central Denver. It is a small school of only about 3,500 undergraduates and 5,000 graduate students. Its campus is located south of the intersection of Evans Avenue (named for John Evans, who founded the Denver Seminary in the late 1800's after establishing Northwestern University and Evanston, Illinois) and University Boulevard. It is surrounded by pleasant residential neighborhoods on three sides and Interstate 25 to the north.

Its campus is a compact collection of mostly red brick buildings, highlighted with copper trim, over an area of about five square city blocks. Despite some new construction occurring in all four corners, there are pastoral open lawns and many trees lining the walkways between its buildings. It's a beautiful place surrounded by residential neighborhoods. Because of its size, both physical and student population, it's hard to become "lost in the crowd" at DU, unlike many large state universities. Each student feels that they are a significant presence during their years there and the faculty tends to form personal relationships with many of their students.

Some 35 years earlier, I had walked this campus and attended classes in pursuit of my Master of Science degree in Business Administration. I remembered spending my time in the Student Union transfixed by the televised Watergate hearings. I had history there. And, now, so did my son, Michael. We are both DU Pioneers.

After visiting briefly with Michael in the morning, I left Dana watching over him while I drove to DU. Driving from DHMC was like taking a mini-vacation from the cold, mechanical, clinical environment of the SICU. I felt some relief from the constant strain and tension of the hospital. But, despite being back in Denver's familiar surroundings, I was anxious about what lay ahead that morning.

The drive from Denver Health Medical Center to the University of Denver is not a long one, perhaps only five or six miles. As I drove, time seemed to warp and return me to the time in the 1970's when I lived in Denver as a graduate student. I drove past many familiar sights which stimulated many memories ... of happier times. The day was warm and sunny. The trees threw beautiful shade over the streets. But didn't those lovely tree lined streets know that my son was in the hospital fighting for his life? Even the drive felt abnormal now.

Having Michael receive his diploma while he was in SICU was surely not our most important concern. But at the time, while school was still in session and Mike's accident was still breaking news to many people, I felt compelled to ensure Mike's graduation from the school. No one knew whether he would ever again be able to pursue his education or complete coursework which might be incomplete. To have attended the school for one week short of the full four year term and not to come away with a diploma to certify the completion of college would have been so unfair. Although he would not walk in the Commencement ceremony, I was going to make sure that he got his diploma.

I pulled into the parking lot to the south of the Mary Reade Library. Old Main, the administration building which was one of Denver University's first structures in the 1800's, was nearby. I looked for the Registrar's office, which I found was located in the basement of the building. The young man attending to the reception desk was busy talking with a student who was trying to obtain her transcripts. So I took a seat to wait for my turn. When, after five minutes, the student left with forms to fill out (*What a surprise! Some things never change!*), I approached the desk.

"I hope you can help me. My son was to graduate this week but was in an auto accident. I would like to see someone about obtaining his diploma. Can you direct me?" I inquired of the young man behind the desk. I struggled to keep my voice from shaking; I was getting very emotional. *Be calm! Stay calm!* I told myself, although I could hardly contain the emotions welling up inside of me.

"Well, no one here can help you out. That stuff is handled down the hallway in the graduation evaluator's office. But she isn't there right now; she's in a meeting discussing the Commencement ceremony." His tone of response was so matter-of-fact compared to my own anxious stuttering that I was truly surprised and taken aback. *Couldn't he tell how upset I was? Can't he see our family's trauma on my face and hear it in my voice? Didn't he appreciate how serious the accident was? Why doesn't he ask how Michael is doing or if he is still alive? And didn't he know how much pain it caused me to know that Michael would not be at the very Commencement they were planning?* Then, I knew. I realized that I was no longer in the hospital, but back in the world of everyday concerns. This was normal; the hospital was not.

"Will the meeting be a long one? Should I wait?" I asked. "If you want. Their office is down the hall and to the left. Take a seat and they should be there soon," the receptionist replied. I sat down in the hallway as instructed, silently deciding to give the meeting 15 minutes before I would get up and leave. I couldn't afford to spend too much time just sitting in the hallway. *What if I was missing out on something critical happening back at the hospital?* I fidgeted with my notebook as I sat there... for 10 minutes, an eternity.

The door to the conference room opened and several people exited. Only two of them approached in my direction. Standing up, so as not to go unnoticed, I inquired if one of them might be the graduation evaluator. The older woman of the two said it was she and asked me what I wanted to see her for. I believe she could tell that I wasn't a student! I repeated that Michael had been in an automobile accident and he faced a graduation dilemma. Her face wrinkled up. She looked personally put out by this news and told me to wait there in the hallway.

After another five minutes, the graduation advisor approached me and invited me to her desk. She did not, however, invite me sit down. I again told her about Michael's accident, his status in the Denver Health Medical Center's SICU and his anticipated graduation the next Saturday. Without a moment of hesitation or consideration, she said she couldn't help. She said she didn't know if Michael could graduate because grades for the last quarter had not yet been submitted. Even if he was qualified to graduate, she couldn't (or wouldn't) get us his diploma since diplomas would not be printed and ready to be mailed until mid- to late July. I asked her how I could find out if Michael had completed his course work. She told me that I had to go see his advisor. However, she hastened to add that she didn't know and couldn't find out who that was. Instead, she directed me to the General Student Advisory office, located across campus in Sturm Hall.

Trying to keep some semblance of calm, but irritated by the graduation evaluator's cold, impassionate response, I exited the Administration building. I was certain of only one thing ... this was not going to be easy. Walking across the campus, past the Penrose Library, which had first opened the year I attended the graduate school – 1972, 34 years earlier, I felt completely out of place. I was 55 years old and not in college anymore. My grey hair made me stand out from the young students making their way across to Sturm Hall. I continued on over the foot bridge which spanned Evans Avenue and into the Student Union / Sturm Hall building. Following the directional signs, I went down the stairs to the lower level where the Student Advisors office was located.

I walked up to the reception desk and explained (yet again) to the young woman sitting there that my son, Michael Adler, was supposed to graduate at the end of this week but that he had been in an accident. I asked if I could talk to his advisor. The young woman behind the desk asked if Michael had a major. I said, "Yes, English." She told me that students with majors were advised by the individual departments and that I would have to go to the English department to see his advisor. I asked if she could look up in the computer who that might be. She replied that she wasn't allowed to. I was feeling more frustrated now and was sure it showed in my face. Seeing that I was troubled and looking a bit defeated, the receptionist asked me to wait while she tried to find someone who might be able to help me. I thanked her and sat back down in a waiting chair.

Five minutes later, a professorial-looking gentleman came out to me and introduced himself, "Ned Muhovich, head of Advisory Services." He invited me to follow him around the corner to his office, which was a small, cramped closet of a space, typical for college settings. "How can I help you?" he asked me. I took a deep breath and, again, began to describe the situation. I explained that I wanted to learn if Michael could get his diploma despite missing Commencement that upcoming weekend.

Dr. Muhovich was sympathetic and told me he would look into the matter immediately. Despite not being the advisor for students with majors, he said that he would call the English department, find out if Michael was qualified to graduate and get back to me. He took my phone number and said he would call the next day. He also said that he was sorry for Michael's accident and hoped he would be better soon. These were the first words of compassion that I had heard in over an hour on the DU campus. I thanked him for helping. This meeting was the first of many with the staff and faculty which showed that the University of Denver indeed had a heart to go along with its institutional intellect. Feeling some relief that I had been able to enlist someone/anyone who could help on this quest for Mike's diploma, I left his office and passed by the reception desk, stopping to thank the young girl for her assistance. Her initiative set the wheels in motion for what turned out to be a very special Commencement and Graduation.

That evening we were visited in the SICU by two of Michael's professors: Susan Schulten, Professor of History, and Ann Dobyns, Professor of English (Rhetoric). Word of Michael's accident and hospitalization had spread quickly from the Advisory Services department to other DU departments, particularly the English and History departments, where Michael had studied for his major and minor, respectively.

Initially, we met Professor Schulten in the Waiting Room of the SICU. She was extremely reluctant to disturb Michael, Dana and me. But we assured her that that was not the case. We greatly appreciated her visit. She told us that Michael was one of her favorite students and that he had been in all three of her classes during his senior year, one each quarter. She loved having him in her class. She told us he was always bright, energetic and engaged in class, even at 8:00 a.m.

As we walked with her through the security doors over to Michael's room, we could tell that she was nervous and anxious. The first sight of Michael upset her greatly. Her legs buckled slightly and she cried. "I'm sorry," she said trembling. "I thought I would handle this better." Dana put her arms around Dr. Schulten and told her not to apologize. His swollen eyes, tubes emanating from his nose and mouth, IVs feeding him, the sound of the respirator, all were too much for her to take in at first. She asked if she could hold his hand. We nodded and said, "Yes, of course." She wept as she gently touched his hand, which lay inert by his side on the hospital bed.

Professor Dobyns had taught Michael a year earlier in her Rhetoric class. She was older than Dr. Schulten, maybe the same age as Dana and me. She too said she had loved having Michael in her class and felt very close to him. She was also deeply moved, seeing Michael laying in his hospital bed. They stayed with Michael for quite a while, staring down at him, both wondering out loud, "How could this have happened?"

Following their visit, in the hallway outside of the ICU, Dana and I thanked them both for coming to the hospital. Meeting them meant a great deal to us and we knew Michael would appreciate their visits. I told them about my visit to DU earlier in the day and how important it was to us that Michael receive his diploma on time. Susan and Ann, as we would come to know them, promised to help and assured us they would take care of it. Both Dana and I were relieved to hear that people who so cared for Mike were going to help us. We smiled one of the few smiles of those first few days.

Email received June 6, 2006

> ...I am still numb. I just can't understand the "why" of the accident. My thoughts drop in on you several times a day. I see you both being strong, resolute, and sad. How in one flip of a second does Michael go from driving his car down a street in Denver to being a trauma victim?

You have a new challenge, one you never expected. What you are doing is far from Temple committees and cooking lessons. Life has grabbed your attention in a way no one ever expected. Committees and lessons were so simple... if only you could awaken in Tucson and recall Denver as a bad, bad dream. I can ask "why" a million times and not get an answer. It is what it is, and you have the love and support of a huge network of friends and family. I ask the Universe to restore Michael to health and to bring you both back to your busy, happy lives.
Stay strong.

S. and R.

Chapter 7
Just the Facts, Ma'am

On June 6, the fifth day following the accident, Michael was unconscious but beginning to move his arms and legs "purposefully" [Rancho Los Amigos Level 2-Generalized Responses].

When we arrived at the hospital, we were shocked to see the change in his condition. *Were we losing him?* He was still septic. His temperature was 103° F (38.4° C). Despite being unconscious, he was sweating profusely and his limbs moved restlessly about in his bed. His bedclothes were soaked with perspiration. To address this, the room temperature was reduced to 60° and the nurses placed a special blanket over Michael which circulated cold water above his body. The hope was that this would lower his body temperature. After a few hours of this, Michael was shaking with chills (reflexively, not consciously). To mitigate his shaking, the nurse tried to place the circulating blanket under Mike's body instead of over him. This helped for a short while until he began to shake once again. Over the next day or two, we would come into the SICU room to see the water blanket under or over him depending on the nurse on duty at the time. It seemed that each nurse had her own individual preference on how to apply the cold water blanket rather than any specific medical protocol to follow. As the positioning of the water blanket changed, especially when its weight was on top of his injured pelvis, Mike showed some irritability and discomfort, moving about spasmodically on the bed... as if possessed by some demon.

On this day, I met with the ENT specialists. We had heard from a nurse that Michael did not need facial or skull surgery to repair the various fractures of his skull. But I wanted to understand how that conclusion had been reached. Because we had never even seen the ENT doctor, I requested (no, *I demanded*) that the doctor spend the time to explain that to us. We went over Mike's CT scan – a truly amazing technology which provides images of the body in 1.3 mm slices. It showed that he had multiple complex fractures of the orbit around his left eye – especially the bridge of his nose. Also, the parietal skull (left side) was fractured. But, because the fractures were not severely displaced (i.e., they matched up and were aligned pretty well), the doctor explained that they believed there was no need to surgically repair them. Also, he pointed out that there had been neither a collapsed sinus nor leakage of cerebral fluid – both of which supported his conclusion that surgery on his face was unnecessary. Knowledge is power, as we all know, and we left reassured by his explanation. Yet, I wondered why the doctor had not chosen to tell us these things… before I had to ask.

Still fighting infections and pneumonia, Mike needed intravenous antibiotics. Meanwhile, he was still awaiting his orthopedic surgery for his pelvis/acetabulum, which had been postponed, bumped from the schedule, as it were, by the arrival of more acute orthopedic emergencies at DHMC's Emergency Department. He was also scheduled for a four vessel angiogram which would look for tears in his posterior and anterior cerebral arteries and the carotid arteries in his neck, lest he throw a clot from some injury there, which would result in a stroke. There was much of this activity going on throughout the day.

At the same time, Mike had many visitors; too many to list here. But they brought baskets of food and fun goodies like a fortune ball (much like the old "8" balls) and gossip magazines. Although grateful for their generosity, Dana and I wondered to each other who would bring magazines to a patient in a coma and we wondered if Mike would be able to read them if and when he woke up from the coma. His friends had pizza delivered for lunch (the first of many we consumed over the next several weeks). His visitors brought flowers and teddy bears and photos. Dana and I were so very proud of all the loving connections our son had made in his time away at school. It was no wonder then that he preferred living in Denver to Tucson!

During the afternoon of June 6, Mike had a central line (IV) inserted below his clavicle in order to ease the delivery of the medications. His arms were bruised black and blue from being poked frequently. It took the surgical resident two tries to get the central line tube to point downward to his heart instead of upward toward his arms. After each try, X-rays were taken using a portable x-ray machine to confirm the tube's placement. Next the technician performed a head CT Scan and the four vessel angiogram. The results were positive in both cases, i.e., they found no more bleeding within his skull and no obstructions of the arteries in his neck. These were bits of good news and we began to appreciate how fortunate Mike was to not have to deal with any added medical issues than he was already faced with [later he required further treatment of some uniquely TBI-related medical issues]. The nursing care Mike was getting was wonderful and appeared to us to be highly professional and competent. We were fast developing greater confidence in the abilities of our nursing and physician staffs.

Dana and I were now pretty worn out from phone calls, visitors, doctors, tests, and emotional highs and lows. We both had had our own breakdown moments. That day we also learned that the preliminary police report, a copy of which we had obtained from the Emergency Department, named Detective J. Estrada of the Denver Police Department (DPD) as the investigating officer of the accident. We phoned over to him at DPD Headquarters to try to learn the status and whereabouts of Mike's car. He was, of course, unavailable but we learned that we could come see him between 7:00 p.m. and 3:00 a.m., which were the hours of his shift. We made an appointment to come down to DPD Headquarters around 11:00 p.m. that night.

Dana, Darcy and I visited Mike in the evening, noting little change in his condition. Then, after visiting hours ended, the three of us drove the short distance between the hospital and police headquarters which is located at the corner of 13th and Cherokee. We parked on the street to the south of the building and walked around to the front. We entered through the plaza between the administrative building and the lockup. It was deserted at this late hour like most of Downtown Denver. Once inside, we were confronted by a female officer who was sitting behind the protective window which served to separate the police from the public in the reception area. The officer looked at us coldly and asked, "What do you want?"

"We have an appointment to see Detective Estrada," I replied. "What? All of you?" she asked indignantly. "Yes." I said, looking back at Dana and Darcy, rolling my eyes to try to communicate, *Here we go! Hang on! This roller coaster is about to leave the station.* "Show me your id's," she ordered. No community relations training in evidence here! We each pulled out driver's licenses and she made some notes on a log sheet sitting on the counter before her. Then she called upstairs and told the detective that we were waiting downstairs ... with her. Then she told us to take a seat there in the lobby.

The lobby of the Denver Police Department Administration Building is decorated with pictures of policemen who have been killed while on duty. The little memorial plaques below each picture gave scant information about each. Aside from these, there was little to look at. Only one other person sat with us in the waiting area. We did not engage in conversation; we waited – in silence.

A man entered the waiting room from a side door to the left of the glass wall which separated the public from the policewoman who had "greeted" us. He was about equal height with me, wore a jacket and tie, not a uniform. He did not smile as he came into the room and looked over toward where we were sitting. We introduced ourselves as he continued to scowl at us.

"They're lucky to be alive; I thought they should be dead." He spoke almost matter-of-factly. Hearing this put so bluntly caught us off guard. I felt a shock, like a bucket of cold water had been thrown in my face, by his seeming lack of concern for our son and, perhaps, also for our feelings. He offered no sympathy, no words of comfort.

He described the accident to us as if it were a scene from the TV show "Dragnet" ("Just the facts, ma'am."): The car had wrapped itself around a tree. Mike was drunk and in very bad condition.

He had interviewed Mike's roommate, Dave, on the scene. Dave asserted that the car hit the median, then swerved across the right lane and jumped on the curve, hitting the tree on the far corner of the intersection of Alameda and Fairfax. The detective said he could not find evidence on either the tires or the curb that the car had actually run up against the center median curb before sliding across the street sideways. (I made a mental note to go check this out for myself.) He said he noted 1/8" of standing water in the street and that both lanes were wet with drainage from the sprinklers. He smelled alcohol on both occupants of the car and took a blood sample only from Michael to test his blood alcohol content (BAC) because he was the driver. There was vomit in the car, although it was not clear who had vomited, but he suggested that perhaps both Mike and Dave had thrown up.

The detective then told us that a citation was likely, pending the police BAC analysis. He said the citation could be for a DUI charge or for the lesser charge of careless or reckless driving. He told us that witnesses, neighbors on this street, one of whom was in bed and the other working in his garage at the time of the accident, heard the crash. These neighbors had called 911 and the paramedics from a nearby fire station had responded in just minutes and, given the severity of the damage to the driver's side door and roof of the car, they had had to use the Jaws of Life to remove the roof in order to extricate Michael through the top of the vehicle. The term "Jaws of Life" refers to a brand of several types of piston-rod hydraulic tools known as cutters and spreaders, which are used to pry open vehicles involved in accidents when a victim may be trapped. During emergencies, when a few wasted seconds can cost lives, the Jaws of Life are brought in to remove victims from the crashed vehicle.

Once again, Detective Estrada repeated, perhaps for emphasis, that Michael was lucky to be alive. He handed us a copy of the preliminary police report, which he said was a "huge" favor to us because we would not have to apply for a copy and wait several weeks to see it. Clearly, his tone indicated that he wanted us to feel beholden to him. Then he told us that the car had been towed to the DPD Impound lot in north Denver, near I-70. He did not offer us any help beyond that. I asked if I could call him to follow up, and he said, "Sure, if I am on duty and in the office."

We left the DPD administration building after midnight, physically exhausted due to the late hour, but curiously aroused by all of this new information. There were a lot of details to absorb. As Dana, Darcy and I drove to Bert and Jo's home, we talked about the accident, in particular, going over the diagram of the Alameda/Fairfax intersection again and again. We came to the conclusion that there was simply no good reason for the accident to have occurred at this time and place. We tried to appreciate that Michael had been lucky, as the detective had suggested, but none of us really felt all that fortunate at that moment. Luck, at least good luck, would have to wait for another time and place.

Late the next morning of June 7 (Day 6), I left the hospital once again. This time it was to meet with attorney John Purvis. Although his main office is in Boulder, we were to meet in another law office near downtown Denver that was shared with other attorneys in a small office building which had been rehabilitated in an older, but up-and-coming, neighborhood. I entered the second floor office, but no one was there. Nor was there anyone in sight. The office seemed deserted. I decided to just sit down and wait until someone passed by.

After a minute or two, a woman, who must have heard me enter, stuck her head out of the first doorway down the hall and asked, "May I help you?" I didn't really need help. So I replied, "No, I am waiting for John Purvis." "Oh, is he coming in today?" she asked. "I hope so. I have an appointment with him at 1:00." I took a seat in the waiting area, looking into the library/conference room, a glass walled room at the front of the office, filled with legal texts and books filled with papers from many transaction closings.

Mr. Purvis appeared a few minutes later. We shook hands, I thanked him for seeing me on such short notice, and he showed me into the conference room/legal library. We wasted no time getting down to the matters at hand. He interviewed me to get the pertinent facts of Mike's accident and I summarized his current medical condition. He explained what I would get from the police:

a police report, which might affect the auto insurance claim, and a notice of impound regarding the location of the car and how to get it and its contents released. He expected that there would be an investigation into the accident. He also said that our insurance company might investigate the accident.

I asked about the potential or possibility of a lawsuit against the City and County of Denver for negligence in watering the medians on Alameda too much so that the water ran off the median and into the road. I postulated that the excess water might have increased the likelihood of hydroplaning during a car's steering correction. Purvis told me that, in Colorado, as in many other states, cities were protected by liability limit laws so that it was unlikely that Michael would recover very much in the way of awards by the court. In fact, he estimated that legal costs would eat up much of the potential award as he estimated that a lawsuit against the City and County of Denver would take a long time, perhaps years, to litigate. He also indicated that a product liability claim against Toyota for a side collision was not a cause of action which could likely be won. The facts were that Mike was intoxicated, or, at a minimum, impaired while driving the car and that most likely he was the cause of the accident.

I left the law office more informed, but with some of the fight taken out of me. I wanted someone to take responsibility for this terrible thing; I guessed it would have to be Michael, although my parental instincts wanted to protect him from that. Deflated, I drove slowly back to the hospital.

While I was meeting with the attorney, back at the hospital, Dana was learning that Michael was going to have his pelvic fractures repaired in surgery the next day. Michael's nurse reported that they had Michael's fever under control and that the combination of antibiotics, Motrin and Tylenol were having their desired effects. We thought his color was improving. We talked only about his physical condition because we didn't have any signs of cognitive recovery to discuss. Six days after the accident, he remained in a coma. He lay there in his bed in SICU #15, his body was still except for the respirator assisted chest heaves as he breathed. He was fed through a tube and was diapered to catch his waste. He didn't complain, joke, smile or frown. We knew that there was so much going on inside his body as he fought to overcome his injuries, but outside there were few signs to stir our hopes. He was mostly quiet and immobile. And we were waiting, just waiting.

Dana and I had fallen into an uncomfortable daily routine by this time. We awakened in the morning, ate breakfast, checked emails, considered what the day might hold, and, without hurrying, arrived back at the hospital each morning at 10:30 a.m. We first checked in on Michael, and then we took turns answering or making phone calls in the reception area of the SICU, taking 30 to 60 minute breaks from our vigil by Michael's bedside.

Michael's friends, teachers and our relatives visited frequently. We tried to provide them some solace by updating them on the latest news of Michael's condition. We were also visited often by our new acquaintances from Congregation Emanuel. Everyone had come back to be with Michael for at least a few minutes each day. We believed he appreciated and might somehow be aware of their presence and devotion. Dana and I were grateful and deeply moved by their visits and, unexpectedly, found enjoyment in making new acquaintances. Without their company, we would only have had ourselves and the medical professionals to talk to and the sight of our son passive and still in his hospital bed.

Chapter 8
Breakthrough

We arrived earlier than usual on Thursday, June 8. Michael was scheduled for surgery that morning and we wanted to be in the Surgery Waiting Room during the procedure. The surgery had been postponed from the day before due to the orthopedic surgical team's availability. The orthopedic team was indeed busy performing over 50% of all surgeries in DHMC's Emergency Department.

Prior to going into surgery, the doctors performed a tracheotomy in Mike's throat and eliminated the breathing tube from his mouth. Having a hole cut into one's throat and a tube inserted into one's lungs doesn't sound very appealing. However, it helped Michael breathe more easily by eliminating some of the distance air would need to travel in his windpipe to enter his lungs. Whether Michael felt any relief or was consciously aware of the change, we could not know. However, removing the tube allowed his mouth muscles to relax and his mouth to return to a more normal expression. His whole body seemed to relax also without the strain of respiration through a tube in his mouth.

Surprising us, his SICU nurse leaned over Michael and spoke directly to him. She asked him to raise two fingers. In response, Mike made a slight effort to lift his right hand. Then talking louder and closer to his face, she loudly asked Michael to give a thumbs up sign, "like the Fonz," a reference to the trademark move of the character Arthur Fonzarelli of the 1970's television show "Happy Days." Responding to her loud voice, Michael clenched his right fist and, with great effort and purpose, raised his thumb and arm off of the bed. A moment later, his arm fell to his side.

The thrill! The joy! The elation! Dana and I were so happy, excited and relieved that we both cried. Everyone present in SICU #15 hugged each other, smiles burst out from ear to ear, we laughed and then cried again with happy tears. Our hearts literally leapt for joy and, for the first time in a week, I felt that I could breathe again.

Michael had moved on his own! He had responded to voice, and, for the first time, we knew he could hear. He had not only heard her voice but also had understood the nurse's command. That is, he had been able to translate that understanding to a motor response. With that smallest of actions, a raised fist and thumb, Michael had shown us the first sign that his mind was waking from its coma. He had started to progress to Rancho Los Amigos Level 3: Localized Response.

"Thumbs up" became the informal signal of doing well through the rest of Mike's stay in DHMC. The hand gesture became the sign we all used to indicate that Mike was going to recover and return to us. This seemed so appropriate for Michael. "Thumbs up" is derived from ancient Roman times and signified the people's desire, and the emperor's decision, to spare the life of a gladiator in the cruel and often fatal games put on in Rome's Coliseum. Oh, how Michael would have appreciated that. Ever since taking Latin in middle school, he had been an ancient history *aficionado*. Now, he was our gladiator, fighting for his life and being rewarded for his good fight. Thumbs up!

Later that morning on June 8, seven days after the accident, Mike finally had the surgery to repair his acetabulum. The operation lasted three hours. While we waited in the Surgery Waiting Room, Beth, the surgical nurse, came out and said all went well. We felt tremendous relief. The surgeons had placed six titanium screws in Mike to hold him together. They reported to us that there was no need for plates and no further repairs were needed once they could clearly see the other pelvic damage. He was left with a scar that ran from his right side all the way across the front of his stomach, below his belly button, and around to his back on the left side. Mike stayed in the recovery area until he was later taken back to his room in the SICU.

While we were waiting in the Surgery Waiting Room, I

received a call from Professor Schulten. She told me that the Dean had cleared the way for Michael to receive his diploma on time. Susan said she would personally deliver it to us on Friday! Dana and I were overjoyed by this news. We were so proud of Mike for this accomplishment. But we were even prouder of the fact that his relationships at DU with so many schoolmates and professors were being recognized and rewarded with their kindness.

That day, his friends continued to visit – including: Helen, Julia, Lindsay, Liz and Ann, and Professors Schulten and Gilbert. Marcy, one of Darcy's oldest friends from her middle school and high school days, and Matt, her fiancé, who were soon to begin internships at Denver's Childrens Hospital and DHMC, respectively, came by to visit as well.

Most happily, Mike's best friend, Eric, arrived on this day from Tucson and visited with Mike. Eric is a wonderfully compassionate young man. It was clear that he was devastated by Michael's accident. He was nervous about entering Mike's hospital room, but, once inside, he quietly sat by Michael's bedside for many minutes, holding Mike's hand in a warm handshake. If Michael had had a brother, we would have wished that he would have been like Eric. It warmed us to see them together in this time of crisis.

Despite all of the exhilarating events at DHMC on this day, life's more mundane issues kept coming at us. A claims agent from Liberty Mutual called and explained that Mike's car would have to be appraised by a field appraiser and then valued at Actual Cash Value based upon some special valuation chart used by insurance companies. She informed us that Liberty Mutual would send us a check for $1,000 for medical expenses per the policy's terms, without any further delay. Pretty good service, Dana and I agreed.

Then, at 7:15 p.m., Detective Estrada called and informed us that, like the blood sample taken by Denver Health upon Michael's arrival in the ED the night of June 2, the DPD blood sample taken at the scene of the accident showed that Michael was not legally Driving Under the Influence (i.e., above .08 BAC) but showed that he was legally impaired (i.e., his BAC was somewhere between .05-.08). We took this, also, as good news.

This had, indeed, been a good day! A very good day!

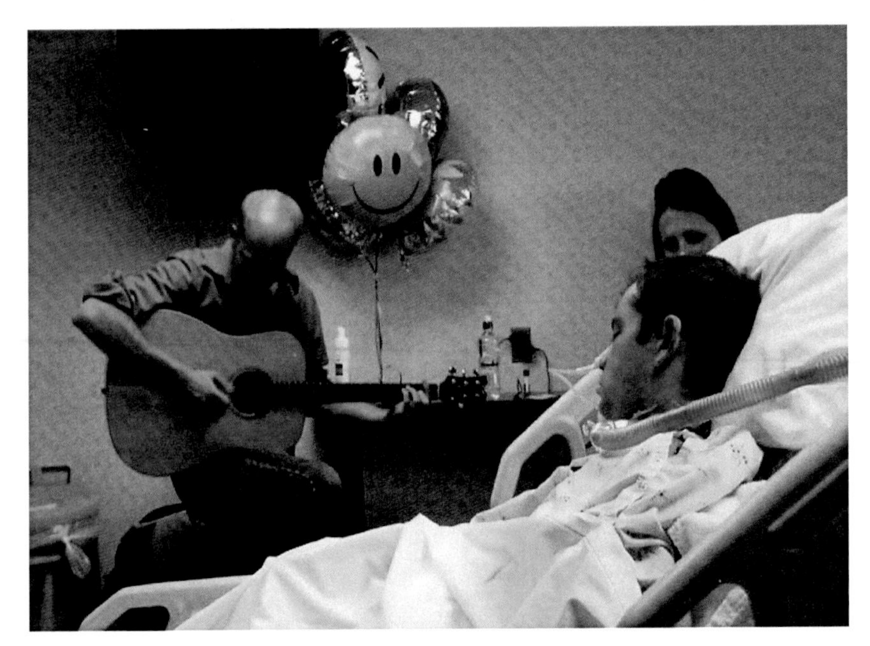

Eric serenades Michael in the SICU. Before the end of the summer, Eric had written a ballad about their special friendship, which brought tears to all who were fortunate enough to hear Eric perform it for Mike.

Chapter 9
Graduation

Sometimes we experience life in ways which fill our hearts with love and lift our spirits so high that we feel like we are soaring, in-flight. At those times people perform such great acts of goodness that they brighten even our darkest moments. Then, only joy colors our world, and our sadness is pushed back, if only just temporarily. **June 9, 2006** was such a day.

Early that Friday, DU Professor Margaret Witt, who was both the chair of the English Department and Michael's advisor, came to see Michael. Dr. Witt arrived at 9:30 a.m., before visiting hours and, so, we missed seeing her. Nevertheless, Dr. Witt left us a warm note of concern for Michael which we saved in his welcome journal. She later returned that morning to visit with Dana, Michael, Darcy and me. She brought with her a copy of Mike's freshman year orientation class portfolio, which included photographs taken by Michael during his first quarter at DU. It was a glimpse into the type of student and person that Michael was when he first started at the university. She left the portfolio with us. Her genuine affection for Michael warmed our hearts and, I'm sure, would have strengthened Mike's resolve if he had been aware of her presence.

That afternoon, Professor Schulten accompanied by Jennifer Karas, Associate Dean of Arts, Humanities and Social Sciences, came to the SICU. They carried with them the printed program for the Commencement ceremony for the University of Denver, which was scheduled for 10:30 a.m. on Saturday, June 10. They also brought Michael's diploma and the red collar of the Pioneers which would be worn by the undergraduates over their robes as they graduated the next day. Susan and Jennifer stood by Mike's

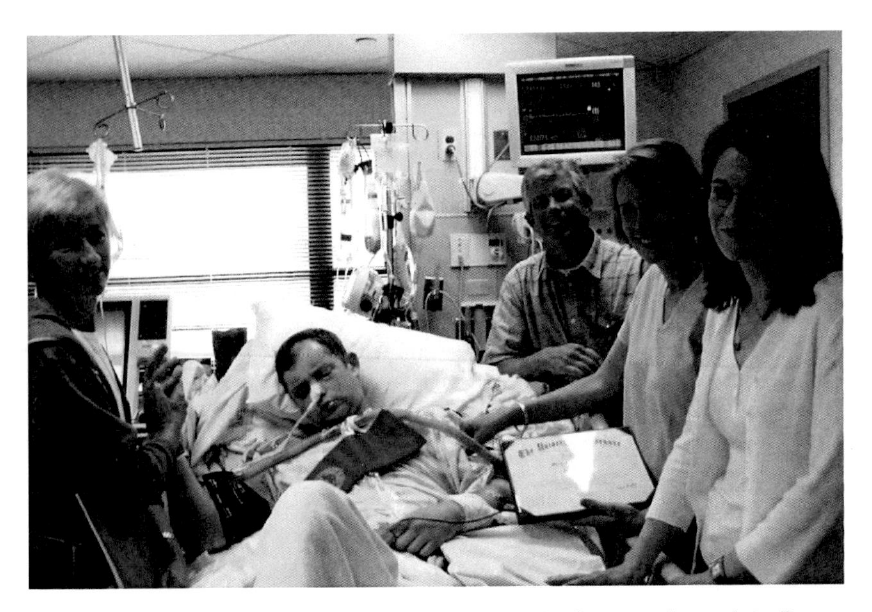

June 9, 2006 Graduation: (l. to r.) Dana and Ira look on as Associate Dean Dr. Jennifer Karas and Dr. Susan Schulten of the University of Denver delivered Mike's diploma, sash and cap in an impromptu graduation ceremony held in SICU #15. With Commencement scheduled for June 10, Michael thus graduated "first" in his class.

bed while Dana, Darcy and I stood close by. With all the pomp we could muster, we gathered formally around Mike in his bed in SICU #15. Dean Karas presented still-comatose Michael with his diploma, gently placing the red sash on his chest without disturbing any of the tubes and wires running from his body to the monitoring equipment, and placing the diploma on his stomach.

Dana and I, overcome simultaneously with pride, joy and sadness, both quietly cried, while Darcy smiled broadly. And Michael... well, we believed he knew he had completed a wonderful achievement, earning his Bachelor of Arts in English. From that day forward, he would forever be a DU Pioneer graduate and alumnus.

Dean Karas handed me a DU alumni pin, which, she said, every graduate pins on his/her neighbor at graduation following the Commencement roll call. I vowed to wear that pin on my lapel every day during Michael's recovery as a symbol of my pride and support for my son. And, in fact, I wore the pin every day until we returned to Tucson... over two months later.

Dean Karas and Dr. Schulten wanted to leave quickly so as not to disturb Michael, but we encouraged them to move closer to the bed with Michael in it so that we could take a photograph of the ceremony, preserving the moment to share with Michael when, not if, he awakened. As we pushed closer and closer, forming a circle of love around our son, we were deeply moved by this alternate Commencement. It was time for Michael to "walk" with his classmates. It was time for Michael to wake up!

I will always remember that, on Friday, June 9, 2006, the University of Denver community, including the provost, the associate dean, the director of advisory services, the English, History and Graduate Studies departments, and our new friends on faculty showed their support and love with their embrace of our son. What a wonderful special memory DU had given to all of us.

Progress Report #2 – June 9, 2006

Thank you for all of your wonderful emails filled with kind thoughts, warm wishes and prayers for Michael's recovery and in support of our family. We feel the love, support and energy all working for him.

Much has happened in the last two days.

- *Michael's fever is under control. He is on several antibiotics for pneumonia and a blood infection and all of that should be eliminated with time.*
- *A tracheotomy was successfully performed yesterday. The advantages are numerous: this will enable him to breathe much easier when he is weaning off the respirator; oral hygiene is better maintained; the irritation of a tube down his throat will be eliminated; and case studies indicate patients heal faster and better on a trach rather than a tube. He also looks 100% better without the tube being adhered to his entire face. He's so cute!*

- *Michael had surgery Thursday to repair the fractured acetabulum, the bone within the pelvis that holds the femoral ball. Everything went very well and the surgeons were able to align the fracture and secure the bones with screws only (no plates). They found no other injury and the other fracture of his pelvis is deemed relatively insignificant and expected to heal by itself. They did have to sever a nerve that will result in a permanent numbness to the surface around the thigh area but will not affect his ability to walk or his strength. One of Michael's anesthesiologists was Dr. Amanda Selwyn, daughter of Dr. Jeff Selwyn, from Tucson. This provided us a great deal of comfort.*

- *All of his vital signs are stable and good.*

Now for the miracles of life...

Rabbi Cook from Congregation Emanuel in Denver has come to visit Michael two times. On Wednesday, before he left, he said a Mi Shebeirach (a prayer for healing) for Michael. As we were leaving the room for Michael to be bathed, his nurse said, "Hey Michael, can you show me two fingers?" And, Michael lifted two fingers. He was next asked to wiggle his toes, which he was able to do.

Michael's left eye has also opened, albeit not all of the way but enough so that we can see his iris and pupil. When Darcy was speaking to him he was looking at her and then, when Ira was speaking to the surgeon, he turned his head and was looking towards Ira.

Michael continues to be very purposeful in his movements when not deeply sedated. He is also extremely strong so the nurses have his arms tied down very tightly to keep him from reaching up and pulling on the various tubes and wires. He becomes more active as his sedatives wear off.

Just before going to surgery yesterday he was coming off his medicine so the nurse told him he was getting ready to go on a road trip and asked if he could give us a "thumbs up, like the

Fonz." Let us tell you, a thumb has never looked so beautiful as he raised it twice on command, making a fist and lifting his thumb upwards.

The accident occurred the evening after his very last college class. Michael had one graduate level class that required a final paper for the entire grade, which Michael is obviously not able to turn in. Ira visited DU (the University of Denver) to inquire about the status of obtaining his degree and was told by the Director of Student Advising that the decision was up to his professors. The Director said he would contact all of his professors to find out his status. Since Michael has been in the hospital he has been visited by two of his favorite professors and, yesterday, we received a phone call from one of them informing us that Michael's diploma will be hand delivered to him today! We are so grateful to all of those at DU who helped make this happen for Mike. We are so proud of him.

Yes, we would have to say that the last two days have been very good. As one nurse said, "Michael came to us broken, and then he got sick. Our job is to get him well, fix his breaks so that he can begin the healing process."

This is so true and with the love, support and prayers from all of you and his strong will and determination, we know he's on his way!

Love to all of you,
Dana and Ira

We had been up in Denver over a week and we had become accustomed to the rhythms of the SICU. We knew the routine doctors' rounds occurred before we arrived at 10:30 in the morning. Michael had been seen by the attending physicians, and the nurse, who had arrived for the daytime shift, had been briefed by the nurse who had just spent the nighttime hours with our son. The bedclothes had been changed, the sheets replaced and the room cleaned up.

Despite the medical apparatus hanging from hooks everywhere, the scene upon our arrival each morning looked almost normal now. The sounds and sights of respirators, IV monitors, and the

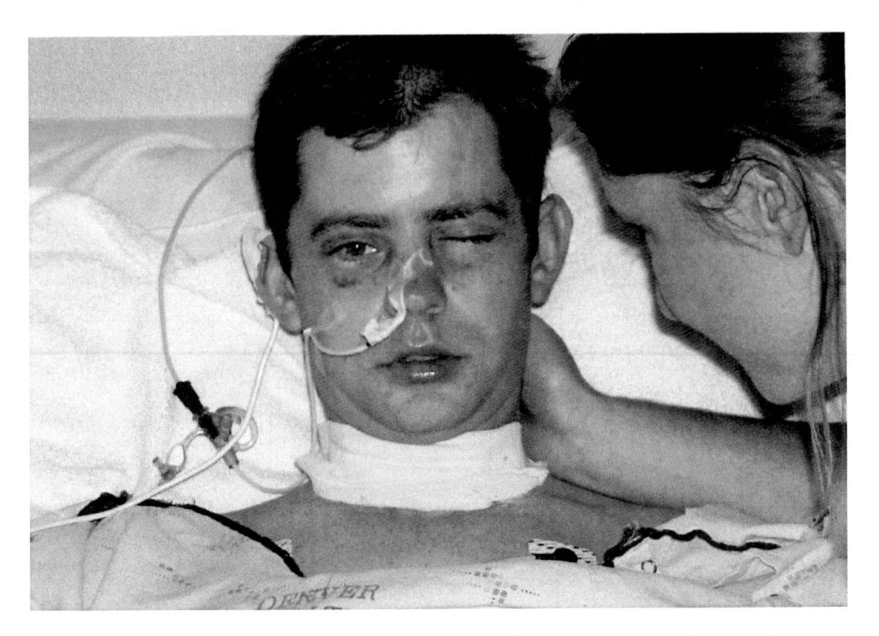

Michael winks (with Darcy): As he returned from the coma, Michael gradually opened his eyes. His eyelids, still bruised from the impact of the tree in the accident, would flutter and his pupils would search for something to focus on. His mind worked hard to make sense out of what he was seeing.

others were all too familiar. We checked their data monitors as soon as we entered SICU #15 for another day of surveillance over our son's recovery: heart rate, blood pressure, oxygen levels, and respiration rate. He was connected to the monitors by an array of wires and tubes.

Michael was generally unresponsive and passively lay there in his bed. He moved without stimulation, but not in a reflexive way. He seemed to be trying to stretch out his muscles, extend his legs, and feel his body. His actions could be characterized as "mild thrashing about," but his movements seemed more "purposeful."

Michael was able to open his eyes only with great difficulty. His eyelids flickered as if any light was too bright to be tolerated by his optic nerve. And yet, he struggled to raise his eyelids in a series of fluttering blinks, opening further with each try. *Can he see anything? Does he know what he sees?* When not asleep or receding back into coma, he seemed to labor to connect to the visual world.

The external signs of his injuries had begun to subside. The darkest bruises had lightened up and his color was returning. The swelling around his face had significantly subsided. He looked like Mike again. His hairline, shaved for the implantation of the bolt on that first night in the Emergency Department, had begun to fill in, but it was still a prominent reminder of which part of his body was most critically injured.

We will always remember Saturday, June 10! This was to be Michael's graduation day from the University of Denver and, indeed, it was a day of commencement and of new beginnings. Many of Michael's friends came to the hospital for a graduation party. We gathered in the Family Consultation Conference Room of the SICU which had been decorated by Mike's friend Charla with DU red and gold crepe paper and balloons. She also set out soda pop and cupcakes on the conference tables. We were joined by Mike's co-workers from the Grille, friends from college, fraternity brothers and dorm mates. We took pictures, signed poster boards, cried and laughed together. Considering the surroundings, it was quite a joyous gathering. The only person missing from the conference room was Michael himself.

June 10, 2006 Graduation Day Party: In the Family Conference room next to the SICU, friends gathered to celebrate Michael's graduation from the University of Denver. Standing (l. to r.): Ira, Matt, Marci, Leslie, Dave S., Helen, Charla, Evan and Darcy. Seated (l. to r.): Cousin Debbie, Dave, Erin, Dana and Maria (Marci's mother).

At this time, Mike was allowed to have only two visitors at one time. Thus, two by two, Mike's college friends and co-workers left the conference room to go to SICU #15 to visit him at his bedside. When the first two were done visiting, the next two would go in to join Mike, until everyone had had a chance to spend time with him. *Surely he must know how great these friendships are*. We wished that they could all remain friends throughout his life time!

It was reported to us that Michael's name had been announced *in abstentia* at DU's Commencement ceremony. His was the first name to be read in the alphabetical order. The announcement was followed by clapping and cheering of students and teachers in the audience despite a stern admonition by the Chancellor to hold all applause until all the names had been called. We felt Michael had been honored by the other students but sad that we could not be in attendance celebrating with them.

Later that evening, as if motivated to see what all the fuss was about, Mike opened his eyes wide for the first time! His eyes stayed open, blinking and fluttering constantly, for about an hour. This signaled another sort of graduation. As we watched his eyes flicker in and out, Dana and I teared up (yes, again) with happiness. I grabbed the general surgery resident in the ICU who was just passing by the room to show him that Mike was awake. He smiled and said to Mike, "Awesome, Mike, awesome!" capturing our feelings as well.

Following a day in which Michael had hardly moved at all, resting peacefully as friends and family were asked to keep the external stimulation to a minimum, Mike had opened both eyes. He may have had trouble focusing or understanding what he was seeing and why, but he clearly did see the light and followed us all about the room. He particularly focused on Darcy, reaching out with his hand to touch her bracelet and sweater. Our hearts were lifted sky-high by this momentous sign of progress, another graduation present given to us by Michael.

That same day we were informed that Mike would likely be moved to the Step Down Unit (SDU) in the next day or two. The surgical resident discussed Mike's medical condition with us and he told us that Michael would soon be deemed non-critical, despite not being fully conscious. All that *medically* needed repair had been repaired or was in the process of healing. Mike continued to fight fevers, high blood pressure swings and rapid pulse, but we were told that these were all positive signs of his body's internal struggle to heal!

Dana and I had become strangely accustomed to the environment in the SICU and felt comfortable with the level of care Michael was receiving. Hearing that Mike was to be moved, we became anxious and fearful once again. Sensing our discomfort with the thought of leaving the SICU for the SDU, Theresa, the day nurse, offered to escort us over to the SDU, which was located in the then new addition of the Denver Health Medical Center. She explained that the rooms there were much more conducive to the patient's comfort, yet still fully capable of, and equipped for, acute care. The SDU rooms are more like private bedrooms than medical cubicles. While we would miss the extremely close care and attention of the SICU nurses, we were very happy that this change of location indicated that Mike was, indeed, getting better. We ended the day on this positive note.

The next morning, while Dana returned to the hospital, I went to Michael's condominium for the first time. I had been reluctant to go there and had put it off for over a week. To get there, I drove right past the location of the accident. The tree stood with only a few scars in the bark from the impact. As I went by, I stared hatefully and silently wished the tree would die as punishment for the pain it had inflicted on our son.

At the condominium complex, I parked in Michael's parking space, got out of the car and climbed the three flights of stairs to the third floor hallway. When I opened the door and entered the small hallway entrance to the apartment, it felt familiar, yet uneasily empty. Dave, Mike's roommate, who had survived the accident relatively unscathed, at least physically, was there. As I walked from room to room, I could "see" Michael everywhere. His photos, his new furniture, his books… everything reflected Mike's tastes. In his bedroom he had hung two enlargements of pictures taken by him that spring in Panama. One picture was a head shot of a monkey taken during a river boat trip; the other was a close-up of a tropical flower. They were both beautiful photos! *Mike has such a good eye for photo composition*, I thought to myself… and then I wondered if he would still be as creative when he recovered from his brain injury.

The curtains covering the windows in the living room of the condominium were a dark blood red – opaque to keep the light out during movie showings on the new flat screen TV. I looked around the room further and saw that there were surround sound audio speakers. His dining room table was a dark wood with a triangular pattern on the surface. Through the glass door, I could see that the patio was also fully furnished with four chairs, a table and a large gas grill. I walked to the end of the hallway off of the living room and looked into Dave's bedroom. It was pretty sparsely furnished and decorated only with a few family pictures.

Dave and I sat in the living room on the huge green sofa which he and Michael had picked out together. We talked about Mike, the condo and the future. I told Dave to expect that Mike's recovery would take a very long time and that he faced a difficult road ahead. I sensed that Dave was not comfortable with this discussion. But he walked over to the kitchen, reached up above the refrigerator and brought down a bottle of rum from Grand Cayman which the boys had bought for me during their Spring break cruise. He handed the bottle to me and said that Michael and he had intended to break it open with me following graduation. I held the bottle in my hand. It was a sad reminder that, but for the accident, we were all supposed to be celebrating this weekend… with rum toasts. But now the celebration was on hold indefinitely.

I tried to suppress my feelings in Dave's presence. But, when I returned to the hospital, as I walked down the hallway through the locked doors leading to the SICU, I could keep my feelings inside no longer. I stopped, turned to the wall, shuddered and began to sob uncontrollably. Through my breaths, I repeated aloud over and over, "I want my son back! I want my son back!" Dana held my shoulders with her hands. I don't know why I broke down at that exact moment, but my pent-up emotional turmoil seemed to pour out of me all at once. All my fears, like emotional magma, came pouring out in wet tears and loud sobs. I turned to the wall of the corridor to support myself as my knees buckled. It took me a full five minutes to regain my composure, and, with some deep breaths, and Dana's hand in mine, I returned to Michael's side.

Progress Report #3 – June 11, 2006

First of all, we can't thank you enough for all of your emails of concern and support for Michael, Dana, Darcy and me. Your kind wishes and offers of assistance sustain us each day.

We continue to have only good news to share. Each day Michael makes some small progress and has had no setbacks. The path he is on is going to be a long one, but we believe, also a good one. He remains just under the surface of consciousness and we are hopeful that he breaks through soon.

- *Great news! Michael has opened his eyes and kept them open for long periods. He is slowly "awakening" and we hope to see him recognizing everyone very soon.*
- *He is breathing completely on his own now as well. The respirator was removed early yesterday.*
- *He spent his day upright in a chair and strongly grips the hands of all who visit.*
- *There have been no complications from his successful pelvic surgery on Thursday afternoon.*

All of this adds up to a strong and improving physical condition while showing small, but continuous, signs of neurological improvement. As a result, Michael will be moved from the Surgical ICU to the Step Down Unit for interim care prior to being relocated to a longer-term care facility or rehabilitation hospital.

Because of the interim nature of the Step Down Unit, we will need to decide in pretty short order on where Michael will go next. While we will be consulting with the staff at Denver Health Medical Center, we would like to ask any of you or any of your contacts for assistance in identifying facilities that specialize in rehabilitation and care of traumatic brain injury patients. We are looking at facilities in Denver, but would also like to investigate facilities in Tucson, Phoenix or other locations. We recognize that we need to match Mike's needs with the facilities capabilities, but right now we are casting a wide net until Mike's needs can be further evaluated and more specifically defined. Any assistance or referrals would be greatly appreciated.

Dana, Darcy (who left to fly back to Richmond today... we are missing her already) and I are heartened by Mike's progress and convinced that he will not only endure this difficult episode but will also emerge stronger than ever.

Love to all of you,
Dana and Ira

P.S.FYI – We were planning a family vacation to Lake Tahoe 7/1 – 7/15 on the north shore area. Obviously we have cancelled these plans but unfortunately were unable to get our money refunded. If you, or anyone you know, are interested in renting a 5 bedroom, 3 bath, mountain home in a gorgeous location please let us know.

This call for assistance in finding a rehabilitation environment suitable for Michael brought another wave of valuable email from the Tucson community. However, because of the specialized nature of his injuries, many suggestions led us to facilities which were either not appropriate for Michael or significantly distant from either Denver (Michael's home) or Tucson (our home). With the aid of the internet, we read about Atlanta's Sheperd Center, the Northwestern Neurological Institute in Chicago, and others in the Midwest and East Coast. We looked into Barrows Neurological Hospital in Phoenix and considered both inpatient and outpatient therapeutic environments. We focused on the smaller radius of the area around Denver because it had the advantage of not having to transport Michael in aircraft accompanied by nurses to what might have been a place unfamiliar to each of us. Dana and I considered and visited several of the rehabilitation hospitals around the Denver/Aurora, Colorado metropolitan area.

The one place we kept coming back to was Craig Hospital, just "down the road" in Englewood, Colorado, adjacent to Swedish

Medical Center. For years Dana and I had been aware of Craig Hospital's reputation as one of the finest spinal cord and traumatic brain injury rehabilitation facilities in the country. Many famous people were reputed to have been treated there... including several of the Denver Broncos and actor Christopher Reeve. But we never before, in our wildest imaginations, thought we or our family would want or need its specialized capabilities.

We performed our own research to confirm Craig Hospital's services. Dana's father, Bert, provided valuable assistance by driving over to Craig, just a few miles from his home, to collect some printed information about Craig and its admission policies and procedures. He returned with pamphlets and a video which described the hospital.

Events were moving quickly now. Not so much in Michael's SICU room where signs of recovery were gradual, yet continuous, but there was so much for Dana and I to think about, to plan for, and to deal with. We have always thought of ourselves as well informed, educated and actively engaged parents. At this juncture, we had to absorb so much information in so little time. We were getting a time-compressed medical, risk management, social and spiritual education. I could not keep track of it all without making a list. On June 12, I wrote the following lists of organizations to look into:

Notebook Entry – June 12, 2006 (Day 11)

Brain Injury Association of America www.biausa.org

National Directory of Rehabilitation Services

BIA of Arizonainfo@biaaz.org

St. Josephs Barrows Neurological Institute – just a little better than Tucson

Craig Hospital – best anywhere near the West coast

Carondolet St Mary's – has outpatient "Bridges Now" program

Scottsdale Healthcare

Lisa Sternberg Tucson

Spalding Rehabilitation Hospital

Kindred Hospital

Select Specialty Hospital

Colorado Acute Specialty Care Hospital

Chapter 10
Moving Up to Step Down

On Sunday, June 11, Mike showed us his baby blues again. He looked but his eyes were unfocused and rarely moved from side to side. His head did not turn.

He was moving around in bed continuously now. He still had a fever and was sweating profusely while fighting several infections. Dana spent most of her day standing by Mike's side and wiping his brow and face with a cool, wet washcloth. Sally was his nurse on this day as she was when we first arrived over a week ago. It was a routine day by SICU standards.

Sunday evening we left the hospital as usual to return to Bert's and Jo's house for dinner. They were out for the evening – chanting with their Buddhist friends. Just as we sat down to our meal, the phone rang. Sally was on the line. *Why was she calling us at home?* Still skittish about phone calls from the hospital, my heart must have skipped several beats. But the news was good. She told us that the doctors had decided that Mike was stable enough to be moved immediately to the Step Down Unit. More accurately, I thought to myself, a bed had opened up in the SDU and they needed the room in the SICU for more critical patients. We told her that we would drive right back to the hospital. We gulped down our meal and jumped into the car.

At 8:00 p.m., Michael was moved to the SDU, Room 349, in the new West addition of DHMC. The environment and atmosphere of the SDU was much nicer than the SICU. The room had its own wood door instead of a wide sliding glass door and curtain. The lighting was less bright and less stark against the walls, which had more natural wood trim and cabinetry than the SICU room. There was a large vinyl recliner near the foot of the bed and a sofa bed for visitors to sit and rest on by the window which faced north toward downtown Denver. The room also had a closet for Mike's personal items. And it had a private bathroom. Michael's first SDU nurse was Cheryl – from Trinidad – a very caring person with a gentle "Caribbean" accent.

Michael's gift to us on this evening was a yawn and the first appearance of his tongue. He opened his mouth voluntarily for the first time (9 days post-injury)! Again, we celebrated at the sight of this relatively minor accomplishment. It signaled another step on his path to full consciousness. It seemed as if his brain was finding small motor skills and cognitive "software" programs and rebooting them one at a time. Once Michael was settled in his new room, connected to new monitors, we left again for our home away from home so that we could return refreshed in the morning.

When we arrived that next morning, we decorated the room with the cards, photos and signs we had collected in the SICU, all expressing hope for Mike's quick recovery. By the time we were finished, the room looked like it had been Michael's room for weeks.

Mindy, our niece by marriage to our nephew, Adam, was then a first year resident at the CU Medical Center. She had been helping us all along by reviewing doctors' notes, translating medical jargon to layman's English and generally helping us to communicate with the medical staff. With Michael now in the SDU, it became even more imperative to identify a rehabilitation facility to which Mike would move when he improved further and was no longer qualified for SDU level care. Mindy made a call to Craig Hospital seeking admission information; she wrote these remarks regarding their admissions policies:

> *"6/12/06 Dr. Pappas: Physical, medical and Rehab, informal consult*
>
> *-pictures of head would indicate severe brain injury*
> *-Michael semi-purposeful on R side, neglecting L side*
> *-Physical therapists will start working with Michael tomorrow*
> *-Acute Rehab Facility – shorter-term, participate 3-4 hours per day*

-Long Term Care Facility – longer term, less intense rehab
-Karen (Social worker at DHMC) needs to contact Craig Hospital for them to come do evaluation. Dr. P. said he will ask Karen to contact Craig.
-Dr. P. will speak with primary team (neurosurgery) regarding hopes for going to Craig.
-Dr. Christine W. is running the inpatient rehab facility here at Denver Health. She is my (Mindy's) good friend, I'm sure we could talk to her."

The first days in SDU, Monday through Wednesday, were a bit of a blur. Each day Mike presented us with new gifts, i.e., new signs, albeit small changes, that he was awakening from his coma. For example, his eyes began to track and focus on specific people or objects. His overall look was still one of bewilderment and he stared at nothing in particular, wide-eyed, from his hospital bed. He had turned his head toward some activities in the room to both see and hear. Also, he continued to raise his fingers on command, tightened and then released his grip. He even began to try to smile. Still, he did not try to speak and showed no awareness of his situation.

His grin, which he showed us occasionally, seemed forced, slightly contorted to one side. He showed more strength on his right side, more in control, and showed significant weakness, almost paralysis, on his left. However, he surprised us by snapping his fingers on both of his hands – although in this, too, he favored his right side. He was slowly re-discovering the left side of his body. I thought that was strange since I had always understood that the right side of the brain controls the left side and the left side of the brain controls the right half of the body. I took this as a sign that there was more right side damage than the CT Scans had indicated. However, this was never confirmed by any medical information provided to us.

Yet another good sign, Mike held a stress ball in his right hand, dropped it, located it on his lap by feeling around with the same hand, and picked it up again, indeed, several times. And then, incredibly, he tossed it at me!

While in the SDU, Michael was constantly surrounded by his closest friends – Liz and Tim, Julia, Helen, the other Julia, the Daves (yet Dave S. seemed to be having trouble dealing with Michael's condition and chose to go home to Chicago to "chill"). Dr. Schulten returned repeatedly to visit with Michael. When she was on vacation in California visiting family, we had missed her visits. We were also visited by a radiologist at DHMC who was an old friend from internship days with friends who had moved years earlier from Tucson to Sacramento. Dr. Richard Albert, Chief of Medical Services at DHMC, a friend of one of Michael's professors at DU, came by to see Mike in the SDU, shocking the SDU nursing staff who sat around amazed at this impressive array of visitors. We were grateful for each one of these visits as they provided us with much needed relief from the boredom of sitting and waiting in the hospital. We were pleased to meet and talk with new people, people who could appreciate ours and Michael's circumstances. Their expressions and offers of assistance were kind and generous.

Mike was more attentive the next morning. He was attempting to smile, shaking hands with me, following people and noises around the room. At one point, Dana reached down holding his

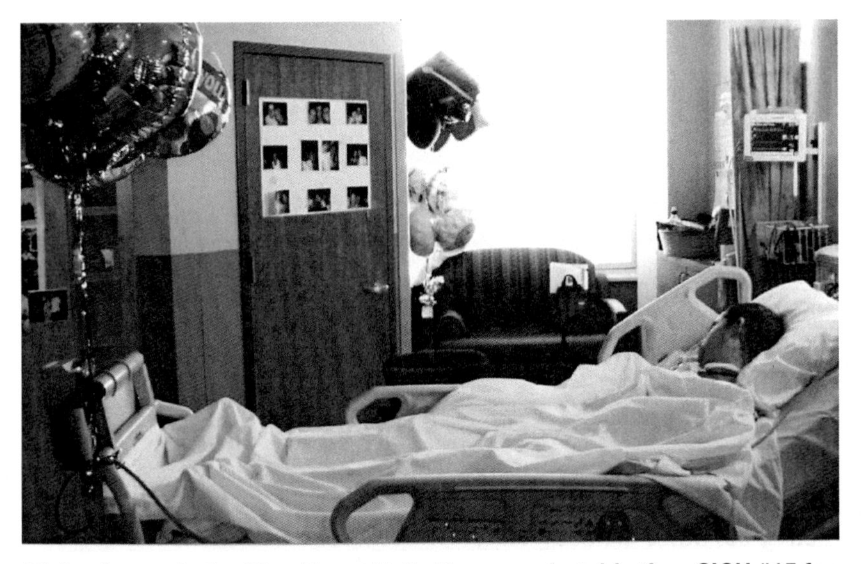

Michael rests in the Step Down Unit: More comfortable than SICU #15 for visitors, Michael slowly emerged from the depths of his coma.

hand and asked him to kiss hers. He pulled toward her and placed his lips on her hand. She leaned toward him and asked for a kiss. He pursed his lips to her cheek. I followed, leaning in for a kiss also. He touched my cheek with his lips. I whispered, "I love you, Mike." To the surprise and joy of everyone standing there, including Dana, Adam, and myself, Mike mouthed "I love you" back to me.

Has so simple a phrase ever been packed with more meaning? More hope? More of a sense of relief? "I love you." Yes, these words are regaled by literary writers, poets, people of every walk of life throughout the history of humankind, but, believe me, never before have they been more meaningful, hoped for and appreciated. With these few words, Mike showed not only that he knew who we were but also his first language skills and speech *after two weeks* of terrible silence! He was reconnecting the circuits of his complex brain, motor skills with language. He struggled to form a crooked smile. We could see that he was trying so hard to come back to us. We felt elation at this latest indication of Mike's progress. Can one's spirit soar up any higher from the depths of fear and anxiety we had experienced? My joy was uncontained.

Despite these moments of happiness, we asked ourselves: *Has it only been two weeks since the accident? Can so much experience really be compressed into so little time?* Time seemed to be racing by – as days ran together, as sleep seemed only a momentary interruption to the incessant need to care for Michael, to plan for the future and to deal with the more mundane out-of-town ordeals of maneuvering through daily activities. We were awake at 5:00 a.m. Not because we didn't sleep well – sleep felt good but short – but rather because we awaken still in the vise grip of anxiety and mindful of many small tasks not yet completed or addressed.

By Wednesday, June 14, we had been in Denver almost two weeks. On this day, we were visited by the evaluator from Craig Hospital. Just having her show up to review Mike's case generated great excitement in Dana and me. We had so much of our hope tied up in his being admitted by Craig Hospital. The evaluator was a heavy set nurse whose years of experience were evidenced by her graying hair. She sat outside Mike's room for about three quarters of an hour, thoroughly reviewing his medical file. We stayed with Michael in his room but kept one eye on her facial expressions, looking for a sign of either acceptance or rejection. Experienced as she was, her face betrayed neither.

Finally, she put the notebook containing Mike's file down on the nurse's table and entered the room. She introduced herself and went over to Michael. She talked to him directly, trying to make a connection. He didn't respond to her at all. Nor did he continue to give thumbs up or move about. It was late afternoon. He was getting tired and distracted. After a few minutes of trying to stimulate a response from him, the evaluator made some notes and left the room, saying she would be back in a few minutes, after she had called into Craig to report on her findings. Dana and I sat with Michael like parents of a child waiting to be told he had passed the interview and had been accepted to private school. We felt that so much was riding on her analysis. If he was accepted, he would be transferred to one of the finest rehabilitation hospitals in the country, which would give him the best opportunity to recover fully from his injuries. If not, we would need to go back to the drawing board and find a facility nearer to home, probably Barrows Institute in Phoenix, also a fine rehabilitation hospital.

The evaluator returned as promised and invited Dana and me into the family conference room across the hall. We sat down at the table facing her. Without much in the way of preliminaries, she described the process of admissions to Craig Hospital and said, without hesitation, that Michael was an excellent candidate for Craig. In her opinion, Michael met the critical criteria for admission, i.e., he could and would benefit from their rehabilitation services. A wave of relief swept over both Dana and me, bringing new tears of hope to each of us. Perhaps other parents could be stoic when moving through these poignant moments in the long journey of TBI recovery, but not the two of us. We were flooded with relief and excited anticipation about the next few days...and yet another transition for Michael.

She said, however, that there were no beds available immediately and that discharges would occur in the middle of the next week, on Tuesday and Wednesday. The hospital would not know, until just before they occurred, how many cases would be discharged and how many new cases would be accepted from around the country. We recognized for the first time then that specialized facilities had limitations, their own need to triage patients, both coming and going. Like classroom space at a private school, the competition for available beds and therapies was fierce.

We had hoped that our proximity to Craig Hospital was a plus. That Michael could be transported with little difficulty would help. The fact that he was progressing rather rapidly so soon "out of the accident" certainly worked in his favor. Yet another positive which supported the case for Michael's admission was that he was well insured and would be a paying customer. Not all patients have the financial wherewithal to meet the cost burden of prolonged treatment and, while hospitals may not openly cite this criterion, we believe it helped Michael get accepted quickly into Craig's rehabilitation program. In this regard, we were one of the lucky ones. Blue Cross / Blue Shield of Arizona still needed to pre-certify the Craig program under his policy, so there was some uncertainty and delay which that process would entail. The evaluator said they, at Craig, would begin the admission process immediately.

As we waited to hear from Craig Hospital about a bed opening up, drained both emotionally and physically, Dana and I were in need of some time alone. Marci and Matt, the friends of Darcy, came to our rescue by offering to let us stay in their home in Park Hill while they were away at their own graduation from medical school at Stanford University. Excited by the prospect, we accepted their generous offer, packed up our things in the basement bedroom and moved up to Park Hill. Marci's and Matt's home proved to be a wonderful change of scenery. Upon entering their home, we were welcomed by a dining room table covered with local menus, local sightseeing brochures, and a warm welcome note from Marci and Matt. In addition, there were two tiny carved fetishes. According to the note left alongside their tiny feet, we were to place the fetishes beneath our pillows at night to relieve our worries while we slept. We enjoyed their home for several days; we will be forever grateful to them for their kindness.

Progress Report #4 - June 15, 2006

Sorry for the delay in sending this news to you all, but Dana and I have temporarily moved from her Dad's house to get a little respite at the home of a friend of Darcy. We arrived there only to find that there was an internet connection but no computer. And, of course, we don't have laptops with us. Thus, the delay.

There is lots of news to share with you about Mike's progress, all of it good. From the medical standpoint, Mike is now eating without a feeding tube and breathing without a trach! Both were removed today after he showed that he could swallow food and clear his throat and lungs safely. [Note: Unassisted eating was short-lived. The N-G (nasal-gastro) tube had been removed to test Michael's swallow reflex, but, when swallowing, he aspirated the food into his windpipe and so the tube was quickly replaced.] He is awake most of the day with eyes open, tracking people in the room, responding to requests to move his limbs. He remains weaker on his left side than his right, but that is improving each day.

He has amazed his parents, his friends and doctors with the following: he has snapped his fingers to music, has dropped and retrieved a small stress ball while sitting up, has smiled broadly, kissed his mom and mouthed the words "I love you" in response to my telling Mike that I loved him. He sometimes moves his lips as if singing with the music playing from an I-Pod loaded up with some of his favorite tunes by his friend Julia.

In short, he has made great progress this week. He does, however, remain only partially cognizant of his surroundings and the people around him. He is physically active (agitated some might say) when he is in his "awakened" state. [Rancho Los Amigos Level 3: Localized Responses]

In addition to all of Mike's personal improvement, he has been preliminarily accepted into the Craig Hospital rehabilitation program. As many of you know from your many great references and referrals, Craig Hospital is one of the premier rehabilitation / long term acute care hospitals for spinal cord and traumatic brain injuries in the Western U.S., and just happens to be located in Denver. Michael was evaluated yesterday by a Craig evaluator in his Denver Health Medical Center room and was medically stable and alert enough to qualify for their program. Pending insurance pre-certification and bed availability, we are hopeful that Mike will move there by early next week.

We will also move there because they have a patient-family residence attached to the hospital which is funded solely by donations. It is an environment meant to accommodate ex-patients returning for their follow-up evaluations, but will help us be close to Mike during these critical early days at Craig.

Because we don't know exactly when Mike will be moved, please do not send any more cards or packages to Denver Health Medical Center, but instead send them to Michael's grandfather's address: Mike Adler c/o Bert Dendinger, Quinn Place, Denver, CO.

Michael, Darcy, Dana and I have received so many letters, packages, flowers, etc. containing many wishes for Mike's quick recovery and sentiments of support for the family that we can scarcely begin to thank all of you.

We miss Tucson dearly, although we have been enjoying a Denver "heat wave" with temps in the mid-90's. Everyone here is complaining about the heat!

We look forward to reporting continued good news to you. All of our deepest gratitude and best wishes to all of you,

Ira and Dana

Chapter 11
The Car

Thursday, June 15, Michael's condition was rapidly changing and improving; we were able to breathe slightly easier. Physically, he was better. However, he was still not aware of his surroundings or why he was in this precarious situation. We, on the other hand, were keenly aware of his condition and how we had gotten here.

That morning I received a phone call from Officer Henry Jones, Denver Police Department technician for Community Services at the Denver International Airport. Henry had been referred to us by Janet Bronitsky of Denver's Congregation Emanuel. He had recently converted to Judaism in April 2006 and, therefore, was closely connected with the temple. Over the phone, Henry said that he was able to assist me in getting through the red tape of the city's automobile impound facility. Because we had been so coldly received by Detective Estrada, I was very grateful for Henry's contact and eagerly accepted his offer of assistance. We arranged to meet at DHMC's main entrance after lunch. He pulled into the circular driveway in front of the hospital at 12:45 p.m. He bounced out of the car and quickly extended his hand to me. He was the smiling-est police officer I had ever met. Without further ado, I climbed into his unmarked white Chevrolet Impala, which reminded me of my first Tucson Electric Power company car, an old Dodge Aries K, with its blue cloth seats and its plain white exterior.

Henry is an extremely affable and talkative fellow and we quickly got past our initial greetings and down to talking about how best to deal with the police bureaucracy. He suggested that we first needed to get clearance to enter the Impound lot from the supervisor of the Traffic Investigators office. Leaving DHMC, we drove down to the DPD Administration building, the same building where Dana, Darcy and I had met Detective Estrada late at night almost two weeks before.

This time, instead of entering from the public entrance from the plaza in front of the building, we entered through the underground parking garage directly beneath the building where all the official and personal cars of the DPD are parked. We entered the building by going up the elevator to the third floor where Henry escorted me through bleak institutional beige hallways to the Traffic Investigators offices.

Henry asked to see Sergeant Farr. Unfortunately, the sergeant was at a policeman's funeral. While riding his motorcycle off-duty, an officer had been killed by a DUI. So we waited for a half hour until the sergeant's supervisor arrived. Henry explained to him why we were there and the supervisor immediately called down to the DPD Impound, telling them to give us permission to get Michael's personal possessions from the car. We thanked the supervisor, returned to the garage to Henry's car and headed to the Impound lot in north Denver near I-70 and York. Each step took me closer to an understanding of the full severity of Michael's accident.

While we traveled, Henry filled the time with talk about his conversion to Judaism and his being drawn to the "chosen people" concept. He also surprised me by relating the story of his own spinal injury years before, which resulted from an auto accident while on duty. He described his own recovery at the DG trauma unit. Weeks later, when we had gotten to know each other much better, he would show me the surgical scars across his back. He told me that he had been severely injured and had undergone a lengthy rehabilitation. I thought to myself that this might explain why he had been reassigned to Community Relations and Security at Denver International Airport from the Traffic Investigation division and Mayor's Security Task Force. We also talked about Denver, the city… as it was twenty years ago when our family had lived there and the growth it had experienced since then. If we hadn't arrived at the Impound lot, I'm sure we would have kept on talking for hours, perhaps discussing world politics next.

We wound our way through the streets of Commerce City, one of Denver's industrial districts. Inside the Impound lot's office, in the waiting room, there was a wide assortment of people waiting to pick up their old Dodge Darts, new BMWs, Ford pickups and a host of other makes and models. Crashes don't discriminate between makes and models nor between the economic status of the car's owners. No one in the waiting area seemed happy to be there. Henry spoke briefly to the desk clerk. I gave her our control number – 244055 – and, like magic, we were promptly invited through the locked door into the Impound lot. The lot was huge and completely filled with all manner of vehicles: coupes, sedans, wagons, trucks of all shapes and sizes. Many, crushed and crunched in accidents, were hardly recognizable. Ruined vehicles stretched out in front of us, row upon row. It was quite a disturbing sight to see so many destroyed vehicles all in one place.

The yard attendant told us that Michael's 2001 Toyota RAV 4 was at the north end of Row #2. At first, we couldn't see the car as we walked down the long line of vehicles. Finally, after passing 20 or 30 cars, I could see its tailgate emerging from behind another car. As I hesitantly approached, more of Mike's car came into view. Even though I had tried to prepare myself ("Mike had to be extricated from the car through the roof using the Jaws of Life," Detective Estrada had said), the sight of what remained of the once-attractive silver RAV 4 hit me like a punch in the gut and sucked the breath right out of me.

The devastation to the car was extreme, especially on the driver's side. The door was crushed well into the interior of the car, making a "V" where the tree trunk had impacted. The driver's seat, where Mike had been sitting, was crushed and crumpled like an accordion toward the right side of the car so that it was now only one third of its designed width. The windshield was shattered and partially missing. Broken glass lay on the floor. There was dried blood on both of the front seats and dried vomit on the passenger's side floor and door. Just as the police report had said, the roof had been ripped off and the door to the back left side of the car had been removed from its hinges and was laying across the back seat of the car.

How had Michael survived such an impact? Pinned in the wreckage, how helpless he must have been!

The sight of the car spoke volumes to me about the heroics of the EMT's, who were on the scene the night of the accident, fighting to extricate Mike from his driver's seat and, at the same time, working to preserve his life. The terror of the accident reflected in the car's condition set off a surge of adrenaline inside in me and I was thankful that Dana had not come with me to the lot.

I took some photos of the car for insurance claims and to show Dana and, perhaps, Michael at some time in the future. The front was relatively undamaged. The driver's side was totally destroyed. The rear and right sides of the car were not damaged at all. But the car, with no roof, was a total loss. I checked the tires for signs of sidewall rubbing which might confirm the version of the accident which Mike's roommate had described. He had told us that the car had come into contact against the median curb on Alameda before careening across the street and into the tree. But I could find no evidence to confirm that.

Looking inside through the crumpled driver's side door to the front passengers' compartment, I saw a pack of Camel cigarettes on the floor on the driver's side. *Had Mike been reaching for a cigarette when he lost control of the vehicle?*

I began to remove Mike's personal items from the car with Henry's help: Mike's roller blades, his golf clubs, his copy of the "Book of the Cosmos," and his CD collection. We left his pack of Camels, the Starbucks coffee cups and other assorted papers and paraphernalia on the floor of the driver's compartment. I retrieved several personal mementos/bracelets, sliding them over the top of the stick shift – which was still in gear! I looked inside the center console between the driver's and the passenger's seats and found a small pipe with nothing in it. I recognized the type of pipe it was and, silently, was thankful that drugs had not been found alongside the corked bottle of wine which the police report spoke of. For some inexplicable reason, though, I left the pipe in the car.

Henry and I carried the salvaged items back to his car and loaded them into the trunk. As we left the Impound lot, I hoped that was the last time I would ever see that car and this place.

When we had returned to the hospital, I loaded Mike's things into our rental car. I invited Henry to come up to the SDU to meet Michael and Dana. When we arrived in Michael's room, I could see that Henry was deeply moved by the scene. He stayed for a few minutes and promised to return in the near future. Not even a full day later, Henry arrived back at Michael's room bearing several gifts embroidered or embossed with DPD logos. He brought Mike a pair of sweat pants, a tee shirt, a baseball cap, a coffee mug and a DPD teddy bear. We were moved by his genuine generosity, and we thanked him on Michael's behalf. We got to know Henry fairly well over the next few weeks as he was a frequent visitor to the hospital and a regular attendee of Friday night services at Congregation Emanuel.

But I was left with an unsettled feeling about our experience at the police station late at night with Detective Estrada, about his version of the accident as set out in the copy of the police report he had given us, and the sight of the devastation which had been Michael's car. *How did this accident happen? Why did this happen?* These questions rolled around, again and again, in my mind. This was not just idle curiosity but also my internal ranting against the reality of the hospital setting. *Our son was laying in bed, struggling to heal his body and his mind. Why had he been victimized by this accident?* Knowing the answers to these questions would never change the consequences, but it took me a long time before I came to grips with that reality.

Disturbed by these thoughts, which never seemed to go away, I thought that experiencing the location of the accident at the time of night at which it occurred might provide some clarity, some understanding. So, after being with Michael the whole evening, and then delivering Dana and Darcy back down to my in-laws' home, I drove back across town and, just after midnight, parked my car at the southeast corner of Alameda and Fairfax, where the accident occurred.

Sitting in the car, I observed that the median sprinklers were not yet on and the road was dry. *If only Mike and Dave had been driving back home an hour earlier than they actually did!* Getting out of the car, the neighborhood was quiet except for passing cars. There were no lights on in the adjacent homes. I walked up to the tree where Mike's car and Michael had come to a violent stop. There were gashes and grooves in the grass between the curb and the tree where the car's tires had, moving sideways, gouged out a path. The tree was scarred on its trunk, about four feet off of the ground, and the thick branch which jutted out from the tree's trunk toward Fairfax had also had its bark scraped clean by the impact of the car and/or Michael's head. In my mind, I could hear the screech of the tires on the pavement, the metal crunching suddenly against the immovable tree, and I could envision Michael's head snapping sideways into the tree trunk and limb. It all played out in slow motion in my mind. I reached up to touch the tree as if I could recapture some of Michael's life force and return it to him in the morning.

Then I turned and walked along Alameda in front of the Lutheran church. I made a wry note to myself that the cross in front of the church had provided no protection to Michael and Dave as they travelled by on June 2 at 1:30 a.m. The median showed no signs of any collision, just as the car's tires had shown no signs of bouncing up against the cement curb. I wondered again about Dave's version of the accident. *Had he imagined the car hitting the curbside? Had he conjured up this reason, frightened by his close escape while his roommate lay in a coma at Denver Health? Was he afraid to recognize that the blame fell on the two of them for being too inebriated to control theirs and the car's actions?* Whatever it was, I found no evidence to support his claim of the initial cause of the accident.

There were also no tire marks on the street. Of course, this was almost two weeks after the fact, but I looked for evidence just the same. And, finally, when, at 1:00 a.m., the sprinklers in the median started up, they started in sequence farther down the road to the west and there was no excessive water flowing on the street after a few minutes. It began to sink in more firmly that the accident was most likely the result of Michael's impaired ability to drive, his lack of attention to the road or, perhaps, some distraction occurring within the car. There was nothing on the scene to indicate otherwise. And being right there at the street corner did not provide any clues or answers.

I got back into the car and sat in the darkness absorbing the scene in front of me. I stared ahead through the windshield and tried to envision how such a peaceful, quiet place could be the sight of such a terrible accident. *How had my family's serenity and happiness been shattered just as Michael's body had been shattered against this innocent looking, but malevolent, tree?* As I sat there, I was suddenly shaken out of my own thoughts by the appearance of a disheveled and dirty man carrying a knapsack right in front of my car. He noticed me sitting in the car, stopped, and stared at me. Then he stumbled his way past the hood of the car and turned down Fairfax staring at me all the while as he walked down the street, not three feet from my driver's side door. I had left the window open on this side to let in the cooler summer night air, but his proximity made me feel unsafe. I kept watch on him as he receded to the rear of the car and further down the street. *Had Michael swerved to avoid this person walking in the dark on the night of the accident?* Shaken, I turned the key in the ignition and rolled up the window as quickly as I could. At that moment, I

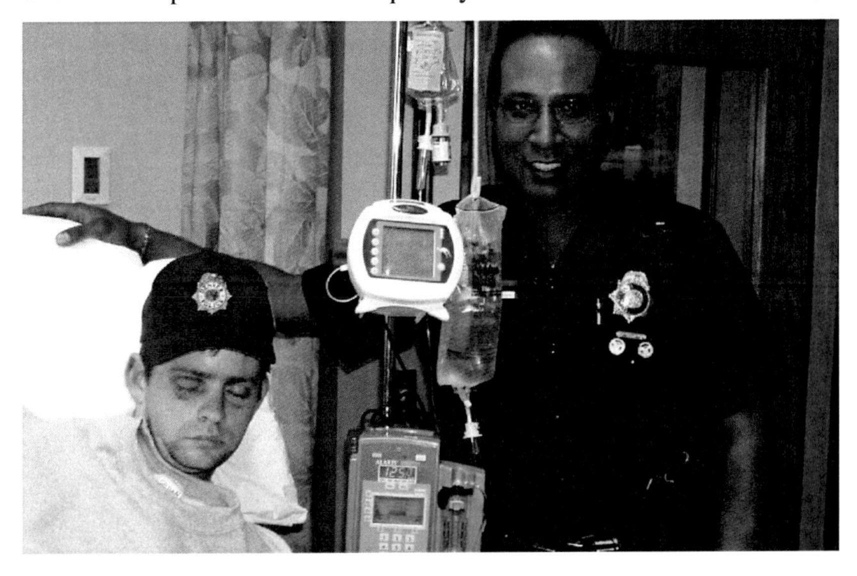

DPD Officer Henry Jones brought many official DPD gifts for Michael while he was in the Step Down Unit. Officer Jones became a close friend over the next three months.

realized that many dangers (real or perceived) lurked in the night, even in that quiet little neighborhood by the church, not two miles from Mike's apartment-condo.

I started up the car and returned home. I would think back on this night many times as I sat beside Michael in his hospital rooms and during his therapy sessions.

Progress Report – June 18: Father's Day

Wishing a Happy Father's Day to all of you. This is an especially poignant day for us as you might expect. Not only are we able to enjoy a full lifetime relationship with both of our fathers, but we are also blessed by both of our wonderful children.

Both of our fathers have overcome health issues and yet continue to thrive. They share their love and wisdom with us, making our lives fuller as a result. Of course, we are also blessed with the presence of both of our moms as well.

Darcy makes us proud every day with her caring spirit and loving ways. She is a dedicated friend to so many and a devoted sister to Michael. We could not have made it through the past two weeks without her presence in Denver. We wish she was nearer to us physically, but we know we are as close as can be in so many other ways. She makes us proud everyday in ways large and small.

Michael has just entered a new phase of his life. Postgraduate work, if you will. We know he will excel here just as he did at the University of Denver. He will soon pass from Denver Health to Craig Hospital where there have been many successful "graduates." He has already amazed us with his early recovery and strong will. His presents for Father's Day were the several smiles, responsiveness to music (we listened to a Beatles collection together and he mouthed many of the lyrics…yeah, yeah, yeah…and tapped his hands with the music) which seems to stimulate him greatly, and a special kiss goodnight.

So, on this Father's Day, our best to all of you,

Love,
Ira and Dana

Michael's time in the SDU was similar to his stay in the SICU. Perhaps there was less drama as he had overcome the critical, life threatening injuries and continued to improve without any major medical setbacks. He was getting better, but the extent of his recovery was still uncertain.

Thankfully, the SDU's shifts were not the same as the SICU's. Therefore, the visiting hours were much less rigidly enforced and our pattern of day visiting extended up to early evening. We did not always return to visit after dinner.

During the day, Mike would be visited by respiratory technicians checking on his breathing following the removal of his tracheostomy tube. We found it interesting that the hole in his neck, covered with just a piece of cotton and some tape, began to heal almost immediately and was closed up within a week's time. It was as if his body knew that it was important for his windpipe to be closed to the outside, except through his mouth and nose. He was also visited by a physician specializing in physical therapy. He would move Michael's arms and legs and help him to alternatively bend and extend them to begin the process of strengthening his limbs as well as restoring his control over his motor skills. Mike was a cooperative, almost passive, patient. He never fought the therapist nor became aggressive with anyone in the Step Down Unit. In fact, he tried to smile as if welcoming the nurses and technicians into his space.

With each passing day, the signs of improvement kept adding up. He would move his head, reacting toward a sound in the hallway. He would look up at the television hanging on the wall across from his bed, looking but not watching, fascinated by the sights, colors and sounds but with no comprehension that we could discern. He would never react one way or another to what was on the screen. He would occasionally tap his hands to the beat of music emanating from the IPod loaned to us by one of the Julias.

And he began to have short conversations with us. Not really conversations, these were more like responding to test questions which we posed as we probed and looked for answers to the question of what information Michael's brain still knew, what it could use and whether there was a connection to the pre-accident Michael we knew.

"Can you read the sign on the wall?" I asked in order to learn whether his eyesight had returned sufficiently to see forms clearly and whether his brain could translate the visual stimuli to a useful cognitive piece of data. "Where are we, Michael?" Did he have any understanding of where or why he was in bed there in the Step Down Unit? In most cases, the responses, if any, were disjointed, almost random, speaking. However, he did seem to know Dana and me. His understanding of the concept of family seemed to be intact.

But the question of who Michael would be when he was finished recovering hung over us every moment we were with him. The question colored every conversation at every meal we sat down to and was of primary concern in our thoughts every evening when we returned home to the basement bedroom.

Chapter 12
Let The Games Begin!
Craig Hospital – The First Days

On June 20, 2006, 18 days after first arriving at Denver Health Medical Center, Michael was discharged and moved to Craig Hospital.

Throughout this Tuesday, we anxiously waited at DHMC for word from Craig Hospital that: 1) they had a bed opening up for Michael and 2) Blue Cross/ Blue Shield of Arizona (BCBSAZ) had pre-certified the costs of their rehabilitation services. The morning passed ... no word. On the theory that the squeaky wheel gets greased, we "bugged" the social worker at DHMC to call Craig to see what the situation was. We left message after message on her voice mail. She never called back or came to see us. Trying further to be proactive, we also tried to contact the Admissions director at Craig Hospital.

Then, early in the afternoon, we learned from his SDU nurse that Michael was to be discharged from DHMC "immediately," transported by ambulance and admitted into Craig Hospital. The news was electrifying. Michael was leaving DHMC. Dana and I were excited by the prospects of this new phase of our post-trauma lives. Michael, however, was unaware that everything was about to change. Once again, we packed up Mike's get well memorabilia which adorned all the walls of his room. The SDU nurses supplied us with boxes and plastic bags to pack for the move. Despite the volume of cards, pictures and posters, toys, food and clothing which was collected over the past 18 days, the whole packing exercise took only 30 minutes.

Then we waited for the transport personnel to arrive. And we waited, and then we waited some more. Finally, near the end of the afternoon, hours after the nurse's initial announcement that Michael was moving "immediately," we received the news that the ambulance transport had arrived and that the transport techs were on their way up to Michael's room.

The SDU personnel jumped into action. There was a sudden flurry of activity in Mike's room. SDU nurses bustled in and out of his room, poking and prodding Mike, taking final vital signs for their records. The attending doctor appeared from somewhere with Mike's formal discharge papers, which cordially invited Michael back for follow-up visits over the next two months. The papers instructed Mike to return to DHMC to see the doctors from general surgery and orthopedic surgery. I wondered who would transport Mike BACK to DHMC a month from now. *Would Craig handle this? Would they let him out of their hospital to visit the doctors in another hospital? Would we need to arrange for another ambulance to transport him?* Dana was handed a list of his current medications, which included antibiotics, stimulants, etc.

The transport personnel appeared in the doorway. Within just a few short minutes, Michael was disconnected from all wires and tubes attaching him to the walls and machines in his SDU room, connected to a portable monitor and loaded onto a gurney. In a flash, away he went. Seeing that Michael was becoming agitated from all of the commotion around his bed, Dana opted to accompany Michael in the ambulance. I was left behind to load up all of the personal things into our car for the short drive down to Craig.

In what seemed like a brief instant, his room, which had been filled with visitors, pictures on the walls and gift baskets of food and games, was vacant. Suddenly there was no sign that Michael had ever been there. Standing there alone, I took one last look at the room where so many miraculous signs of recovery had emerged: opened eyes, thumbs up and handshakes, first words and smiles, to name a few.

Dana and I had connected personally with the SDU nursing and therapeutic staff. Every day we were greeted with smiles and, as we left each evening, we were told, "Have a good evening. We'll take care of Michael for you." They truly seemed to care about us and our son. Thus, leaving for Craig Hospital was almost bittersweet as if we were saying good-bye to new friends.

As frightening as our experience had been, DHMC had become our safe harbor, the place where we knew Michael was getting the care and supervision he needed. The terrible fear of losing Michael completely had given way to the almost equally terrible uncertainty of the unknown outcome. Once he had physically stabilized and begun to awaken from his week-long coma, our thoughts had turned to wondering who Michael had become, what persona would emerge. He was still in danger, but the dangers seemed less life-threatening. What had occurred would surely threaten, if not his life itself, his life's plan.

Now he was facing another unknown and foreign environment. But the prospects were better where before they were dreadful. Despite my pre-nostalgic feelings toward the people and services of DHMC, I left the room with a sense that the worst was over. I had a real feeling of excitement and optimism: *the doctors, nurses and therapists at Craig would be working their own miracles with our son.*

I hurried over to the parking lot to retrieve our car and drove down to meet Michael and Dana at Craig Hospital. By the time I arrived at Craig, parked the car on the street between the hospital's east and west buildings and entered the building, Mike had already been taken in a gurney up to his room on the second floor of the West wing in the acute care hallway. He was joined quickly by Dr. David Ripley (believe it or not!), the assigned physiatrist and rehabilitation team leader. Dr. Ripley, a young, but highly experienced, doctor, rolled into the room in a wheelchair! *Was he afflicted with injury just as his patients were or was this just an effort at empathy for his patients?* We didn't know until later that he had had a bone graft in his leg to alleviate an orthopedic problem and would be confined to his own wheelchair for most of the duration of our stay at Craig.

Dr. Ripley's PA, Christina, as well as Dr. James Schraa, the team's neuropsychologist, also arrived when Mike did. Christina is a key staff member who keeps Dr. Ripley on track and on time. She had her clipboard with her, taking notes as they reviewed Mike's case and condition. Dr. Schraa is a tall and lean man, sporting grey hair and beard, and, as we later learned, is very agile intellectually. The team introduced themselves to Dana and me, saying only that we would be meeting with them in a short while to discuss Mike's course of treatment.

They made their admissions review of Michael's condition. During this examination, Michael was agitated and unresponsive to their commands. Dana and I were rooting for Mike to show them how well he had progressed from the coma: *C'mon, Mike, do your stuff for the doctors. Raise your hand and thumb. Smile. Say something! Don't let them change their minds about admitting you*. But, Mike was tired and disoriented from the short trip from DHMC and from the stimulation of his new environment (and,

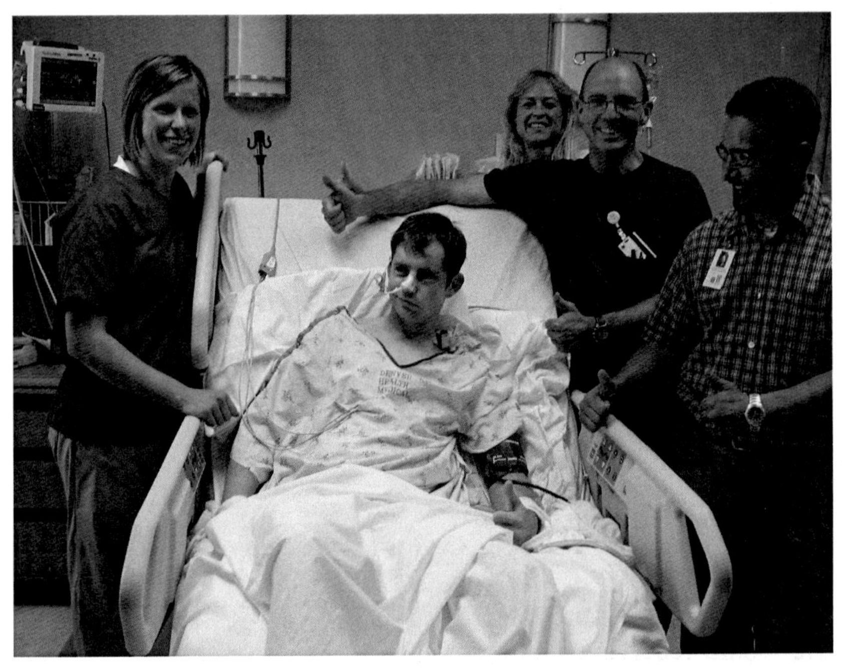

June 20, 2006: Leaving DHMC/SDU for Craig Hospital. All "thumbs up!"

perhaps, as a result of being medicated for the journey between hospitals). Although cognitively unresponsive, he was physically active while laying there in his new hospital bed, kicking and thrashing around. He was, in fact, completely bewildered by the events of this afternoon.

Agitated by the move, Michael aggressively reached up to try to remove his feeding tube from his nose. He reached up to grab the tube not just once or twice, but incessantly. Because of the danger of injuring himself if he were to succeed at removing the tube from his esophagus, Dr. Ripley and Christina covered his hands in gauze safety mittens and strapped his hands to his bed by his sides. Both precautions were clearly for Mike's own safety, but it was disturbing to us to see Michael tied down this way, as if he was a violent mental patient or inmate.

Also, his legs thrashed about, seemingly trying to find a position in which to be comfortable. Dr. Ripley offered that he might be recommending a Craig Bed for Michael until he settled down a little more. A Craig Bed is a six foot square enclosed sleeping pen which sits about a foot off of the floor. The walls of this pen are four foot high padded cushions. Patients who are physically agitated are safe in this environment because they can move without hurting themselves or being restrained. The walls limit external stimulation from noise or other distractions, helping to calm the otherwise confused or distracted patient. If they somehow succeed in "fleeing the coop," they are protected from further injury. Patients can sleep in that bed, tossing and turning without restraints, but also without the risks of falling from the bed and doing harm to themselves.

For the immediate future, however, Mike lay on his back, tied down in his hospital bed. The side rails of the bed were elevated and locked into position so as to keep Mike from rolling out of the bed onto the floor. After this eventful day, he seemed to quiet down with just a small amount of evening sedation.

Dana and I were introduced to a patient assistant, or "tech," who stayed with Michael continually during his first days at Craig. He would receive 24 hour surveillance and assistance by one or more techs. He was monitored this way for the first two weeks of his stay at Craig. If we were in the room with Michael, the tech left us alone in the room but sat stationed just outside the door in the hallway. When we left the room, the tech came in to sit by his side to continue his/her vigil.

The Craig team's professional manner, their keen attention to detail, their obvious concern for keeping us informed, and the fact that they had been there immediately to greet Michael upon his arrival, all contributed to our sense of relief in having Michael admitted at Craig. Still, we did not know then just how good Craig Hospital would turn out to be. In fact, having just entered the third hospital environment (SICU, SDU and now Craig Hospital) in just the past three weeks, we ourselves felt unsettled, displaced and anxious. After the next sixty days there, we were to learn a great deal more about the people and programs at Craig.

Although we were remotely familiar with Craig Hospital when we resided in the Denver metro area, we quickly learned much more. Craig Hospital had been founded 100 years earlier, in 1907, by Dr. Frank Craig. At that time, he established a tent city in Lakewood, Colorado, for the treatment of indigent men with tuberculosis. Dr. Craig, himself, died at age 37 in 1914 of tuberculosis. But the organization lived on after him expanding to several buildings west of downtown Denver. It was not until 1957 that its mission became specialized in TBI and spinal cord injuries. By that time tuberculosis had become less of a problem given the advent of antibiotics. In 1958, Craig was renamed Craig Rehabilitation Center and eight years later, Craig Rehabilitation Hospital. In addition to rehabilitation, it began to offer medical services related to TBI and SCI. Expanding its facilities, Craig built the 80-bed rehabilitation hospital on its present site adjacent to Swedish Medical Center. As its reputation grew, it needed still more facilities and built a unique patient-family living facility across the street to the east of its main building. In this new building, patients and family members could practice "living together" while becoming accustomed to the routines and regimens required by the patient's injuries. The two buildings, separated by Clarkson Avenue, were connected by a glass skyway, which allows patients and families to easily move from one building to the other without crossing the street. In 1975, in order to accommodate the healthcare insurance industry and to avoid being pigeon-holed as a rehab facility only, the word "Rehabilitation" was dropped from the hospital's name. Innovative programs with adaptive equipment for SCI and TBI patients, recreational programs beyond the hospital's walls and important research into rehabilitative techniques are all characteristics of Craig's world-class reputation.

Craig's philosophy of dedicated teams of physicians, therapists, patients and families guides all therapies. Reflecting this all-encompassing philosophy, the Patient Family Residence was built in 2002 providing housing for outpatients, inpatient families and patients returning there for follow-up examinations and treatment. This unit replaced aging apartments throughout the neighborhood which were used previously to provide housing.

As Dana and I explored the hallways of Craig Hospital, we passed by an antique wooden wheelchair sitting by the front door of the east wing of the hospital. It served as a constant reminder of just how far medical and therapeutic treatment of SCI and TBI patients had come. And we took great comfort knowing that Michael would be getting the very best in care as he struggled to recover from his injuries.

Progress Report #5 - June 21, 2006

Greetings from Denver, where the high temperature today is going to be 81! Following our Father's Day greeting, I was given a great Father's Day gift ... Darcy returned to Denver! She has been able to stay these past few days and has been great medicine for Mike, who lit up when she entered his hospital room, and for Dana and me. We all do better when we are together as a family. Unfortunately, she must leave again today, but we look forward to her return as soon as she is able.

As many of you know, Dana is a Denver native and I lived here for 16 years following college. There are many aspects of Denver, and the Rocky Mountains, which we enjoy, and in many ways Denver is our home base. But being up here these last three weeks has been wearing on us as we miss all of you and our little nest in Finisterra.

We had a wonderful dinner a few days ago with our neighbors from Tucson who have their "other" home in beautiful Genessee, just west of Denver. Thanks to them for a wonderful evening of respite and friendship. And, being up in a place like Denver which is so familiar to us, and being able to come back to Dana's Dad's home each evening, has been one of the not-so-small blessings we have to be thankful for.

The big news of yesterday is that Michael was moved from Denver Health Medical Center to Craig Hospital in the afternoon. We said a tearful goodbye to our many doctors, nurses, therapists, clerks, and support staff at Denver Health, vowing that Michael will be back to thank them all personally for the excellent care and attention he received while being in their acute care. We have a long list of those who touched Michael's life these past few weeks, from paramedics and EMTs, doctors, nurses and technicians in the ED, SICU and SDU, speech and physical therapists, receptionists, ...really too many to enumerate here. But we are deeply grateful to all of them.

Michael is now one of the about 40 patients at Craig with traumatic brain injuries. (There are 60 others with spinal cord injuries.) He spent his afternoon looking around at his new surroundings, not quite trusting where he was and where he had been (Craig is a short 10 minute ambulance ride from Denver Health). We met with his team leader, Dr. David Ripley, who will coordinate Michael's rehabilitation. This first week at Craig will be made up of many tests and base lining so that the rehab team can plan out his path of treatment. They also gave Dana and me homework in the form of a notebook, "The Traumatic Brain Injury Manual," so we can better understand what has occurred, what the process of recovery is, and what to expect going forward. Craig has an excellent website if you are interested in learning more about the facility. You can find this at www.craighospital.org

Michael's new address is:

Michael Adler
c/o Craig Hospital
S. Clarkson Street
Englewood, CO

We will be staying with Dana's Dad and Joanne for a little while longer and then will move into the Craig Hospital family residence in order to participate more fully with Mike's rehabilitation and to learn more about our role in caring for him.

As always, we thank you for all of your emails and expressions of love and concern for Mike, Dana, Darcy, and me.

Dana and Ira

First impressions are often the most difficult to appreciate; it took weeks to fully understand the environment and the purposes of all that we observed around Craig. Craig Hospital is not a regular medical hospital; it is a medical *and* rehabilitation hospital. Consequently, the sights and sounds of Craig were very different from those we had experienced at DHMC's SICU or SDU.

We first noticed that the patients were much more visible to us. In the SICU or SDU, patients were acutely ill or hurt and, therefore, were confined to beds in private rooms. They were not seen in the hallways. We could only glimpse those patients in their beds as we travelled down the hallways past the few open doors. At DHMC, outside the rooms, only doctors and visitors were visible. At Craig, the hallways were filled with patients moving about in wheelchairs, walking with walkers, sitting at tables eating their lunches or dinners. Instead of being dressed in hospital gowns, those dreadfully drafty linens, Craig's patients were dressed in shorts and t-shirts or athletic warm-ups. Most were accompanied by a father, mother, other relative/friend or technician. Few were capable of making their way about on their own.

There were patients who looked as if they would never recover their motor and/or cognitive skills. This perception was more a reflection of our ignorance than their condition. There were patients with half of their skulls missing or large tracks of staples across their scalps from surgeries. Some wore protective helmets. There were patients who sat in wheelchairs, unable to lift their heads or move their arms or legs. However, a few patients moved through the hallways in their wheelchairs, self-propelling by pushing the floor with their feet. Then, there were patients who looked like they were fully recovered, walking and talking, as if, to the untrained observer, they were normal, uninjured people. But we have learned since that that is one of the characteristics of TBI; survivors of severe brain injuries can look normal and healed. Any continuing cognitive deficits may only be noticeable to those most familiar with the patient's pre-injury personality and intelligence.

Given all the activity in the halls and therapy rooms, and the heavy traffic of visitors coming and going, there appeared to be fewer rules being observed than in DHMC's SICU or SDU. The nurses and techs at Craig didn't seem to be "policing" the way they did at DHMC. What we later learned is that it was not a lack of rules we had observed (for there certainly were strict rules and protocols being followed), but that there was a degree of freedom given to the patients and their families necessary to allow them to explore the full range of the patients' physical capabilities and cognitive functions. At first, we did not notice the belts around the wheelchair-confined patients, which locked them in their wheelchairs to keep them from falling out. Nor did we recognize the individual techs walking a step or two behind each patient, ensuring that they didn't lose their balance and fall while they moved through the hallways to their appointed therapies.

We also noticed that most of the patients were male. We later learned that most TBIs result from accidents of one sort or another – automobiles, motorcycles, bicycle, diving, etc. We concluded, intuitively, that men might be more physical risk takers than women.

However, we also learned that not all brain injuries result from traumatic injuries caused by external forces such as auto accident or falls. Hypoxia, the deprivation of oxygen to the brain, and/or strokes which alter or deprive brain cells of blood flow can also cause brain injury. In those instances, the neurons are not severed but are injured or have died due to lack of oxygen or the toxicity of the blood chemistry itself to brain tissue. The results can be similar to an externally caused traumatic brain injury.

Mike's first room at Craig Hospital was a private room down the north hallway. The rooms along this hallway were for patients who had either just arrived from acute care hospitals or were in need of acute care and constant surveillance. Each room was fitted with a camera which was focused on the bed. The cameras allowed the nurses' station at the end of this hallway to monitor patients in their beds 24/7. Patients on this wing were either highly agitated, confused and/or unaware of their surroundings and their condition... they were like our son!

Although his room was designed for two patients, only Michael occupied it. His first bed, to which he was restrained, was quickly removed and replaced by a tented hospital bed, known as a Vail Enclosed Bed System.[3] The Vail bed was designed for patients who are agitated and restless enough that they might find a way to fall out of bed, but not enough to require a full Craig padded bed. The tent screen encompassed the bed like mosquito netting, but was zipped down to attach and enclose the bed fully. If Michael had been more aware of his surroundings, this treatment might have been viewed by us as cruel – from the outside, he looked like a caged animal. But his level of awareness of his surroundings was so low that he was only first rediscovering his own body parts and appendages, not yet aware of his zippered imprisonment.

Mike was, indeed, agitated. He was still fitted with a nasal gastro tube (N-G tube) for feeding because he had pharyngeal dysphagia; that is, he couldn't yet swallow food properly without risk of aspirating. The N-G tube was pushed up into his nose, down his esophagus and into his stomach. Understandably irritated by this plastic intrusion, he constantly fought to pull it out. Focusing all one's attention on one thing or thought is known as "perseveration." Michael perseverated on this feeding tube for many days, until it was finally removed. His hands remained "mitted", i.e., covered by gauze-like mittens, which were supposed to prevent him from grabbing the N-G tube and pull it out. The cumbersome mittens and this intrusive tube occupied Michael's full attention throughout each day. Indeed, he quickly established himself as the "Houdini" of the mitten set by finding ways to

---

[3] Vail Products, the maker of the Vail Enclosed Bed System, has since been closed down by the FDA following several deaths associated with these tented bed systems, and possible neurological damage due to the possibility of becoming entangled in the netting which surrounds the patient.

wiggle his hands free from the mittens enough to squeeze the N-G tube between the heels of his hands in order to give it a yank. He succeeded several times in pulling the tube out at DHMC and at Craig. Each time the tube was removed, a nurse had to be called to re-insert the tube into his stomach and an x-ray taken to confirm that the tube had been properly positioned. The battle between Michael and the N-G tube lasted for several days at Craig; so much so that Dana and I became friends with the technician who operated the portable x-ray machine ("Nice to see you...again!").

During the first day, Mike was only semi-conscious. Perhaps this was the stage of recovery or perhaps the effect of the meds he was taking. Dana and I couldn't tell. He was awake, but didn't speak to us. He looked around the room, at us and the hospital personnel but his face showed no significant recognition or understanding. His facial expression was blank. The people and the environment were strange to him... and just as foreign to us.

Every time we entered or left Mike's room, we would pass by the patient from the adjacent room who would be sitting in his wheelchair, half in/half out of his own doorway... never moving, not talking, just staring. Several weeks later we learned that this patient's name was Jerry. Jerry was a burly man who was always dressed in wife-beater type t-shirts. We guessed that he was somewhere in his forties. Later we learned that Jerry had been a car mechanic in Greeley, Colorado. He had crashed his motorcycle on the street pavement to avoid a collision with another vehicle. Unfortunately, he didn't have a helmet on. As I walked past Jerry into Michael's room, I always said "hello" but his expression never changed. There was no recognition. Jerry just sat there smiling at no one in particular.

Chapter 13
Life in Craig Hospital

Approaching Craig Hospital on Clarkson from the south, one can see the glass bridge which connects the second and third floors of the West wing of the hospital to the East wing. The bridge is a two story walkway which arches above Clarkson so that patients can travel from one wing to the other without leaving the building to cross the street itself. It also protects the patients from the Denver weather, which can be quite variable... from sunny to rain/snow, from warm to cold, from calm to stormy... in just a matter of moments.

For us, the bridge symbolized the journey from acute care (West wing) to sub-acute care (East wing). To travel across the bridge required that the patient exhibit a certain degree of physical and mental recovery and represented an increased degree of freedom earned by hard work and perseverance in one's therapies, as well as the trust earned by exhibiting cognitive improvements measurable by the staff. A bridge of dreams? No, more a bridge from injury and despair to hope and promise. Each time we approached the hospital from the south this bridge loomed above and ahead of us.

Craig Hospital is a place of miracles. It is also a place of cutting edge science. It is a place where rehabilitation therapy is paramount. Every staff member, every scheduled therapy session, and every aspect of non-scheduled time are designed to help the patients recover from their injuries. That the success rate at Craig is as high as it is a testament to the dedication, skill and caring spirit of the caregivers, doctors, nurses, therapists and technicians. Every staff member was compassionate, optimistic and, most of all, patient. Their knowledge and specialized expertise were obvious; their compassion for the people they were treating as well as for the families who were just learning about the challenges ahead was genuine.

The hallways were filled with patients in all variety of wheelchairs – manual, mechanized, hand rolled and even those which are steered by controlled breathing through straw-like tubes. These latter chairs' occupants puffed and sucked air in and out, generating mechanical commands understood by miraculous software connected to sophisticated hardware. Ambulatory patients walked around the floors aided by all manner of walkers and canes. Some wore helmets made of white plastic with holes to keep their heads ventilated. These helmets are protection which provide cushion from another devastating impact to the brain should their wearer slip and fall.

The sound of electronic beeps could be heard everywhere, emanating from timers hung on the backs of wheelchairs. Those tones alerted the techs and/or family members to stop whatever they were doing, to lock the wheels of the wheelchairs, and to tilt the chair back, shifting the patient's weight from their seats to their backs so as to stimulate the flow of blood through all the parts of their sedentary bodies. Tilted upward, the patient eyes stared up at the only thing they could see, the ceilings, or they were forced to squint into the sun. This weight-shifting occurred for three minutes following every 20 minutes of being seated upright for those confined to their chairs.

During his first two weeks at Craig, Michael continued to be generally unaware of his surroundings. He was awake in the present, but could not remember the recent past, whether it was the day before, earlier in the current day, or even the last hour. In the present, he remained totally consumed with trying to remove his feeding tube. His hands, wearing the mittens and tied down to either his bed or the arms of his wheelchair, were incessantly straining to escape their bonds in order to reach up to remove the tube. The tech's attention was, in turn, completely focused on preventing Michael from succeeding. As we walked behind Mike's wheelchair, we also helped to keep him from yanking the tube from his nose, pulling his hands down from his face – over and over again. If I have repeated this aspect of his recovery several times, it is because this is what consumed our time during the first days at Craig.

Like other patients' family members, we accompanied Mike around from therapy session to therapy session as if tethered to him once again by his umbilical cord. We tried to assist Michael by lifting, pointing, exhorting, but our efforts were met by the blank stares that only TBI, and its cousin, post traumatic amnesia (PTA) (See Appendix B) can generate. Michael was out of it, zombie-like. His stares were not dull and vacant. Rather, he moved as if he simply could not respond to his environment or even to his own body. He seemed unable to distinguish between live beings and inert objects.

Email received June 21, 2006

> ...It's that circle of energy: people giving and receiving that makes the journey a whole lot more manageable... and it's love and support that creates strength for you... to give to Michael ...and so it goes..."

Email date June 23, 2006

> Dana and Ira,
>
> Susan S. forwarded your email to me. I cannot tell you how wonderful that news has been to read. I'm so happy for you all!
>
> ....
>
> I am continually struck by the number of students who come up to me to chat about Mike. Annie L. and Julia B. have both talked to me recently...What wonderful friends Mike has.
>
> Jennifer Karas
> Associate Dean, Arts, Humanities and Sciences
> University of Denver

Progress Report #6 - June 22, 2006

"Wonder of wonder, miracles of miracles..." so goes a lyric from Fiddler on the Roof. Today, we have one of those wondrous events to report to you all.

When we arrived at Craig Hospital today, Michael had just returned from some testing over at the adjacent Swedish Medical Center. As we approached his room, his nurse told us that Michael was talking up a storm. Not knowing what that meant exactly, we entered his room. He saw us and said to Ira, "Hi, Dad." He then said hello to Dana and, with those greetings, we began the wonderful first real conversation with our son. He was confused as to why he was there, but seemed to accept for the moment the explanation that he had been in an accident and was in a special hospital to help him heal and get better. The tech asked Michael what day of the week it was, and he replied, "Thursday." What date? "June 22," he said with a little prompting. We were so amazed at this exchange that we called Darcy, now in Richmond, and put Michael on the phone with her. They talked to each other for several minutes. Then we called his roommate, Dave, and they talked together. Finally, we asked Mike to read something from a poster we had taped to the wall, and he was able to read the large print, "Friends Forever."

This clarity of mind lasted for a good part of the morning, until he got tired and seemed to withdraw once again. But the signs of recovery, and the potential for a significant recovery, were never better. This new alertness had been stimulated by one of the medications prescribed by the rehab doctors, but proved that Michael's cognitive abilities simply lie hidden waiting for his brain injury to heal.

He had physical therapy (strength and balance), occupational therapy (mobility), speech therapy (swallowing and some language), twice each, today for short sessions. By the afternoon, he was pretty wiped out and was quiet during visits with his friends and family.

On another note, Dana and I learned that we will be able to move into the family residences tomorrow afternoon. This will make our participation in Mike's therapy sessions more convenient. And, by not having to commute too far, we will perhaps be more rested and, hopefully, better able to participate.

So again we have good news to share with you. There will be days when Mike has bad days as well as he climbs his mountain to recovery, but today was a good day for us all.

Love to you all,
Dana and Ira

On the 20th day following the car accident, Michael welcomed us as we entered his room, "Hi, Dad. Hi, Mom." We were floored. For three weeks, we had had virtually no communication with our son. How, after just one day at Craig, was he able to speak? The answer was that a medication, a stimulant, which had been administered early that morning, had "awakened" Michael's mind and he was now speaking. Once again, our hearts soared with elation and relief. *Oh my God, he's back!* I thought, clearly a premature conclusion on my part. Dana asked him if he knew where he was and he just looked quizzically back at her. "You're at Craig Hospital. You had a car accident and you hurt your head. You are here to get better," she told him. He looked back as if he understood fully. But, in truth, TBI doesn't work that way and we had to repeat this information to him many times over many days before he would retain and understand. As the day wore on, and the stimulant medicine wore off, he talked less and less. It became clear that at DHMC they had not given Michael anything that would stimulate his brain or body. Their entire focus was to keep Michael alive and overcome his physical injuries as well as his body's reaction to them. In fact, he was sometimes sedated. At Craig, the entire intent of the rehabilitation was to wake him up, to "reboot" his cognitive functioning.

Several medical tests were repeated in Michael's first days at Craig. He had a CT Scan, more blood work and a neurological workup so that Dr. Ripley could have his own data, a baseline from which to assess Mike's medical progress. To get to the testing labs, the techs would transfer Mike from his bed to a gurney, wheel him down to the elevator, taking it to the basement level of the hospital.

From there, he would be pushed through a tunnel-like hallway which connected Craig Hospital to Swedish Medical Center. In SMC's radiology department, they repeated tests performed at DHMC. The new CT scan was used by his new team to develop Mike's early therapy schedule and protocols.

After just three days, Mike was moved from his room on the acute hallway to Room 262 around the corner to the west. His new room was also equipped with a camera to monitor his movements but the room was quieter and much more spacious. We eagerly helped move his personal items to this hospital room (the fourth room he had stayed in since his accident...not including the Emergency Department at DHMC). This room had two windows which looked out to the north, over the driveway entrance to Craig Hospital. This entrance was only used occasionally by cars either picking up or leaving off patients who had ventured out of the hospital on off-campus trips or were returning for outpatient services. Therefore, there was little outside traffic noise. In his new room, Michael was no longer entrapped in a tent bed as his general level of agitation and perseveration on the N-G tube had lessened.

For the fourth time, Dana and I redecorated the walls with the pictures and cards by which family and friends wished Michael a speedy recovery. Julia, who had loaned Michael her IPod while he was at DHMC, allowed him to keep the music player at Craig and it was placed on the window sill opposite his bed. On the far window sill, we placed the CD player which we had borrowed from Bill and Anne's son so that we could continue to play Cantor Heit's Mi Shebeirach for Mike each evening before he went to sleep. The room also had a television suspended above the patient's bed. His clothing was neatly folded in a built-in dresser between the windows. In the far corner opposite Mike's bed, there was a sink and mirrors in the corner and a door leading to a commode which was shared with the patient in the adjacent room. His new quarters were large enough for half the room to be set off as Michael's bedroom; the other half was for daytime activities like washing up, eating and visiting.

Room 262 was to be Michael's home for the next four weeks. During this time, we saw Michael heal and recover in ways that never failed to amaze us. He arrived unaware… of his accident, of his environment, of his mind; he would leave this room to advance to another level of recovery with renewed spirit... aware but challenged. But that gets ahead of our story…

During the first two weeks, the techs cleaned and dressed Michael in his scrubs, T-shirt and slip-on shoes each morning. He was unable to dress himself but could lift, squirm and arch to help. His clothing was loose to allow easy access for blood work, blood pressure taking, etc. which occurred each day. It also allowed considerable freedom of movement needed for physical and occupational therapies as well as maneuvering the wheelchair up and down the halls of 2 West.

Transferring Mike from his bed to his wheelchair was a multi-step process performed several times each day. A tech would arrange a canvas-like seat beneath him as he lay on his back in bed, helping him to shift from left to right and then right to left as the canvas was pulled underneath his body. Then the corners of the canvas seat would be hooked like a playground swing up to a mechanical lift, which was oddly similar to those hoists used to lift and mount car engines. Controlling the motion from a control box which hung down from the hoist on a cable, the tech or nurse would "lift" Mike up out of the bed. Once airborne, they would guide him carefully, swinging him out over the wheelchair, and then gently lowering him down into the chair. When Michael was sitting up in the wheelchair, the canvas seat was unhooked from the lift and slid out from under him. This act of aerial acrobatics was required so long as he was not allowed to put any weight on his left leg as a result of his pelvic surgery and so long as he was not fully aware of the dangers of falling during a transfer. The procedure also prevented falls during the time period when he showed general weakness on his left side of his body. When hanging in this contraption, Mike was totally passive.

Following the transfer procedure, he was pushed in his wheelchair through the hallways to each of his therapies. During these earliest days at Craig, therapy consisted of helping Michael regain his sense of balance, his range of motion, his field of vision, his coordination and improve his responsiveness to verbal commands. After laying in bed in a coma and/or only sitting up in a hospital room chair for several weeks, Michael was pretty unsteady. He could not sit up without support. His arms, legs and feet were stiff and inflexible, showing the spasticity which often follows an accident of this nature. He could focus his eyes straight ahead, but had difficulty perceiving objects in his peripheral vision. Still agitated to distraction by the N-G tube threaded up his nose, down his esophagus and into his stomach, he was not attentive to the verbal stimuli of either our voices or those of his therapists, nurses and doctors. Nor did he ever complain or show any anger.

His first therapy sessions were down the main hall of 2 West, past the nurses' station in the center of the floor, in a large open room called the Gym. The Gym served several functions. First, it was the primary location for physical and occupational therapies. It contained equipment to help patients regain their physical coordination and strength as well as to re-learn simple cognitive activities such as shape recognition, and to speed responses to stimuli, both visual and aural. Second, it served as a makeshift cafeteria for those patients who were allowed to eat outside of their rooms.

Entering the Gym, I thought I had just entered an exercise studio. In the center of the room were three raised 10'x10' exercise mats. They sat about 3 feet off of the floor. To the left of the hallway door were parallel bars and specialized equipment used to stimulate, stretch and strengthen arms, legs and hands. There were balls and bean bags for tossing and various other more specialized adapted "play" things. Along the wall, also to the left upon entering, four small private rooms allowed for therapies to be administered to patients without the distraction of the sights and sounds of the larger room. The Gym also contained a small "practice" kitchenette in which patients who were further along in their recovery would be tested and/or retrained in the processes of planning and organizing for shopping, cooking and cleaning.

Looking around the Gym, it was always a beehive of activity. Some patients were sitting at tables working on what looked to be board games with peg boards and wooden sticks, trying to place square pegs in square holes and round pegs in round holes. Card games were used by the occupational therapists to help patients with their ability to organize objects in a series, while physical therapists used mechanical devices and rubber balls in exercises designed to test and enhance strength and balance.

Patients were individually being attended by therapists who were lifting them from their wheelchairs onto the exercise mats. Some patients were unable to sit without assistance; others tottered uneasily on the edges of the mats with their feet on the floor. Therapists were stretching the muscles of their patients, while others were lifting and bending legs and feet. There were patients who were standing near the mats holding onto walkers and, with great tortuous effort, moving one leg in front of the other as they re-learned to walk. Those, who were strong enough, stood unassisted within parallel bars. Another patient sat exercising his arms at the arm bike. Still another patient was playing "catch" with his therapist. Looking around, ten or more patients were occupied in either physical or occupational therapies around the Gym.

One patient in particular caught my attention the first time I accompanied Mike to the Gym. Matt looked to be a fit, young man…standing on his own…lifting free weights with his arms. He appeared to be about Michael's age, but was moving about and conversing as if he had no apparent injuries. I wondered if Michael would recover to that degree. I later found out that he was a U.S. Marine who had been injured while driving drunk in his hometown on the Western slope of Colorado's Rocky Mountains. After a case of beer was consumed, he had rolled his topless jeep down an embankment and suffered a brain injury. While he looked and acted "recovered" physically, he was angry and antagonistic, often loudly expressing disdain and hatred of everyone and everything around him. To Dana and me, his normal appearance, yet abnormal behavior, was but one lesson in the complexity of brain injuries.

This same room also served as the dining room for patients able to leave their rooms for meals, but not yet free to leave the supervision of the floor. During meal times, the dining tables, which folded away the rest of the day when not in use, were set out by the hospital's staff and surrounded with an odd collection of office and salon-type chairs. A metal rolling shade to the right of the hall doorway was lifted to reveal a buffet line with counter service staffed by the culinary staff of the hospital. But it would be weeks before Michael was permitted to join these patients and their families in the Gym for his meals.

Thus, as the therapeutic and gastronomic center of the TBI floor, the Gym was the focal point of the TBI community at Craig.

As I looked about, I was struck by the variety of injuries: some injuries were obvious from scars crisscrossing scalps left there by various head surgeries. Tubes emanated from the patients' various orifices, including many throat holes left by tracheotomies. Indeed, the sight of tracheotomies and trach scars became common. The patients presented a wide range of physical strength and communication abilities. Some patients were on respirators which made talking extremely difficult, if not impossible. Michael fit right in.

Communication is a bi-directional function: one must give and receive information. Despite being able to speak sentences without any difficulty, Mike's understanding and responsiveness were limited. While in PTA, there was little continuity in speech, thought and focus. He couldn't really communicate very clearly or effectively. This, then, affected his ability to participate in therapy.

He could not stand without assistance and, even when helped up, he was not allowed to place any weight on his left leg. His balance was adequate but not steady, and he would list to one side or the other after a few moments of being erect. His physical therapist and his occupational therapist worked together, helping to lift him onto mats, into chairs, and just generally keeping him from falling over.

He had been in the SICU and SDU only 20 days so his muscle tone was better than most of the patients, who may have been comatose for many weeks rather than just one or two. He was weak on his left side and had trouble grasping with his left hand. *Would this be a permanent handicap?* His visual tracking showed limited peripheral vision to both the right and the left sides. He only really saw things in front of him, not on either side of his central field of vision. He worked each day with his therapists on exercises to address each of these deficits. *But what if his vision did not improve?*

Arriving for a physical therapy session, Michael was transferred by another hoist from the wheelchair to the elevated mat. His therapists, both young women in their mid- twenties and no bigger than 5'5", worked together to lift him from the wheelchair and swing him over and above an elevated exercise mat. Using the button controls, they then lowered Michael onto the mat, either into a reclining or sitting position. Their teamwork provided a tandem approach which increased their social interaction with Michael as well. Together they were strong medicine and Mike was happy when working with them.

Barb Grota, Mike's physical therapist, would begin the session by helping him stretch his legs, arms and back muscles. His muscles were tight not only from being confined to bed for the prior three weeks at DHMC, but also spasticity in response to the brain injury. Barb would lay him on his side and push and pull his legs up and down, and side to side. She would make him reach from one side to the other, twisting his trunk. She would tell Mike to lift his legs and hold them up in different positions in an effort to begin the process of strengthening his core (abdomen and lower back) muscles without putting any direct pressure on his left pelvis. Mike strained to raise his legs just a few inches from the mats and held the position for as many as thirty seconds. Then he would roll over onto the other side, and he would repeat the exercise. He never complained, and he always strived to comply with her instructions. The results were good; we saw him getting stronger each day.

Kim Brown, his bubbly, always smiling occupational therapist, would take over next. She would tell Mike to reach for objects placed on his sides, below him and above him. In this way, Mike worked on his eye-hand coordination, peripheral vision as well as his listening skills. Occasionally, Michael and Kim would play catch with bean bags as he sat on the mat. This exercise game was intended to improve not only his coordination but also his balance. He would sometimes reach too far and begin to fall sideways, unable to maintain his upright position. But Barb and Kim were vigilant and caught him before he was allowed to fall over fully onto his side. Throughout the physical acts of stretching and reaching, pulling and pushing, following his therapists' instructions, Michael's brain worked to reconnect language, motor skills and overall spatial awareness.

Dana and I watched each therapy session with intense interest. We sat in a row of the chairs which would later be used around the Gym's dining table. We studied how his therapists were manipulating Michael's body and working to stimulate his thinking processes. We would try to repeat these when we were later alone with Michael and on the weekends when no regular therapies were scheduled and we were left to our own devices.

At the end of an hour of physical and occupational therapies, Mike was hoisted again by the mechanical lift from the mat back into his wheelchair. Then, without intermission, Dana and I would take turns pushing Mike in his wheelchair down the grey and beige hallways to his next therapy, which was usually a meeting with his speech-language therapist, Carlyn Muselman.

Speech therapy had both physical and cognitive components. It was a combination of oral physical therapy designed to improve Michael's ability to swallow, to eat, and to speak, as well as cognitive therapy to improve his verbal reconnections. In these first few days at Craig, his speech therapies, which came in half hour segments, focused on practicing to speak and enunciate words clearly. Mike needed to work on these in order to overcome the left side impairment which caused him to slur some words. Carlyn and Michael also worked on his oral motor skills, so that he could regain his ability to eat without the aid of an N-G tube.

In Speech therapy, Michael was subjected to a great deal of additional testing to properly establish a base line in his verbal functioning. Michael was asked to read, to try to relate words on lists, to count and to keep track of days, therapy appointments, etc. Tracking his verbal skills would be critical over the coming days as he progressed from one stage of recovery to the next.

His Speech therapist introduced the use of the patient notebook, which would become a permanent appendage while at Craig. The notebook contained basic information such as the name of Craig Hospital and the date as well as the schedule for the week's appointments and activities. It was used to help Michael to become aware of his schedule during each day and to remind him of where he was. Until he could emerge from PTA, remembering such details was extremely challenging. By referring to the notebook and searching its contents, he could determine for himself where he should be, who the therapist was at the session, and what type of therapy was coming up next. In the first few days at Craig, Dana and I relied on the notebook more than Mike to keep us on schedule getting Mike to his therapies, but, as he gradually became more aware of the hospital routines, he would himself refer to the notebook many times throughout the day... searching for answers to his own questions, "What's next?" As we made our way through the hallways from one session to the next, Mike might refer to the notebook three or four times within just a few feet... looking through the pages of the notebook, searching the schedule and trying to remember what he had just read just moments before.

Finally, after being physically and orally "manipulated" for two hours in the morning, Michael moved down the hallway to meet with his neuropsychologist, Dr. Schraa. Dr. Schraa's primary activities consisted of testing Michael's awareness and ability to retain information, also laying down a base line for future measurements. Dr. Schraa would go over a map of Denver with Michael to see if he could locate where Craig Hospital was and where his condominium was in relation to Craig. He would ask Mike to read a list of words, to try to memorize them and, a few minutes later, to repeat them back to him. I have since learned that that test is called the California Verbal Learning Task (CVLT). The CVLT tests not only memory but also encourages memory strategies like repetition, semantic elaboration and grouping, and phonetic similarity. Because of his short term memory deficiency during PTA, these tests were extremely difficult for Mike to perform successfully. In fact, when it came to long lists of words,

Occupational therapist Kim Brown brought smiles to the party.

Mike's Therapists: Physical therapist Barb Grota (l.) and Speech and Language therapist Carlyn Muselman (r.) flank Ira.

Dana and I had trouble remembering them as well! But with each session and passing day, small improvements were noted as more and more words were remembered as the days past.

The schedule of therapies changed every day, yet always consisted of each milieu. Day after day, the routine of Michael's therapies, with Dana and me in tow, felt as if we were all in some fog-like dream state. We moved from activity to activity, not fully conscious of our purpose. Generally, all three of us did as we were told by the Craig staff. It was a surreal experience. Michael, who only a few weeks earlier had been preparing to graduate college, was now learning how to sit up, walk, eat and even how to speak. Dana and I could never have anticipated finding ourselves following Michael around a rehab hospital rather than vacationing in Lake Tahoe with our two adult children.

Because Michael was in the early stages of TBI recovery, and still deep into post traumatic amnesia, having little short term memory of events occurring in the immediate past, it was difficult to assess his emotional state at this point. In fact, Mike was very calm, even complacent. But for perseverating on his N-G tube, he was a very cooperative patient. All of Mike's energy seemed to be spent on just comprehending this odd and unexpected environment – what he was seeing, what he was hearing, who he was with, why was he here – leaving little room for happy or sad emotions. As awareness gradually returned, his emotions also returned. But during those early days at Craig, he was neither unhappy nor angry. He was simply bewildered. And, by the end of each day, he was exhausted...both physically and mentally.

When the morning therapies were over, Michael returned to his private room. At first, because he was being fed through an N-G tube, there was no need to bring him lunch. Later, after he was cleared for swallowing and chewing, he would go back to his room while either Dana or I would retrieve a menu for lunch from the Gym. We tried to gently guide Michael in his selections from the menu by helping him circle the food and drink selections. Then we would return to the Gym to pick up his lunch, and brought it by tray to his room so that he could eat in private. We often took turns eating with him, limiting the level of stimulation so that he would not be distracted from the effort needed to eat the meal. Following lunch, after being lifted yet again by the hoist from the wheelchair, this time returning to his bed, his hands were again restrained to his bed for a midday nap. He showed us that he was, indeed, exhausted by the morning activities, unable to speak clearly or to stay seated without moving about in an agitated manner, shifting and squirming. However, the midday nap would revive him for the afternoon, when he would repeat each of the therapies again.

At 1:30 or 2:00 p.m., following his nap, he was transferred by hoist to his wheelchair to begin the afternoon circuit of therapies. PT and OT often were the same as in the morning session, working toward the same goals. SPT was usually last. And, by late afternoon, Mike again was exhausted by that day's travels through the hallways and by his therapeutic exertions. At 3:30 or 4:00 each afternoon, he was more than ready to retire to his room. But even late in the day, he wasn't finished. Mike always rewarded us with his smile, even when he was exhausted from all the physical and mental effort that was required of him.

As Dana and I accompanied Michael through the therapies, we looked for and celebrated even the littlest improvement. Outwardly, we urged Michael to stay energized, cheering him through his exercises and offering up praise for his accomplishments and his efforts. But, on the inside, despite Mike's apparent improvements, we both fretted over what seemed like slow progress. We were often reminded by staff: *This is not a sprint; this is a marathon.* Quick progress was not as important as continued progress. I feared that Michael would plateau at some premature level of recovery and that his progress would stop. Fear is not the same as pessimism. Fear was an expression of our concerns; pessimism would have drained our energies entirely.

Often, in the late afternoon, visitors stopped by his hospital room --- his friends, family, co-workers, professors, our newest friends from the Denver community. Mike would try his best to keep up with all of the conversations and activities going on simultaneously in his room but to little avail. Seeing visitors and hearing their words of support were wonderful. Yet it was difficult for Michael, tired from the day's mental exertions, to concentrate on and to comprehend the sights and sounds of these visits.

Consider the mental activity required to comprehend three or more people talking at once, while they move about the room. The mind must filter what the ear hears, blocking out some sounds and attending to others. At the same time, another part of the brain must receive images and interpret them. Who to look at? Where is the sound coming from? What is the content of the visual and auditory messages? Making sense of multiple stimuli, such as three or more people all talking at once, some directed at Dana or me, some at Michael, plus music playing on the IPod in the background was hard on him in these early stages of recovery. If more than one discussion was going on at a time, Michael could not keep up. If the words and images came too quickly, too loudly or too softly, he could not make sense of them.

Dana and I observed that Mike would lose his ability to participate in the visits as his fatigue increased. He would just drift off into his own disconnected topics of conversation or he would simply stare past the people in the room. Not only could he not participate in these visits while they were occurring, but he would have difficulty remembering them as well.

One of the effects of TBI and the subsequent "re-booting" of the brain's software is that current events, memories of past events and prior knowledge can all become confused. The patient can connect to part of his/her current environment but then confuses the current context with the past contained in longer term memories. What the patient can't remember, he/she fills in with other memories or fantasy events. The result is a confabulated mixture of truth and fiction, "now" and "then."

Confabulated conversations were sometimes funny, bringing us a light-hearted moment in the midst of all the very serious work of recovery. For example, Michael told us about his trip to Panama accompanying Dave to see his parents in Panama City. The trip occurred in March 2006. While there, he said, they saw a wonderful concert performed by the Dave Matthews Band. But in fact the concert had been in Denver at Red Rocks Park during the summer of 2005. Mike, Dave and several other friends had attended. But Mike was adamant in his assertion that the concert was in Panama. How these two memories got linked together and intertwined in Michael's mind we couldn't know.

Yet his mind was waking up to so many things and in so many different ways that it was hard for him to absorb it all. We arrived one morning to find his room had been posted with a notice for all who entered: ***Low Stimulation***. The floor nurse on duty explained that, when confabulation increases or when the patient seems to get more and more confused despite being more "awake," he/she may need to avoid multiple stimuli such as several visitors at once or more than one person assisting during meals. The warning notice reminded everyone of the need for Michael to have his own space and time to recover from the rigors of his daily therapies.

After several days of therapies which were followed by visits with many, many people, the head nurse had imposed strict limits on the length of visits (5 minutes each), on the number of people who could visit at one time (one person at a time preferably, rarely two) and on other stimuli around Michael (music, television, etc). We tried to have just one person speaking at a time in his presence. In this "*low stim*" environment, as it was called by the staff, Mike ate alone or with just one of us present. We were instructed by the nurses to eliminate outside stimuli (noises, people walking by, alarms, TV, etc) as much as possible which might distract him from concentrating on the task of eating. Even the smallest outside stimulus -- a voice in the hallway or a truck going by outside of the hospital -- could distract him from his immediate task and he would forget to return his attention to eating.

Thus, Michael had transitioned from needing to be talked to, reassured and generally stimulated so that he would awaken...as he did when in the SICU and SDU at DHMC, to needing a quiet, controlled environment where he could focus his thoughts on one or two tasks at a time. He exhibited behaviors which were, in part, Rancho Los Amigos Level 4: Confused and Agitated, and, in part, Rancho Los Amigos Level 5: Confused/ Inappropriate/Non-agitated.

Progress Report #7 - June 25, 2006

Today is the 24th day since we received that fateful phone call at 1:15 in the morning. From that moment until this one, Dana and I have remained steadfastly optimistic that Michael's recovery will be full and complete. We are realistic in knowing that success in this may take many months, years perhaps. But if the progress Mike has made so far is any indication, our confidence and all of your prayers will be rewarded.

Each day Mike presents us with some new and welcome sign of recovery. Today, he was alert a good part of the day, able to focus on tasks when not too distracted by too many stimuli at once (like too many visitors talking all at once), conversant and often making attempts at humor (a very good sign), and showed a few new signs of physical recovery.

This morning Michael ventured outside for the first time since June 2 (other than being transported by ambulance to Craig Hospital six days ago). With Michael in his wheelchair, we all went out for a walk around the Craig Gardens. It was a beautiful, partly sunny, warm day here with gentle breezes. Michael enjoyed the fresh air and sights and sounds of the neighborhood. So much so that he asked to go out again later in the day.

There is no formal therapy on weekends, so Dana and I tried to continue the work that the therapists began last week. Mike tends to respond to those he knows better than to the therapists, so we had pretty good success having him respond to requests for arm and leg movements and answer our questions. We believe Mike now knows that he was in an accident and is in the hospital to recover from severe trauma. He has discovered his scar which is healing from his pelvic surgery and he knows he has been in the hospital for many days. This new awareness is another sign of recovery.

On a social note, we dined tonight with our neighbors from up the road in Finisterra in Tucson, at the new restaurant, Sazza, owned by their son and daughter- in- law. We were joined by their cousins and some of their Denver friends. It was a fun time and the food was superior: organic pizza and salads served on ecologically friendly tables, dinnerware and utensils.

Keep up those prayers, kind wishes, and keep on sending us your healing energy. It's working!

Our love to all of you,
Dana and Ira

Craig Gardens is a small planted patio and deck area at the southeast corner of Clarkson and Girard, just north of the East wing of the hospital. There is a small path which forms a half circle around a small depression in the earth covered with wild grasses and many varieties of flowering plants. On the east side of the garden is a small stone fountain with water bubbling from the top down its sides in which birds bathe and patients' stares are absorbed. A kinetic sculpture by the side of the path, a helix of patina copper cups, rotates, fueled by the wind. And on the west side of the garden, the path turns north across a foot bridge to a redwood gazebo for sitting in the sunlight alongside of the flowers. Under the blue skies of Colorado, and, if just for a moment, the patient is freed from the antiseptic interior of the hospital.

Chapter 14
What is precious?
Thoughts from June 27, 2006 (Day 26)

What is precious?

Something is considered "precious" when the object of the adjective is so rare that it may be considered unique, one-of-a-kind, and, therefore, extra special. When personalized, the word "precious" may describe someone that we love dearly.

What is precious to us is felt most intensely inside ourselves. Thus, what each of us determines is precious is highly personal.

Our son was precious to me. And, as I write that, I realize that I am talking about our son as he was "before", i.e., the person I knew before June 2, 2006. I guess I don't know whether or not the person he is today (June 27, 2006) is as precious to me as before that date. But, as I write this, I feel a deep sense of loss. Will post-trauma Michael be as precious to me as I felt he was before? I don't know, but I confess it is my greatest fear that he will not.

When Dana told me she was pregnant with our first child together, a primal reaction took place that filled me with extreme joy as well as a heightened sense of responsibility. I was filled with many feelings including the joy of legacy, the hope of enduring Self, and a sense of – funny to say now when death's shadow passed over us so recently – immortality.

I recall that, when Michael was just a toddler, he glowed like a gemstone. His blue eyes gleamed so brightly as a baby that they seemed to emit their own light. His hair was fine, a light yellow, almost white, and straight and floppy on his head. His giggle was contagious, making all within earshot laugh along. His cheeks were covered by a band of freckles which crossed his nose – raccoon-

like. He gleamed with youth, curiosity and promise. He was our "prince" – not that he was princely or aloof – but he was our Jewish Prince, as it were. Everyone adored him, fawned over him, wanting to touch his cheek or hold his hand. Later he developed a smile (no, really a smirk) that hinted at the intelligence which was growing within him.

A child is a renewal of oneself. Mike and I were so close to one another that we knew each others' thoughts as they are formed: a like memory, a parallel association; a similar conclusion or way of doing. Sons and fathers, just as daughters and mothers, share this connection and this bond, this organic link to one another.

It is with this strong sense of connection that I think about how precious, how irreplaceably valuable, Mike is to me. For over twenty years, from conception to June 2, 2006, this love has grown inside of me. I tried not to dominate him with my opinions nor interfere with his decisions, but I admit that I was still deeply involved, hopeful and prideful.

Before the accident, Michael had been approaching his graduation from college. Is there any moment in one's life which should be more liberating, full of hope and expectation than completing one's education? It is like the seed, long ago planted, nurtured over time, has sprouted and leafed out. Michael was ready to blossom. He was one week away from declaring to his family and friends and to the world, "I am now ready to fulfill my own hopes and dreams."

Sitting with him in the hospital, I imagined his future: all the independence, all the explorations of people, places, experiences, all of the opportunities to contribute and all of the precious moments he would be sharing with Dana and me.

Sitting in the hospital, I fight back my tears.

Dad I need your help.

Note left by Michael overnight on the table next to his bed in his Craig Hospital room.

Chapter 15
Not a Sprint

Hospital routines are established quickly. What feels like a foreign country when you first arrive, quickly becomes repetitive, mundane, even boring. Each day blends into the next which blends into the next. However, despite the apparent "Ground Hog Day" effect, health is gradually restored. Day by day, Michael's condition improved. Small signs were daily gifts he offered up.

Ten days into his stay at Craig Hospital, Michael had already been housed in two different rooms. During each day, he attended a series of one hour therapies. Either Dana or I stayed by his side almost every moment of the day as he went from therapy to therapy, taking breaks with him outside in the fresh air, and sitting with him while he ate his meals in his room.

After the N-G tube was removed, Mike ate a diet of softened foods and liquids. This protected him from aspirating his food until his swallow reflex returned. We would spoon feed puddings, softened fruit, hot cereal, soup and the like. These feedings looked and felt to us just as it did when we fed Michael as an infant. Now in the hospital, I scooped up some soft food or soup into a spoon, lifted it up to Mike's mouth and he would lean forward to engulf the spoon with his mouth. *Open the airplane hangar…here it comes*. Spoonful by spoonful, this was repeated until the food was consumed. We noted down on the memo pad how much of each food item he had consumed for review by the nurses who carefully monitored his nutritional intake and his weight. In many ways, we were parenting an infant again, waiting for the adolescent and then the adult to re-emerge from the fog of TBI and PTA.

After a week of being spoon-fed, Michael began to hold the utensils in his own hands, eating with the spoon and fork. Allie, his tech, taught us to supervise Michael's eating so that he would not overload his spoon with food nor shovel in too much to chew at one time. The concern was that he would take too large a portion in his mouth and risk choking on it. Michael, like many with TBI, often did try to load up too much for one bite and would spoon more food into his mouth before he had cleared it of its prior contents. This reflected one aspect of his attention deficit.

Near the end of June, Michael's eating and swallowing was improving to the point where his speech-language therapist, who was the arbiter of the patient's swallowing ability, ordered up a special x-ray test, a videofluoroscopic swallow evaluation, to view his swallow reflex in action. Accompanied by his Speech Therapist and Dana, I wheeled Michael to the elevator on 2 West and took it down to the Ground Floor level, where the corridors connected to Swedish Medical Center. We travelled down the subterranean hallway over to the Radiology Department. There we were permitted to watch the swallow test on a monitor in an alcove adjacent to where Michael was sitting.

Michael was told to swallow radioactive jello under the piercing eye of the x-ray machine. Michael would take a spoonful and swallow as I, along with Dana, the technicians, and speech therapist, watched on the monitor. We could see the food passing by his teeth and tongue and his trachea closing reflexively as the food passed down into his esophagus. Several swallows later, Carlyn was satisfied that he could be removed from his soft food diet and returned to a normal diet of both chewable and drinkable foods. This signaled a major milestone as his food choices increased greatly. Indeed, Michael had lost weight since the accident while living on either a liquid or softened diet, and increasing his food choices would help him regain some of the weight he had lost.

Each new day began with the same orientation routine which helped to establish for Michael where he was and why. In each TBI patient's room at Craig Hospital, there is a white board hanging on the wall in front of the patient's bed. Basic information about the day is written on the board:

Where: Craig Hospital, Englewood, Colorado,
Room 206;
When: Saturday July 1, 2006:
Who: Doctor: Ripley Nurse: Katie Tech: Allie.

We went over the day's information with Michael each morning, repeating it several times. He could read the board and some days he remembered where he was, but he had great difficulty remembering what day it was and who was attending to him. When we would leave his room, as we made our way through the hallways, we questioned him periodically so as to stimulate his retention of these basic facts through repetition. He responded, "This is Ripley Hospital and my doctor is Dr. Craig." We might pass someone, like Dr. Ripley, in the hallway and ask Michael who it was. He might answer, "That's Dr. Schraa." Over a period of a week or more, these names and his ability to remember where he was got less and less scrambled.

In his room, Mike would look over at the photo enlargement I had taken from his condo, a photo taken by him of that monkey in Panama. He would recognize it, but would incorrectly identify it. "That's a picture of Dave (his roommate)," he confabulated. Mike was confused; of course Dave is not a monkey but he was with him when he took the photograph of the monkey on their trip to Panama.

There seemed to be no "eureka" moments anymore like when he first started talking to us; only gradually improving thought processes which seemed to be making their reconnections in Michael's brain. There were no timetables; only the hope that each day would bring some new sign of improved cognition.

Dana and I walked with him through the same four corridors of 2 West every day. We took turns pushing his wheelchair. We greeted the other family members of other patients, whom we had come to recognize, although we didn't really know them. There was little time for family caregivers to get to know one another. Our focus, like each of theirs, was on our patient. The only time during a day we were not with Michael was when he was sleeping. In mid-day during his rest periods, we returned to our family apartment or ran quick errands. And we only left Michael at the end of the day following the nightly ritual of playing the CD of the Mi Shebeirach prayer for healing. As Michael progressed and became more aware, he would mouth the words with the music and then, later, would sing the words out loud with us. Even when not fully conscious, he seemed to relate to its special sentiment of recovery for both body and mind. Whenever another person, such as a friend of Michael's or a nurse or a visitor from Tucson, was visiting at the end of the day, they were invariably moved to tears upon hearing the words of hope and healing.

Bless those in need of healing
With r'fu-a sh'lei-ma
The renewal of body
The renewal of spirit
And let us say: Amen.

Following the prayer, we would bid Mike a good night. Then, physically and mentally exhausted ourselves, we would leave to have dinner at some nearby restaurant before returning to our own one room apartment in the Patient Family Residence.

On the way back to the apartment, we frequently stopped at the All for the Better Gourmet Ice Cream Store located just south of the hospital at the intersection of Clarkson and Hampden. This became our nightly ritual. The ice cream store, a neighborhood parlor owned locally and manned by either the proprietor himself or local high school students, became a link to life as it normally is constituted. A pralines and cream scoop in a cup for Dana and chocolate chip on a sugar cone for Ira. We savored the homemade flavors of the creamy cool confections. We sat at tables located in the front of the store and exhaled the day's events. We would sit and talk, debriefing each other from what we had observed and what had occurred during the day. Each day was stressful and we needed to relax and "come down" from the day. But the uncertainties of what lay ahead for Michael… and for us…always hung over us like threatening storm clouds. We tried to remain patient with the slow pace of recovery even as we worried about what was ahead.

Each day we repeated the day, date and location with Michael in the morning. Each day we sat with him through each therapy: PT, OT, Speech and Neuropsych... seeing progress but at what we thought was an excruciatingly slow pace. We fed him breakfast, lunch and dinner. We took him to the bathroom, we laundered his clothes. We traced our steps up and down the same hallways and the same sidewalks. At night, we listened with Michael to the same music over and over (mostly, Jack Johnson tunes) and we helped him get ready for bed. Each day we closed with the Mi Shebeirach. Returning to the apartment, we answered phone calls and emails and took care of our daily business. Through this routine, we supported each other, sharing our hopes and concerns for Mike's future and plans for our return to Tucson. Just the knowledge that we were just a few steps away from the place where medical miracles were taking place, where broken bodies and spirits were being mended and given the time to find their own healing powers, had its own curative and recuperative effect on us as well.

Chapter 16
A Physics Lesson: Thoughts from July 1, 2006 (Day 30)

The universe is virtually vacant of matter (with the possible exception of dark matter), void of material and only barely lit up with the light of any energy. The average density of matter in the whole of the universe, as scientists and cosmological theoreticians now understand it, is only a single proton per cubic meter of space. And, as the universe expands, the density of matter is becoming less and less. There is so little matter in our cosmos that the likelihood of one piece of matter coming into contact with another piece of matter is ridiculously small, probabilistically infinitesimal, and almost inconceivable. For example, a single molecule could travel for millions of years over millions of miles and never collide with another molecule.

But here we are... an improbable conglomeration of molecules and substance, forming structures and organisms which are incontrovertibly complex in form and intricate in function. We are compactly comprised of matter despite the huge void of the cosmos as a whole. We are so structured, so functional, and so tightly packed as to be utterly incomprehensible to our limited (and perhaps, primitive) intelligence and parochial earth-bound perspective.

Yet, on June 2, 2006 (yes, we remember that time is also relative), during what seemed to be a perfectly normal night on the North American continent of the Planet Earth, all the negative energy and improbabilities of life and physics came together to throw some unlikely dense matter in the form of a tree in the direct path of other densely packed matter, i.e., my son and his automobile. The automobile, an equally improbable composite of matter and energy, had turned sideways in the roadway, jumped a curb corner and careened toward the tree. Although the average individual molecule floating about in the cosmos may never collide with another, on this night my son's head came crashing into one simple, relatively stationary tree. The collision threatened to end his life and to terminate the existence of his unique Self.

Those negative cosmic forces somehow conspired to derail a twenty-two year old male of the human species, born from Dana's and my DNA, from the brightly lit path of life which lay before him.

But that night's cosmic conspiracy was thwarted and failed. Mike's strength of will, his determination to live, pushed back against their challenge. Although slowed down by the impact of the events of that night, he has shown that he is gradually, yet inexorably, regaining his momentum on his own special path through the universe. That is my belief, and my hope, on this night.

Progress Report #8 - July 2, 2006

Greetings from Denver where we are experiencing our first Rocky Mountain thunderstorm since we arrived here a month ago! It seems the entire Western U.S. is experiencing the same drought conditions as Tucson, but, like down in Tucson, the summer rains have begun.

Mike has clearly transitioned from acute medical issues to the longer process of regaining his cognitive functions. Medical treatments for infections, pain and the like have all but ended. However, treatment and rehabilitation of his brain injury are moving ahead.

This past week has been another good week of recovery and discovery. Mike is clearly out of the woods on any serious medical issues. He is in no pain from his injuries or surgery on his pelvic fracture, experiencing just some muscle tightness from being confined to a wheelchair (which he confidently maneuvers by himself now) and his bed. He stands up with a walker without losing balance, a very good sign, but is not yet permitted to put any weight on his left leg due to the surgery. It will be a few more weeks before that will be permitted.

Mike also is doing well regaining his cognitive functions. Each day he puts together more and more of the recent events such as where he is, why he is there, what he is doing now, how to get through a normal day. Daily repetition helps to solidify those thoughts for him. To be fully cognizant and functioning will take time, but he seems to be up for the marathon of recovering. He has also come up with some great/funny things: he remembers, much to the surprise of the PTs and OTs, that, as a child, he had "Osgood-Schlatter Syndrome," a growing pain illness; he announced that the longest word he can remember is "pusillanimous;" and he has spoken at least some words in each of five languages: English, Spanish, Italian, Hebrew and French.

Some of you are aware that I dropped in on Tucson for a day last week to pick up some clothes and drive our car back up to Denver. I'm sorry I couldn't have made contact with all of you but I'm sure you understand. I did have good visits with my parents and Dana's Mom, and it was sure good to see our home again.

We are again lucky this week to have some Tucson visitors in Denver. We will be dining with Ron and Hannah and visiting with Steve and Cindy.

Have a happy and safe Fourth of July. And, again, thank you for your many cards, calls, wishes and prayers.

Dana and Ira

Chapter 17
Holiday Spirit

Can you imagine anything more ironic than celebrating Independence Day, the Fourth of July, at Craig Hospital? The patients, our loved ones, were anything but free in the normal sense of the term. Confined to wheelchairs, unable to move about without assistance, they are locked in by both their minds and bodies. Family members, caring for their injured patients, were imprisoned by their love, concerns and fears.

No therapy sessions were scheduled on this holiday. In fact, with the holiday falling on a Tuesday, many of the staff were away on vacation the whole week. The remaining nurses, therapists and doctors worked double duty to keep things in order on 2 West. But with no therapies scheduled, we family members took up the task of keeping the patients active and entertained.

Dana and I spent the morning with Michael travelling about the hallways and grounds, ending up once again in the Craig Garden. The weather was cool enough to sit outside and enjoy the botanic garden's beauty. We sat side by side, staring at the flowers, squinting into the sunshine, but hardly talking. At lunch, the Craig Staff had set up a traditional Fourth of July barbeque on the patio outside of the main dining room/cafeteria on the ground floor. We joined about 30 others where we enjoyed a buffet of chicken, burgers, potato salad, and watermelon. In addition, for dessert, there were brownies and cake with red, white and blue icing.

All around us were other TBI and SCI patients. The adjacent patio tables were occupied by one or two patients and many fathers, mothers, sisters, brothers and children. Despite the reminders of the grim realities which had brought us all together… the wheelchairs, respirators, walkers and the incessant chiming of the weight-shift timers, the mood was quite festive. Michael, Dana and I ate and then returned to Michael's room so he could rest. Dana and I returned to the Family Residence apartment and waited for the afternoon to end.

The Staff had planned to take the patients up to the roof of the parking garage across Clarkson Street adjacent to the East building in the evening. They intended to watch fireworks from various local neighborhood celebrations. But following dinner in the Gym, a line of major thunderstorms rolled through the city of Denver. It rained in thick drenching sheets of water across the parking lots. No one went outside on this evening. Further, Michael did not want to stay up late to be transported to the garage roof. He had become very susceptible to being irascible and agitated when tired at the end of the day. He could not stay alert and became frustrated when not left alone to rest. So we returned to his room and bid him goodnight.

There were no fireworks until the storms had passed later that evening. They finally moved off to the East around 11 o'clock. Finally, the city's official display began from Coors Field, where the Diamondbacks had been playing when the rains came. Dana and I could see the bursts of light on the horizon to the north from our 4th floor room in the Patient Family Residence. We sat staring out at the fireworks. The dark night was illuminated first by distant lightning and then by a burst of fireworks. While pretty to view, we felt far removed from the holiday spirit as we looked out from the hospital residence.

Mike was fast asleep in his hospital room. None of the patients with TBI seemed to be disappointed at missing the fireworks.

Chapter 18
Phase II of Craig Hospital

On July 5, 2006, the 34th day following the accident and the 15th day since Mike had arrived at Craig Hospital, we had our ***first*** Family Conference with the team from Craig. Up until this time, we had not yet heard what the plan was for Michael's rehabilitation directly from his team or doctors and therapists. The delay had been frustrating to Dana and me as we wondered what their plan was for our son. This was, in part, due to the July 4th holiday, before and after which many members of his team were unavailable. It was also, in part, due to my own trip to Tucson to pick up the car and some clothing.

Dana and I had looked forward to this first Family Conference. The first week (June 20-27) at Craig was given to both physical and cognitive testing. The second week (June 28-July 4) was the start of therapy programs, but there was much down time with no therapies occurring due to scheduled vacations around the holiday. We anticipated that the third week at Craig would be devoted to therapy and addressing any new medical issues which surfaced. We had built up our expectations for the meeting hoping that the team would provide grand revelations, insights and foresight into Michael's condition and prognosis for a full recovery. Unfortunately, the reality was, well, just that, cold, hard reality.

The Family Conference was the first opportunity for Michael, Dana and me to sit down with all of the members of the team assigned to Michael. We met in the afternoon in a conference room on 2 East. Dr. Ripley, Mike's physiatrist, sat at the head of the table. Around the table were Dr. Ripley's assistant, Mike's occupational therapist Kim (his physical therapist Barb was still on vacation and, therefore, unable to attend); his speech and language therapist

Carlyn, his floor nurse and our family counselor Linda.

As they each reported their observations, Michael, Dana and I listened intently. In particular, they told us that there was a strong possibility that Mike would be left with compulsive behaviors and some executive function deficits like an inability to plan, organize or problem solve. There might be difficulties concentrating and remembering (and, therefore, learning and/or experiencing). Like one bucket after another of cold water being thrown at us, their comments startled us, forcing us to face new facts. The future they described was frightful, stark and real. No one tried to give us any comfort that Michael would ever be fully himself again; in fact, just the opposite. They virtually assured us that he would not ever "be himself" again. And they repeated many times that his recovery would be a long process...taking months, if not years.

After the doctors, nurse and therapists reported, the family counselor discussed the issue of social security benefits. She said that qualifying for these depended on Mike's degree of employability. At this point in time, no one in the room, including Dana and me, had any idea whether Mike would be able to hold down a job, any job. But hearing this for the first time was painful.

There were few surprises in their reports on Mike's then current condition. Dr. Ripley, the team's leader, did, however, pull up on the computer images of Mike's CT Scans and x-rays. He reviewed the injuries to Mike's brain with great specificity and described some of the problems which could be foreseen as a result of an injury of this nature and location. Below are my notes from this meeting:

Medical report:

CT: Front left contusions and diffuse
(widespread) axonal injury
MRI: Reads material the density of water.
Front left and back left showed fluid collection
MRI can read the iron in the resolving blood,
shows a back right *contrecoup* injury.

The injuries are so diffuse that cognitive awareness issues likely.
Control will be difficult and impulsive behavior later on.
Planning, organizing, executive functioning will be affected.
Still at risk for developing clots.

Nursing:
Fully continent
Still has problem with moving bowels
Warm compresses on arms to resolve clotting

PT/OT:
Keep non-weight bearing on left leg
Next week will work on transition shifting to chair
Both shower seat and ambulatory device (walker or cane) may be needed at discharge.
Working through routines starting next week.

Speech Therapy:
70%-80% accuracy following directions
Attention and concentration being emphasized

Neuropsych:
Recall is the big issue. Can't process rapidly.
Confabulation/organization issues will be big concerns in the long term.

Family Services:
Insurance issues should be addressed.

Target Discharge Date: August 16
Discharge will be when it's safe to live in the home environment
Several types of therapy will be required
Childlike steps- prognosis for reasonably full adult cognitive skills, i.e., initiate actions and self determination
Long term process

During the meeting, tension increased inside of me, like a clock spring being wound tighter and tighter. I listened intently to ever word uttered. We absorbed the news with outward smiles; but our doubts and concerns churned within. *Will Michael know independence? Will he be able to continue to grow intellectually? Will he be employable?* There were no answers at this point in time. And we were told, repeatedly, "*Time doesn't heal all wounds, but healing takes time*."

And so, after 35 days in Denver, the only resolution we had was a target date for Mike's discharge: *August 16*. Like hearing of the accident itself, the anticipation of Michael's discharge into our own care was terrifying. Dana and I had to jump into action, despite being confronted by a myriad of unanswered questions.

What would we do? Where would Mike go after Craig Hospital? Would he stay in Denver? Would Michael continue as an outpatient of Craig? Would the three of us relocate to Phoenix, where Michael would be treated in an outpatient program? Or would we return to Tucson, finding whatever necessary support services were needed for Michael in our local small medical community? We couldn't know. The question which loomed the largest was: *What would Michael be like on August 16? What level of cognitive functioning would he have recovered to? Who would Mike Adler be on August 16?*

We had seen major changes in Mike's condition since our arrival in Denver on June 2. He had awakened from a six day coma, gradually becoming at least partially aware of his trauma. But after five weeks, he couldn't eat, couldn't organize his day, and didn't know where he was. His ability to remember events in the immediate past, his short-term memory, had not yet returned. *How much more could be expected in six additional weeks?* We understood that there would be many more changes between July 5 and August 16. But how could we plan if we didn't know what we were planning for? Following the family conference, we set out to learn as much as we could about other programs, facilities, doctors and therapy programs. Our focus was on Tucson, as we hoped to be able to return home. But our expectation at this time was that, at a minimum, we would have to commute several times a week up to Phoenix to get the quality and quantity of assistance that Michael was likely to need. I dove into internet research and making phone calls to referral sources while Dana focused on the in-hospital issues.

Email received July 7, 2006

Good morning, Ira.

Not sure if you'll get this message anytime soon. I know you and Dana have been very preoccupied with Michael and his rehabilitation. I sincerely hope things are coming along well. Seems to me Michael is a true trooper and would not let anything hold him back. Peculiar how life has its twists. You never think of these unfortunate things happening especially within your family. Michael is blessed to have such a loving, caring and supportive circle of family and friends I'm sure. Michael has the advantage of being young, strong and I'm sure the right optimistic attitude toward his recovery process.

I have a story to share with you that you might find of great encouragement during your processes of recovery. I know life will never be the same, but I also know there are always better things to come in the future.

About five years ago this month one of my nephews was involved in an almost fatal car accident. Footloose and fancy free, he was going into his second year of college, had the world in his hands so to speak. He and three other friends were in route to Rocky Point when the driver of his vehicle had misjudged a curvy road in Why, Arizona. The car rolled three times off the side of the highway.

He and others were airlifted to UMC Trauma Center. My nephew and another occupant took the blunt of the life threatening injuries –crushed back, broken neck, damage

to spinal cord, paralysis, broken shoulder and arm, road rash and trauma to his head. He was not supposed to walk again much less regain feeling in his limbs.
It was very difficult to hold my composure when I visited him the first time after his accident. I was so torn up inside but I knew we had to be strong for him and encourage him that he still had his life. I can't imagine the fear he may have felt when he finally woke up and couldn't feel anything for the first time.

Well, its five years later and my nephew graduated from the University of Arizona this past May! He walks, he talks, and once again he has life in the palm of his hand. Yes, he will probably be on medication for the remainder of his life and does still have limited movement in his neck as he has a permanent metal rod/shunt in his neck and other invisible hardware. He is a young man of Zen and truly believes in self-healing. He has been an inspiration to all of us. I never heard him say "I can't" – as a matter of fact – during his first awakening some of his first words out of his mouth were "Why are you all looking so sad? When can I get up? How long will I have to lay here like this? When can I go home and did my car make it!" I still have yet to hear him say "I can't."...

I hope this story offers you encouragement towards Michael's recovery process! All things are possible and I know Michael will get through this as I'm sure you know this as well....

M.

Progress Report #9 - July 8, 2006

It has been 37 days since Mike's accident. We have spent 19 of those at the Denver Health Medical Center and the last 18 at Craig Hospital. We are now established residents of the Craig

Hospital Family Residence.

But Craig Hospital is a place where the patients, both spinal cord and/or traumatic brain injured, work very hard, fighting to be as full functioning individuals as they can possibly be. Michael is no exception to this. He works very hard every day, without complaining and with total dedication to the task, to sorting out his thoughts and memories and to re-learning how to handle the activities of daily living.

This past week Dana and I attended a family conference with Mike's medical and therapeutic team. Each discipline was represented: medical, physical therapy, occupational therapy, speech and language therapy, and neuropsychology. The meeting began with a review of his CT Scans and MRI. We learned which areas of Mike's brain were most affected by the trauma of the car accident. Although injuries were characterized as diffuse axonal (neuron) injuries – meaning that there was tearing and stretching and bruising of the neuron connections throughout Mike's brain – areas most affected were pinpointed for us. Some were temporal lobe injuries, the result of the initial impact, and some were contrecoup injuries, the result of the sudden deceleration and reverse impact on the other side of the skull (back right), affecting a section of his cortex [actually, his occipital lobe], as the brain twisted from side to side. From the images we can expect that cognitive functions related to organization, planning, memory and executive (daily) functioning may be affected for a longer period of recovery. Cognition is a complex process and the injuries are such that a long term prognosis is often difficult. In many cases, patients recover more than would be indicated from the scans alone.

We also learned that the brain has significant plasticity, i.e., the ability of the neurons to find new paths where old ones were damaged. This plasticity often makes up for paths which have been lost due to the injuries.

Each discipline reported strong progress and, assuming continued forward movement on all fronts, Michael would be expected to be discharged from Craig Hospital around the middle of August. Where we go from here, and when, will depend in large part on Mike's rehabilitation results between now and then.

Mike expresses his desire to succeed here as well as his impatience with the speed of recovery. He is justifiably tired of being confined to a wheelchair, which would be the case given his pelvic surgery, regardless of his brain injuries. But he is working as hard as he can – and we are very proud of his efforts.

Dana and I are doing well right now. We have finally gotten enough rest to be thinking clearly again. For a while, back in June, we didn't know if we would ever feel full of energy again. We had a great visit with friends from Tucson last week and thank them for the respite their visit afforded us. Their visit also heightened our desire to be back home with all of you, our friends and family.

We will keep you posted as more events develop and as our plans to return home firm up.

Our best to all of you, along with our love,
Dana and Ira

Email dated July 9, 2006

Michael,

Thank you for your call today. Last time I saw you, you were having trouble talking, so to hear your voice was wonderful! You sound fantastic. When you were sleeping, I was worried; but I'm so happy to know you are awake and on the road to recovery. I knew you'd be ok.

I was so happy to have the chance to celebrate your graduation with you even through you didn't realize I was there. Your professors came by and spoke so highly of you. Your friends were amazing which did not surprise me. They have your good nature and kind spirit. It was great to meet them and to see how much you mean to all of them. I can't wait until the next time we can hang out… all the cousins. Keep taking one day at a time and stay patient. You have made incredible progress so far and I know each day you will become the new and improved

Michael Adler. We are all behind you.

Congrats on your graduation!

Lots of Love,
Cousin Deb

Following the first Family Conference, we fell further into a regular routine now that the critical care medical issues had been mostly resolved. Just as a marathoner might not be aware of every step along the way, only to "wake up" and be surprised by how far he/she has come, we raced from therapy session to therapy session, only to realize that days/weeks had passed. Michael had progressed showing more and more of his old self every day. *It's a marathon, not a sprint!*

A typical day for Mike at Craig Hospital in mid-July began with Mike being awakened around 7:00 a.m. Six weeks after the initial trauma and three weeks since Mike had arrived at Craig, he was able to get dressed on his own by slipping and sliding clothes up his body while lying horizontal in bed, still not weight-bearing on his left leg. He wiggled and wriggled into his shirts and pants. This wouldn't be easy for a healthy person to do while lying down, let alone one who was dealing with a repaired pelvis and the mental confusion of post traumatic amnesia.

After dressing, Mike would transfer from his bed to his wheelchair. He was no longer subject to daily hoisting. He was able to swing his legs over to the side of the bed and, reaching for the wheelchair, to hold himself up and slide over into the seat of the wheelchair. His therapists call this maneuver "squat transferring." To accomplish the transfer, Mike was taught by Barb, his PT, to slide a smooth three foot long wood board, like the ones which sit atop roller boards used in exercise classes, under his buttocks and across the gap between the bed and the seat of the chair. He then reached over to the armrests of the chair and slid his buttocks across the board and into the seat. Once sitting up in the wheelchair, he dutifully strapped himself in with a seat belt. The belt was intended to keep him from falling out of the wheelchair while in motion as well as to keep him restricted to the chair at all times so he couldn't attempt to get out of the chair and wander off. Of course, a real risk was that he would stand up from the chair and fall over onto the floor.

The first kind of seat belt was a blue padded affair which stretched broadly across the width of his stomach. The belt's plastic latch attached behind the chair and supposedly out of reach of the wheelchair's occupant. But it didn't take long before Mike was able to detach the belt just by reaching around to the back and, without turning around, squeezing the latch to open. At that point, the nurses, who were perpetually on the lookout for safety risks, changed the belt to one which closed with a keyed metal lock. Possession of a key to unlock the belt was a privilege reserved for the nurses and techs, lest some well-meaning family member (who, me?) loose the patient on the hospital. But one of Mike's nurses, the petite, sweet, freckly faced Katie, surreptitiously handed me a key, so I could assist Michael when he needed to relieve himself without having to wait for a tech or nurse to arrive. Katie made Dana and me swear up and down that we wouldn't let on from whom we had gotten the key. Later, when Michael had shown that he was cognizant of the need to keep himself safe and that he wasn't permitted yet to stand on his left leg until his pelvis was more fully healed, he was released from the lock and key belt and given yet another belt, which was more for show than for safety.

Belted in to the wheelchair, and chaperoned down the hallway as we walked by his side, Mike could now wheel himself, pushing the wheels with his hands (the weakness on his left side, both arms and hands, had substantially subsided now) and "walking the chair" with his feet, over to the 2nd Floor Gym. There in the Gym, breakfast was waiting behind a cafeteria-like glass covered counter. The food was shuttled on carts up and down the service elevator to the second floor (and the third floor for SCI patients), for those who could not or were not allowed to transport themselves into elevators and down hallways to the main cafeteria and dining room located on the ground floor of the hospital.

In the Gym, the menus were in a holder on the wall with

pencils to circle one's selections. Mike could now select his own food... with a little prompting to keep the selections balanced and healthful. No longer confined to soft foods, he usually circled up scrambled eggs, bacon, wheat toast or sweet roll, fresh fruit, juice and decaf coffee. Sometimes he added in oatmeal and 2% milk. Not that he could eat all of this, but he was not at all concerned about the size of his stomach. Nor could he fully appreciate the volume of food that he had ordered. What he did consume, however, was usually well balanced and nutritious. Always a good eater, this part of Michael's personality seemed to be fully intact.

The breakfast tray was piled high by the counter workers and by us, as we added the beverages and fruit cups in accordance with Mike's selections. Dana, his tech or I would then carry the fully loaded tray as we followed Michael back to his room. The food tray was placed on a movable table which was then rolled up to his lap and then locked in position. During the first three weeks at Craig, we fed Michael much like an infant. We would fill a spoon or fork with food and then hold it in front of his mouth. He leaned forward to take a bite or a sip, chewed slowly and swallowed. We would fill another spoon with small bite portions and offered it again. We tried to rotate the food groups we offered to him so that he would awaken his senses to different food textures in his mouth and, therefore, strengthen his swallow reflex. Mike's sense of taste and ability to distinguish one food from another was greatly diminished. These sequelae lasted through the first year of recovery. As he gained strength, Michael would use the utensils and feed himself, an act we would celebrate... another sign of manual dexterity and cognitive recovery! Six weeks after the accident, Mike had "advanced" to the level of his early childhood capabilities.

Kim, his occupational therapist, supervised his dressing (described above) and hygiene routine trying to do so with a minimum amount of external cueing. She prompted him to establish a regular hygiene routine, a necessary Activity of Daily Living (ADL). By following a bathroom and sink routine with multiple steps, e.g., locate the toothpaste and toothbrush, put the paste on the brush, wet the brush under the faucet, brush all the teeth, rinse his mouth and the toothbrush, he improved his organizational and planning skills. At the sink in his room, he brushed his teeth, rinsed his mouth sipping from a cup of water and spitting out the toothpaste and, then, slowly and methodically, Mike would rinse the sink clean. Next, he washed his face with a washcloth, shaved with his electric razor (no blades were allowed while he was being treated with anti-coagulants), and combed his hair…in that order, everyday.

Some lingering health issues were addressed. CT scans of his arms found superficial venal clotting around his elbows. These were likely resulting from all of the IVs which had poked his arms. Also, his platelet count was very high, over 1,000,000, as his body responded to its trauma. As a result, he was at greater risk for blood clotting. Therefore, twice each day Mike received an injection of a medication to reduce the platelet count. He also received a painful anti-coagulant injection in the center of his belly into his stomach muscles twice a day. Ever the good patient, Mike never complained about the needles being stuck into his stomach each morning; he just clenched his teeth until the needles were removed. The anti-coagulant injections left large, dark bruises in his abdomen. Since the injection was designed to keep his blood from clotting, he would bleed under his skin with each shot. After a while, he looked as if he had lost a prize fight taking too many belly punches. In addition, warm compresses were applied to his elbows to resolve the clots that had already formed.

The treatment for his high platelet count posed a paradox to the doctors. The platelet count put Michael at risk for new blood clots and stroke. While platelets could cause clotting, the medications preventing the clotting could induce internal bleeding. Michael's CT scans and MRIs had shown signs of minor subdural bleeding in the brain at the time of the accident. Therefore, a careful balance between medicines to prevent clotting and those to prevent excess bleeding needed to be maintained. Michael's blood counts were taken daily and his hematologic condition was monitored very closely.

Typically, after eating, dressing, cleaning up and being medicated, Mike's rehab therapies began at 8:30. His daily schedule of therapies was printed out weekly by his Speech Therapy coordinator. One copy was posted in his room; another was added to the notebook which was placed in a backpack hung from the back of his wheel chair. Throughout the day, Michael was instructed to reach into the backpack and pull the notebook out in order to look up his next appointment. Still suffering from post traumatic amnesia, he sometimes needed to refer to the notebook several times in the course of a five minute time span. He would read and search the schedule for his next appointment, checking and re-checking. Then he would replace the notebook in the backpack. Within minutes, he would reach back again to retrieve and consult the notebook. After several weeks with the notebook, he became both more adept at referring to the schedule and more aware of what he was reading so that he could move independently to his next therapies rather than relying on us to tell him what and where the next session was going to be and to guide him through the halls.

By mid July, Michael was aware enough, and strong enough, to maneuver his wheelchair without help. He would travel down to the 2nd floor West Conference room for a group session called Orientation Group Therapy. Being invited to Orientation Group was considered a small milestone which implied that Michael was moving out of PTA. In Orientation Group, patients Mike, Barry and Jerry pulled up their wheelchairs around the conference table. Led by Laura, an assistant to the Speech therapists, they attempted to discuss current events and other "orienting" details of their lives, such as where they were born, where they live, the state capitals, etc.

Barry was a TBI patient who was older than Michael, approximately 40 years old, and a father of two. He had hit a tree while skiing with his family in February 2006; he had progressed to the same level of awareness as Mike but over a six month period, while Mike was only one and half months out from his accident. Jerry was about 60 years old and not recovering very quickly at all, i.e., he was almost unresponsive to external events or instructions. He was an avid bicyclist who had been hit by a car down in Florida almost a full year earlier.

Mike did very well in Orientation Group, taking the lead much as he did in his college classes. His memory for people and places learned well prior to the accident was good. Laura asked each of them their names, their birth dates and their home towns; the capitals of their home state, and their addresses. Michael could respond to these questions, while Barry and Jerry had great difficulty with them.

Then, Laura would read a newspaper article or something from a book. The patients were asked to discuss what had been read to them. For example, one topic of discussion was the origin of chocolate, both brown and white. None of them was all too

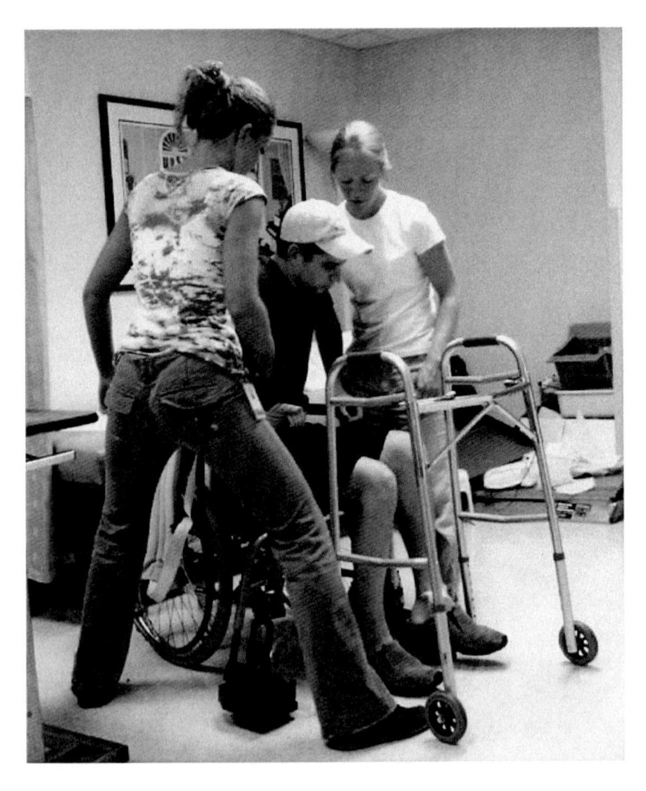

Teamwork: OT Kim (l.) and PT Barb (r.) assist Michael from his wheelchair to a walker, helping him avoid placing weight on his left leg.

interested in this topic, but they played the game as well as they could. Repetition of information, we were told, was a key to re-awakening their short term memory skills.

While in Orientation Group, each patient went through the same exercises and heard the same information being presented; however, there was little real interaction between the three of them. They responded to Laura but showed little awareness of each other. It was obvious that they were preoccupied with their own thoughts, their own histories and their own struggles. We learned later that egocentrism is common with TBI patients.

Following Orientation Group, Mike would travel over to Physical Therapy, Speech Therapy and/or a visit with Dr. Schraa. Each of these sessions lasted from 30 to 60 minutes. In mid-July, physical therapy consisted of stretching, practicing transfers, standing up onto his right leg only from a sitting position, using a walker for support, and hopping about without the use of his left leg, which was still under "toe touch, weight bearing only" instructions from the orthopedic surgeon. Occupational therapy consisted of working on various ADLs, e.g., dressing, washing, eating, bathroom, and, as Mike progressed, into the test kitchen for cooking and cleaning. Mike would work on his verbal skills in Speech therapy, take reading comprehension tests using a computer, spelling words, and writing simple sentences. These tasks, although simple and mundane, were challenging to our patient.

Following these visits each morning with his therapists, Mike returned to his room to rest before tackling the task of lunch. Fatigue, both physical and mental, was still a significant feature of this phase of rehabilitation. Following major surgery, such as Mike's pelvic surgery, one would expect physical fatigue to be an issue as the body has been invaded internally and traumatized. Similarly, following TBI, mental fatigue is usually experienced. Feeling weary and unable to stay energized for more than just an hour or two can be a problem for months or even years.

The midday lunch routine was the same as the breakfast routine. Mike wheeled himself over to the Gym/cafeteria, selected his food from the menu, the staff filled the tray and we carried it back over to his room, where he ate sitting in front of the table-on-wheels. Then, Mike would rest. He would return to bed by squat transferring over the wooden board and nap during this time. Dana and I would leave to make phone calls and eat our own lunch during this rest period.

After his "power nap," Michael was noticeably refreshed and ready to meet the challenges of the afternoon's activities. He returned to the therapy circuit, visiting Speech, OT and PT each day for a second time. Occasionally, his schedule included a half hour in the Therapeutic Recreation (T-Rec) room, where Mike could relax by playing a game such as foosball or billiards. There was a wide variety of activities to choose from in T-Rec. For example, he could have planted some plants in the horticultural room, painted some ceramic or played blow darts. But he didn't venture out of his comfort zone to engage in anything other than foosball and billiards. The T-Rec therapists didn't try to introduce him to other activities, so that these other recreational facilities were left for longer-term TBI patients or those with SCI.

Mike gradually, but continuously, showed signs of improved awareness and cognitive functioning. He responded to the constant repetition, learning his location and the date, the ADL routines, performing the exercises and responding to questions. His strength improved noticeably as the physical therapy increased his leg and core strength. He sat up straighter and moved with improving coordination. He focused on listening better and showed increased verbal skills, both writing and speaking with more clarity with each passing day.

However, as his awareness of his situation grew, he became more emotional and less compliant. For example, Mike increasingly expressed thoughts focused on getting out of the hospital. To all the encouragement and praise for his successes in the various therapy sessions, he would angrily and loudly reply, "If I am doing so well, why can't I leave?" Although increasingly aware of where he was and why, he did not yet appreciate the scope or nature of his deficits. He only heard the praise of his therapists and doctors.... "You're doing so well, making so much progress." His frustration surfaced frequently and grew in intensity.

I could not stop thinking about his future and what it might bring. These thoughts constantly gnawed at me. "Only time will tell..." the constant refrain of the neurosurgeon echoed inside of me like waves incessantly washing up on the shore, only to recede again to the ocean. We were told that only in some unknown amount of time we would see how far Mike would come back to his previous self. His progress was like watching the tide come in rather than individual waves. Just as the tide rises but not discernibly with each wave, so, too, there was little progress moment to moment, although there were more signs of recovery day to day.

In late afternoons and evenings, Mike was spent from the concentration expended in all the therapies. He would wander... not physically, but cognitively and verbally. He confused not only the people and their names, both who had visited and whom he imagined had visited, but also what he had done on that day and the days before. He didn't look confused as he confabulated his memories. Quite the contrary, he looked matter-of-fact about the people and events he would describe. But his mind drew no boundaries between fact and fiction.

Then, around 5:00 p.m., he wheeled himself down to the cafeteria to select and pick up his dinner. Following dinner, he relaxed with visitors, watched television or listened to music. The time following dinner every other day was used by the staff to shower the patient. After showering, they prepared Michael for bed. But Mike is one of those people who would like to shower every morning if possible. While at Craig, he was limited to every-other-evening showers. He was bathed by the techs, who first transferred Mike to a waterproof wheelchair, then undressed him. Covered with a sheet for a gown, they finally transported him to the shower room, which was just a few feet down the corridor, around the corner from Room 206. After a few weeks of this hands-on personal treatment by the young female techs, Mike, ever modest, began to ask if he could give himself a shower. While the answer was still "no," the simple act of asking was taken as yet another good sign of increasing independent thinking on his part.

Dana and/or I visited Michael each evening following our

dinner, if only for a few quiet minutes. We have always recognized how hard it is to be a patient in a hospital, alone in one's room. This was especially true for a person like Mike, who liked to be with people. When we returned from dinner, we routinely and with great ceremony, played the CD of the Mi Shebeirach given to us by Cantor Heit. We liked to hold Mike's hands and place our hands on his hair or shoulders, while we listened to the Cantor's beautiful song and, sometimes, we sang along with her. This ritual had become a very important part of our days in the hospital. By mid-July, Michael began to ask us to make sure we played the prayer for him before he went to sleep. *Oh, the power of belief! The power of hope and reassurance! The power of the mind to heal itself!*

Mike returned to his bed for sleep around 7:30-8:00 every night. His attempts at sleep were interrupted through the night by nurses checking his vital signs or taking more blood or just checking in on him. In the morning, Michael would awaken again at 7:00 a.m., ready to face the day and to take the next step in his long journey.

Craig Hospital Sky Bridge: Connecting the acute care West wing to the sub-acute, transitional East wing, crossing the glass walkway represented both a challenge and the success of therapy. Here it is decorated with posters and signs for Craig Days. (See Chapter 21)

Chapter 19
Thoughts from July 14

I believe we define ourselves by our actions. If we are insignificant in the scheme of the cosmos, we can at least have purpose through what we contribute to the world around us; what we do and whom we affect.

How will Michael define his life, his purpose? Will his actions, and their effects on his family and friends, teachers and co-workers, define a life of purpose and contribution? Will he ever overcome the damage that this one act [the automobile accident] of inattention, lack of skill or foolishness had inflicted on him and those "in his world?"

Am I being too harsh? How can we rationalize or make any sense of this? And if we can't make sense out of it, must we concede responsibility for his actions to some "act of God?" Is there a cosmic plan which was successfully executed by the car crashing into the tree? Or is there some omniscient and spiritual force which actually intervened to make this happen to Michael, and, by extension, to Dana and me?

I think that believing this is an "act of God" is the ultimate cop out, i.e., assigning responsibility to Providence is to try to avoid accountability. Let the chips fall where they may but I believe Michael fucked up and now all of us are going to be affected by this for a long, long time to come, if not for the rest of our lives. There...I said it; I got it out of my system. Doesn't change the result, does it? But at least I feel like I have faced the truth.

Chapter 20
Movin' On

On July 14, seven weeks to the day following the auto accident that Michael will never remember, Dr. Schraa, his neuropsychologist, declared, "Michael has emerged from post traumatic amnesia!" Indeed, Mike's short term memory was improving... finally. Dr. Schraa had performed a series of standardized memory tests: lists of words, numbers and recitation of recent events. Some tests were performed better than others, but a change in Michael's responses was clearly discernible.

This should have been a red letter day, but it just felt like yet another step forward on the long climb out of the Grand Canyon of dark human places. But, it WAS a step forward. "One small step for man; one giant leap..." for Michael.

Michael was taken off Amantadine, the wake-up drug, and was placed on a higher dosage of Ritalin, the focus/attention drug. He reacted quickly to the change. He was like a silly putty ball, bouncing off of one idea to the next, rapid firing his thoughts and attention. He experienced an amphetamine-induced energy spurt. Not only was he more aware and quickly diverted to any stimuli within earshot, but also he was more emotional. He was angry and indignant, "Why am I being held here," he demanded, "when I am so much better? When will I be leaving this place?" He began to express rebellion against the idea of more and more therapy.

Dana had returned to Tucson for a few days of well deserved respite and visits with our family and friends. With no one to trade shifts with during the daily routine of therapies, I spent the entire time with this newly energized Michael and I was exhausted. I was tired physically from standing up and observing him in the hospital, walking beside him in and outside of the hallways and walking paths, and just being in this hospital environment. But mostly I was worn out by the emotional strain of watching our son struggle to be normal again, in his valiant attempts to please so many people during the day: therapists, doctors, nurses, techs, cooks, attendants, and me. I was also tired of being surrounded by patients affected by TBI and SCI, the constant reminder that accidents happen but also that nothing would ever be normal again. Michael's energy spurt required that I respond with equal energy. We had waited so hopefully for the day he would begin to remember, but we were unprepared for the emotional outbursts which came along with memory. I thought, somewhat sardonically, "Be careful what you wish for!"

I felt so weighted down and melancholy. I never believed that I knew what the future held for Michael. After all, I thought, not everyone can be a miracle recovery story... for then there wouldn't be any miracles. These concerns were exacerbated by the angry retorts to almost every inquiry to which Mike responded. "How are you feeling today, Mike?" I asked. "Good enough to leave," he replied. "How was Speech Therapy today?" I tried to change the subject. "I don't know why I have to read stupid stories about things I never cared about, written by some stupid doctor!" he barked back. Although I knew he was not attacking me personally (it was, after all, the TBI speaking), his anger stirred deep sadness within me.

Which patient would walk again? Which one would speak? Who would go back to work or to school? If I was feeling worn out, both physically and emotionally, how then could the patients themselves go on and on? Where did these patients find their strength? How deep was their internal fortitude? And what choice did they have but to go on? But go on to what? Some would live their lives confined to wheelchairs. Some would be unable to speak clearly ever again; some would be unable to think clearly ever again, or grasp a quick joke or comprehend a complex idea or make a decision; and some would never be able to move about like the rest of us. After seeing so many acts of personal courage, so many individual gutsy performances in therapy and the many acts of kindness by the staff and by family members, too numerous to recount here, I knew that what I was observing was really not so many tragedies but rather stories of renewal and rebirth.

Despite all the wonderful sights and sounds of recovery at Craig Hospital, much of what I saw seemed like a needless waste of life and of human potential. A motorcycle accident, an improbable hunting accident, a ill-fated dive into a lake, a horse's hoof coming into contact with the head of a high school basketball coach on his Wyoming ranch... so random, so accidental, so improbable. Yet the probabilities had caught up with these people. And those who lived their lives in close proximity to them, their families, friends and co-workers, had also had their own lives disrupted by these terrible twists of fate. This extended community of patients and caregivers were all survivors of some terrible occurrence. In some cases, personal choices had gone terribly wrong. In others, intentional recklessness was being punished. Few, however, were innocent victims of circumstances (wrong place and the wrong time).

We had all been thrown together. We were compacted within Craig Hospital's walls without regard to education, socio-economic background, religion, race or any other distinguishing traits. The only commonality is that we all have been stung by the whip lash of fate. The song says, "Into each life a little rain must fall?" Bullshit. These accidents and their aftermath are not just a brief rain shower of poor luck. They tossed us about like the typhoon of disastrous fortunes; the hurricane of sadness; a record blizzard of shit. My own anger bubbled over during this time.

We did the only thing we could do in the circumstances. We tried to close our eyes to the horrific events which had brought us together, and to turn our focus, as only conscious humans can do, to the future. We willfully downplayed our present circumstances and we called upon our own human spirits to overcome our fears. We spoke only of "outcomes" and "resolving injuries." We assessed no blame, no guilt. We tried to ignore our feelings of anxiety, anger, frustration and isolation, and we tried to move on.

I asked myself, as I sat alone in the Patient Family Residence room at the end of the day: *Who was fooling whom? Who wasn't facing up to the truth? Who was being willfully blind to their true feelings or squelching them just to make it through another day? Would these feelings surface sometime later when they were least expected or welcome? Could I, and would I, climb out of my own depression?*

Progress Report #10 – July 16, 2006

To all of you who have followed Michael's progress week by week, thank you for being there for us as we struggled through the days of crisis. And thank you for being here with us now as Michael is going to need your support and understanding for his challenging path to full health and function.

This past week was filled with events, some positive and some not so positive. On the positive side, Michael is remembering events from the days preceding the current day. This represents a return to building memories, where once he was captured in the present moment only. Real therapy can only begin when the patient can remember the lessons being taught and this is the threshold of progress that Mike crossed this week.

He began the week by talking about a dinner from the night before; then he remembered who had visited an afternoon the day before; he followed this with a quote from a movie we had gone to see in the hospital's big screen recreation room (despite only having had the attention span to watch about 30 minutes of the film). By week's end, his neuropsychologist indicated that he thought Michael was emerging from his post traumatic amnesia, the period from last memory before the accident to first memory following the accident.

On a not-so-positive note, Michael and Dana returned to Denver Health Medical Center for a follow-up visit with the General Surgery department, the group that oversees the Surgical ICU. For all the excellent care we received in ICU, this visit was a great disappointment. Not only did Michael [along with Dana and Allie, the Craig technician who accompanied them to DHMC] have to wait for two hours in the department's waiting room, but his file was lost (and, of course, no one was told about the problem). When he was finally seen by a doctor, the first year resident with no experience and no time to review the file, declared, "Hey,

Mike, you look okay to me. You are doing very well. You look all healed up to me." The doctor had no understanding of the long term effects of TBI and no appreciation of how a TBI patient might receive such a glowing report. For two days after the visit to DHMC, Michael wondered why he couldn't be discharged from Craig Hospital since the Denver Health doctor had declared that he was "…all healed up."

This coming week Michael has a follow-up visit with the DHMC Orthopedic Surgery department for his pelvic surgery. This is a critical appointment in that Michael is still "toe-touch weight bearing only" on his left leg, therefore, confined to his wheelchair. If he has healed enough from the pelvic surgery, he may permitted to put some weight on his left leg and can begin physical therapy to walk again on both legs. Let's all keep our fingers crossed that we get a higher level of service at this next visit.

Dana went down to Tucson for a few days this week and returned today. She had a great few days of respite from the hospital scene, saw her Mom and my parents, and visited with a few of our friends. I am glad to have her back here with me. Michael is a handful for a solo caregiver!

When surrounded by a hospital environment, especially one where spinal cord and traumatic brain injured patients are, it is difficult to engage in thoughts about the outside world and the global problems with which mankind must struggle. But we, like so many of you, are concerned and distressed about the events unfolding in Israel, Lebanon and the Gaza. We pray for peace to be restored and for the safety of people on all sides of the borders. May higher, more humane values prevail soon!

Our love to all,
Ira and Dana

Email received July 16, 2006

Dear Michael,

We have been touched and moved by the thoughts and

feelings so honestly expressed in your updates. What an extraordinary family you have! We have no doubt the profound love and support you provide one another will enable you to meet the challenges ahead.

Michael, you don't know me however from reading these messages, it is clear that you are so special and loved! Keep Fighting. It's a long, frustrating recovery but take it day by day. You are a strong young man and the prayers for you have reached the depths of all of our souls. Even when the day's progress is disappointing or when you feel cranky, know you're loved. That's what is so amazing about love…it is limitless in its abilities to comfort, heal, and provide hope. We love you, too.

When you were a much younger boy I'm sure your Mom or Dad read you the book "The Little Engine That Could." This is a great story of motivation and the power of positive thinking. But, we're going to change the story somewhat. In the book, the little engine said, "I think I can, I think I can" when faced with what he thought was an insurmountable obstacle. But, luckily, you were born with a different gene set so your mantra is "I know I can, I know I can." And those words will serve you well as you travel on your journey to recovery. There might be times when you say, "I think I can" or even an instance of "I'm not certain that I can." But, deep down inside, your mind is chugging along, just like the train and you will make it to the top of the mountain! And the other train cars will give a loud cheer because you showed them that with much determination, support and love, a lot can be accomplished. So, like the little train, start preparing for your expedition and as one says to a person embarking on a visit to a new place, Godspeed. And know that the Higher Power will watch over you and keep you safe as you navigate familiar and unfamiliar territories.

Lots of love and support
M. and E.

Sunday, July 16, was quiet at Craig Hospital. Sundays, like all weekend days, are less staffed than weekdays. We spent the day visiting with Mike but also found time to simply sit back and reconnoiter. I gazed out of the window of our apartment at the Patient Family Residence. Below, in the parking lot, there was a black cat walking by. I wondered what the cat represented. Bad luck? Or, perhaps, some ancient alchemy which would lead to Mike's full recovery?

The parking lot was filled with cars and trucks and vans from all over the country. There were plates from Missouri, Michigan, Illinois (a car with Chief Illiniwek, the mascot of the University of Illinois, Darcy's alma mater, painted on the hood!), Arizona, California, Montana, Wyoming, and, of course, Colorful Colorado. The majority of parking spaces are designated and sized for handicapped parking. There were several motorized vans equipped with lifts for wheelchairs as well as a small fleet of cars specially adapted for spinal injured patients or those confined to wheelchairs. The specially adapted vehicles were fitted with uniquely designed steering wheels, brake and gas pedals, gear shifting devices, movable seats and/or locking mechanisms to allow for wheelchairs to maneuver within the vehicle.

Looking out onto the patio areas surrounding the hospital I observed several Craig staffers (nurses, technicians and aides) sitting outside, smoking while on their work breaks. I wondered: *Why do so many healthcare workers smoke? Do these caregivers see so many injured persons and hopeless cases that they are numbed to the risks of cancer and other respiratory diseases? Are they educated in regard to spinal cord and brain injury, but not the disease of cancer? Or does the stress of working at Craig Hospital (or any hospital) require some addictive outlet?* It is likely that they are just everyday folks, just like the rest of us. Were they blinded when it comes to their own health risks by their own belief in immortality or, more likely given their chosen professions, resigned to their mortality?

On this quiet weekend day, we looked forward to Michael's first visit to our apartment. Before Michael was allowed to come to the apartment, Dana and I had to be trained so that we would "qualify" as off-site caregivers. So both Dana and I had been taught wheelchair mechanics by Mike's PT, Barb, and learned emergency protocols in the event that Michael would have an unexpected seizure. The wheelchair training consisted of going outside and learning how to maneuver a chair across the street, through gravel or grass, and up and down street curbs, without spilling the patient out of the chair and onto the ground. These are skills that we would need so long as Michael was confined to his wheelchair as his pelvis healed, which we hoped would not be more than a week or two. Then he would graduate to assisted-walker or cane status.

Also, people who have suffered a TBI can be subject to seizures. A seizure occurs when there is either a "short-circuit" or "storm" of the electro-chemical reactions in the brain. These may arise from the axonal tears which occurred during the impact on the brain as it was impelled forward and backward inside of the skull. They can occur as the electrical impulses run into blockages caused by dead neuronal cells following an event which causes a deficiency of oxygen to parts of the brain. Seizures can also occur due to a change in the brain chemistry as a result of the injury. The "electrical storm" can occur in one part of the brain or across several areas of the brain. According to one resource, 35% of open head injured patients suffer this form of post-traumatic epilepsy while only 1% of closed head injured patients develop seizures. Grand mal seizures involve the whole of the body while focal seizures are more localized, affecting limited behaviors, such as tugging of clothing or a sudden loss of concentration or thread of thought.

To qualify as "seizure trained," Dana and I had watched a video on the hospital's closed circuit television in our Patient Family residence. The short video which must have been filmed at least two decades earlier, defined the different types of seizures and showed us what immediate actions to take in the event our patient ever showed signs or symptoms of a seizure. We learned to follow the steps: 1) Protect: Make sure the person is safe by removing physical impediments or obstacles, sitting them or laying them down, protecting their heads with a pillow; 2) Airway: Loosen tight garments, turn the person on their side to ensure a clear airway; 3) Call for help: get help from the police or hospital by calling 911; 4) Evaluate the person: how did the seizure begin, did the person give a verbal warning or do anything to signal the seizure was starting. We memorized the steps using the acronym: PACE. To be cleared for patient care, we took a written test, which was graded by a member of the nursing staff. Lastly, we were consecrated with Craig holy water sprinkled over our heads by the head nurse, who confirmed our qualifications with a brief oral exam ("You did watch the video, didn't you?"). We passed with flying colors, hoping to never have the occasion to use what we had learned. In fact, to this date, Michael has never had a seizure. But I still carry in my wallet a Seizure First Aid Card, which lists the PACE steps... just in case.

Michael came over to visit us in the apartment. More accurately, newly trained in advanced wheelchair techniques, I wheeled Michael in his wheelchair into the Patient Family Residence, up the elevator to the third floor, to where our apartment was located. Michael was glad to be away from the immediate hospital campus and enjoyed the ride up the elevator to our apartment. It had been 55 days since the accident and he was finally freed from hospital premises. It felt like another universe to him, although our one room apartment was only twenty yards from his own hospital building.

Mike observed that he was the first guest entertained in our family apartment "who can't feel his left leg." Then he added, without any segue, his now usual complaint, "What do the doctors and therapists expect to achieve by making me read dumb stories not even written by a doctor?" He had difficulty remembering the content even immediately following the reading. He didn't comprehend the purposes of these exercises and he increasingly lashed out at them, only speaking to us about his frustrations. He tried hard to perform in every therapy session, but he did not enjoy those sessions with his Speech therapist.

Then, Mike said in all seriousness, "Stool softener is nothing more than a colon sanitizer." This cracked us up laughing. He had been fighting constipation for a few weeks and, when he didn't remedy the situation spontaneously, he was given a stool softener to help his digestive processes along. Unfortunately, the medicine was much like inserting a stick of dynamite inside a hole in a mountain to stimulate a rock slide. KABOOM! Relief, which came during this visit to our apartment, was welcome.

Finally, using his cell phone for one of the first times, Mike called his friend, Helen, about her coming by. She said she couldn't. She told him that she has been at the water park all day. We knew she was with Dave. The girlfriend and the roommate seemed to be forming some sort of relationship now that Michael was out of the picture. There were fewer visitors now – coming by less frequently. People were pulling away from Mike, who was anchored at this hospital, while they continued to sail away into their own lives. Michael was becoming more and more isolated from his friends as they moved on. The sadness that Dana and I felt for Michael was increasing as well. He needed his friends, and only a few of them were regulars at the hospital. We tried to compensate but parents are not the same as peers, and Mike was becoming lonelier and missing the camaraderie of his friends more and more as each day passed. His social isolation would continue long after he was discharged from Craig.

The following Monday, he continued his weekday therapies. His awareness and alertness were continuing to improve but his progress seemed more gradual now. He worked hard at physical and occupational therapies, both of which improved his cognitive functioning as they addressed physical activities, like lifting, coordination of eyes and hands, and speed of cognition. One interesting exercise involved a light board in one of the private therapy rooms located to the left when entering the Gym. The light board had various bulbs scattered about a three foot by three foot panel attached to the wall. As the lights blinked on and off, up and down and across the board, Michael had to press buttons connected to an electric buzzer with one or the other of his hands to indicate whether the left side or right side of the board was blinking on and off. The lights moved quickly, and his eyes transmitted the messages to his brain, which in turn transmitted commands to his hands. As the speed of the lights blinking on and off increased, his brain function also sped up and the physical coordination of the response increased.

His ability to recognize shapes and patterns was also tested. Mike placed rubber bands around rows and columns of small pins sticking out of a small game board. Forming a triangle or rectangle with the rubber bands or connecting all of the red pins with one band seemed a simple task for those of us watching, but Michael was very deliberate in his movements as he solved each puzzling request. I was happy to see him successfully complete these assignments but wondered, *Is this the level of aptitude of a new college graduate?* Our feelings of joy at his success always seemed tempered by the realities of the enduring effects of the accident and of the injury.

Further testing his eye coordination, OT Kim, would hold a string out in front of Michael's face while Michael held the other end of the string by his nose. A bead strung onto the string would be moved down the string toward his face as his eyes tried to keep their focus on the bead. Strengthening his eye muscles as well as working on his attention targeted the injury to his occipital lobe. Michael loved this exercise, always smiling back to Kim's equally bright smile. He occasionally complained of double vision, perhaps a sequela of the *coup/contrecoup* to his occipital lobe. He was later evaluated by an ophthalmologist specializing in brain injuries. The doctor believed that the double vision was temporary and would resolve itself soon.

Physical therapy, however, was still impeded by the weight-bearing prohibition while his pelvis continued to heal. He had been confined to his bed or his wheelchair since the beginning of June. According to his orthopedic surgeon, Michael would not be permitted to put weight on his left leg until eight weeks following the surgery. All walking was prohibited. All leg strengthening exercises were confined to the exercise mats in the Gym and in his wheelchair. To keep his arms strong and increase his endurance during this period when he was not ambulatory, Michael would roll the wheels of his wheelchair by himself over to an arm cycle. He would "pedal" the cycle's handles with his hands and arms for 15 or 20 minutes, barely breaking a sweat. This was the extent of his aerobic workouts in Craig's TBI unit.

However, Mike was very talkative during these periods of activity. Stimulated by various medicines which were awakening his mind, he would chit chat about any topic to just about anyone who would listen. He would talk about going back to work or returning to his apartment (the floor plan of which he did not actually remember despite having lived there for five months prior to the accident, a result of traumatic retrograde amnesia which gradually resolved itself) or about events from years prior in Tucson ("Dad, remember when.....?"). His vocabulary was clearly intact and he was as articulate as he had been prior to the accident. He started out slow to express himself, as if he had to find the words before he could speak them. Sometimes he found the words, but they might be the wrong words, out of context. However, as the days and weeks passed, his speed of conversation and expression of ideas improved immensely.

In addition to Michael's therapy sessions, Dana and I were now attending a twice-a-week parent group meeting. The meetings were organized by the Family/Patient Coordinator, and led by one of the neuropsychologists who worked with TBI patients and their families. We met in a conference room located on the first floor of the Patient Family Residence. The room was set up like a classroom, with a table and chair in front of a white board, an easel and student chairs, with their half desks attached, set up facing our "teachers." Only two mothers of other patients attended with Dana and me. The small attendance was either because there are just the three patients who were at that stage of their recovery that their parents or family members were able to consider the topics being discussed or because we, parents representing these three patients, were the only ones who wanted to or could make time during the day to attend. We didn't know why attendance to the group was so limited. Given all the patients at Craig Hospital going through TBI rehabilitation, it seemed strange to us to be selected for these one hour seminars. Nevertheless, we were grateful for the opportunity to ask questions out of the hospital environment and with time to discuss our issues thoroughly.

In the group meeting, we discussed our difficulties communicating with our family members/patients. We also talked about some of the technical information regarding how the various components of the brain operate. One of the Craig neuropsychologists spent the first session drawing pictures of the brain and its components. He lectured us on the functions of each part and listed all of the cognitive and emotional functions which went with each.[4] Lists like this intimidated me. Rather than feeling good about all the functions Michael was adequately performing, these talks seemed to highlight the deficits which might follow TBI. Like the functioning of a finger, which is taken for granted until lost to a sprain or bandage, we never appreciate how important each cognitive function is to daily living...until it is missing.

The other two parents in the meeting seemed distracted and uninterested in the details. Learning about the physiology of their child's injury seemed of secondary importance to them. They wanted help with their own problems: who to see, what to do, how to respond to their patients. I saw both stress and fear in their eyes. I knew also that they saw the same stress and fear in our eyes.

The neuropsychologist made suggestions as to how we might respond to our patients and how to come to grips with the various stages of recovery. He tried to be reassuring, but frank. Each of us expressed feelings of inadequacy in trying to cope with our child's injury. We didn't know how to respond to their sadness, anger, frustration and repeated demands to leave the hospital. Because each injury is unique to the individual, there were only broad guidelines which he could share. These guidelines corresponded to the Rancho Los Amigos stages of recovery.[5]

All of us expressed concern regarding the type of therapy or care which would be needed once our patients were discharged from Craig Hospital and were transitioned to home or another rehabilitation facility. The Family/Patient Coordinator was helpful in outlining the needs of each patient in general terms and explaining insurance-related questions. Unanimously, we expressed fears of

---

4 See Appendix C
5 See Appendix A

financial ruin once our patients were discharged into our own care. But the reality was that each case was so completely different in the level of recovery, speed of recovery, expectations for their continuing needs and unique living environments to which the patient would be returning. Much of what was discussed was only generally applicable and felt superficial.

During the last half of that July, outside of the time we spent with Michael in the hospital, Dana and I researched, for hours on end, TBI resources in Tucson, Phoenix and elsewhere which would be needed after Michael was discharged from Craig Hospital. We had tried to become educated as to who to see and where to go, but, as we feared, we were caught in a confused web of information, indecision and sources.

At the end of the month, we were only 2 -1/2 weeks away from Michael's projected departure date from Craig. We knew that we needed to choose therapists – OT, SLP, PT, a neuropsychologist and a physiatrist. We tried to learn about guidelines to help us evaluate treatment and care options following Craig. The HealthSouth booklet, "Living with Brain Injury" offered the following suggestions for a rehab checklist:

- *Will the family receive regular reports on the patient's progress?*
- *How many people with brain injury has the center treated?*
- *What is the average length of stay? Who determines it?*
- *Are previous medical records incorporated into evaluations and treatment?*
- *Can the family participate in therapies?*
- *If the family lives far away, how much telephone contact is there?*
- *How often are comprehensive re-evaluations performed?*
- *How does the center feel about medication?*
- *Can the center meet the injured person's specific and individual needs, including feeding tube, bowel and bladder control, loss of vision, language therapies, group therapies, and more?*

- *Is there follow-up after discharge? How often?*

These struck me as good questions, but obvious ones. And they did not satisfy my need for finding and evaluating the personnel who would be performing the therapies our son was likely to need for weeks or months following discharge from Craig. One particular requirement had become clear to us during the time at Craig Hospital as we observed Michael's daily therapies: the personal relationship between the patient and therapist is critical to the success of the therapy. In the time at Craig, Michael had related well to his PT and OT, but not to his Speech therapist. He also did not appreciate his neuropsychologist until almost five weeks at Craig when his PTA had passed. Only then did Dr. Schraa become one of Michael's favorite appointments.

Our research found few resources available or easily identifiable in Tucson. Although Tucson has an abundance of many things... sunshine, good restaurants, call centers, and hot, arid desert... it had only limited professional services for the brain-injured. I made calls to hospitals, rehab facilities and to specific doctors and therapists. I contacted in-home nursing services and outpatient treatment programs. I spoke with several neuropsychologists, who told me that they only evaluated and tested patients but did not offer therapy. They claimed that reimbursement from insurance companies was too difficult to obtain for therapy. The rehab facilities dealt primarily with physical injuries and had only limited interest in treating traumatic brain injuries. My frustrations grew as I came to the realization that brain injuries, while common, were simply not a priority in a second tier city like Tucson. Time was running out. *We had to decide where to go, what to do!*

Chapter 21
Craig Days

During the last week in July, all of Craig Hospital celebrates summer with a series of recreational events called Craig Days. Craig Days provided a welcome distraction from the very serious business of rehabilitation which went on otherwise uninterrupted. The staff looks forward to this annual celebration with great anticipation for the fun it brings to them and their patients. A break from the routine of the hospital was an added bonus for everyone. The theme of Craig Days is always *automobiles and racing*. Ironic – given the number of patients at Craig as a result of car accidents where speed is a significant contributing factor!

Michael's Best Medicine: Darcy and Mike during Craig Days.

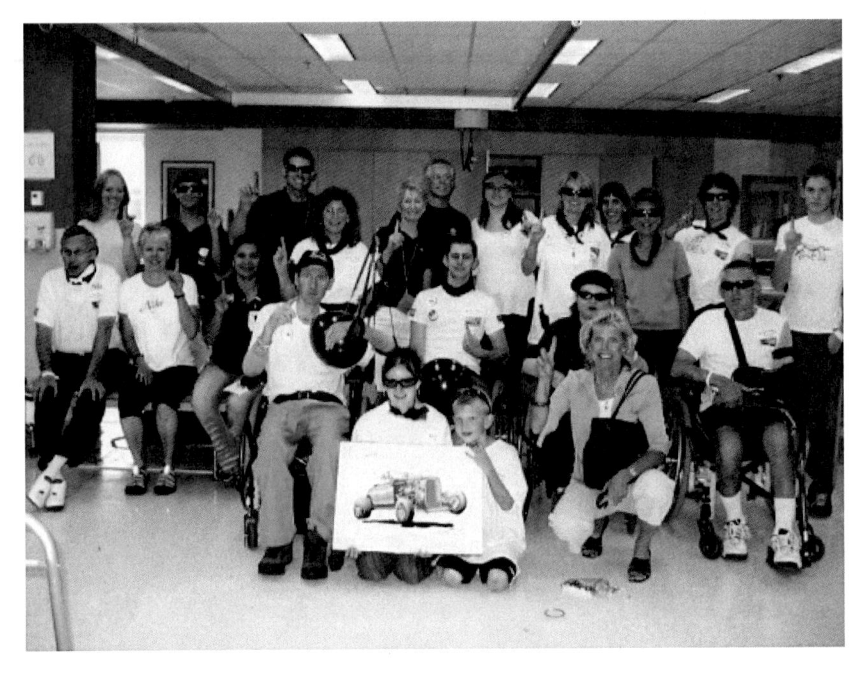

Dr. Ripley's Purple Porsche Team: Patients, family and staff pose for the "winning" team picture during Craig Days. Michael, Dana, Darcy and I are shown in the center of the group.

Dr. Ripley, captain of the Purple Porsches.

The weeklong celebration began with an auto show made up of both classic and new cars donated for viewing by their owners. All of the hospital parking lots were cleared, washed down and then, on the morning of the show, filled with vintage vehicles, from roadsters to today's dragsters, concept cars and beautifully maintained classics like a '57 Chevy. The roadways around Craig Hospital were also lined with these beautiful specimens of our automobile-centric culture. We wheeled Michael around the lots and streets so all three of us could enjoy the sights. Michael is a Corvette fan so we knew he would be drawn to the 'Vettes.

Everyone participated in Craig Days competitions. The hospital personnel and patients were divided into teams reminiscent of color war teams at summer camp. Each team was assigned a color and a team-leading physician. Mike was assigned to Dr. Ripley's Purple Porsche team. Barry, Jerry and a few other TBI patients were also on the team as well as therapists Barb, Kim and Derek, a twenty-something Tech who had befriended Mike. Other teams were led by the other rehab leaders, doctors in both the TBI and SCI units. Their teams represented Maserati, Corvette, Z's, etc.

The teams worked together to accumulate points so that at the end of the week the team with the most points would win. Win what? Nothing really, it was all just for fun. There were hallway decorating contests, crafts contests, and attendance at special events yielded additional team points. The hallways became trails of vine-like streamers hanging from the ceilings and doorposts with walls plastered over with homemade posters touting the various doctors and their teams. The enclosed glass walkways between the West and East wings of the hospital were colorful tunnel of green, red, yellow, blue and purple posters and streamers. The hospital drew the line, however, at issuing machetes to help cut through this jungle of hanging crepe paper.

Throughout the week, Michael and I watched with shared amusement as Dana shopped for purple t-shirts and streamers, fabricated posters on the floor of our apartment to hang in the hallways, cheered for the auto race, and generally, went wild over Dr. Ripley's Purple Porsches. Never one to sit on the sidelines, she enthusiastically diverted her attentions to these tasks, which provided her with a sorely needed outlet for the stress-induced energy built up inside of her as she worried continuously after Michael during the routine of the hospital and rehab therapies. Michael participated in several extra-curricular events in T-Rec and the adaptive aids rooms, including a car wash of the adaptive vehicles located in Craig's basement. We went to special team meals and rallies throughout the week.

The climax of the week was the great "Automobile race" in the hospital's main gymnasium. At the great "Automobile race", wheelchairs, gurneys, pushcarts, all manner of mobile devices, were decorated by the Staff and the patient team members like parade floats to resemble each team's designated car. These makeshift hotrods were raced against one another across the floor of the Main Gym by the team leaders; no patients were permitted to race. Dr. Ripley's Purple Porsche's entry was a sleek contraption temporarily attached to a recumbent wheelchair, powered by Dr. Ripley himself, with running assists from Derek. In two out of three heats, Dr. Ripley powered the vehicle across the finish line first, winning the racing competition. That, along with all of the other points accumulated by the team during the week, pushed Dr. Ripley's team into first place for all of Craig Days. We were all winners that day.

Progress Report #11 - July 28, 2006

"Perseverance and spirit have done wonders in all ages."
-George Washington

We have entered the "dog days of summer" both seasonally and rehabilitatively. Denver is suffering from record heat like much of the nation. It's not as humid as, say, Atlanta or Washington, D.C., but it is sultry for these parts. And, of course, the temperatures pale by comparison to Tucson's. Still, it's been hot, which makes staying indoors in Craig Hospital's refrigerated (it's cold like many hospitals) environment a comfortable alternative.

Michael has just passed his eighth week "out", i.e., since the accident. Most authorities say that the most significant progress for a traumatic brain injury patient occurs in the first six months to one year following the event. If that is the case, Mike is still considered in the early stages of his recovery despite his remarkable progress to date.

After being at Craig Hospital since June 20, Mike feels he is in the "dog days" of rehab. His most frequent refrain is, "If I'm doing so well and am so much better, why can't I leave this place and stop some of these silly therapies." His frustration is a normal phase of TBI recovery which will continue until Mike is more aware of and accepting of his injury. This should come with further healing and time. In the meantime, he still has physical, occupational, and speech therapies twice a day, and neuropsychological consults every other day. He works about 5 hours a day with little rest between sessions and can get very tired by the end of the afternoon.

Significant milestones: Michael has been cleared to begin adding weight to his left leg. He has been only "toe touch weight bearing" on that leg since the accident and pelvic surgery. This kept him confined to his wheelchair and his bed. He began therapy in the pool this week, which allows him to add about 25% of his body weight. Next week he should be able to apply full weight to his left leg and will gradually strengthen it with walking and leg exercises.

In addition, due to his improved cognition, Michael was moved from 2 West, the acute care TBI floor, across the glass walkway to 2 East, a less restrictive hospital environment. He can now transfer from his bed, walker or wheelchair by himself. This indicates the doctors and therapists confidence in his awareness of the need to be careful and safe, so as not to fall over and, God forbid, hit his head again. Moving to 2 East was a graduation of sorts at Craig.

Another milestone occurred last weekend as Michael was given day passes to go out with us on two occasions. We left the hospital and visited Mike's grandfather on Saturday for brunch and toured the Pearl Street Farmers Market on Sunday. Lunch out of the hospital was at Sazza, the organic pizza restaurant, where Michael was able to visit with several of his friends from Denver and Tucson.

We were happy to have Darcy with us last weekend to visit. She is great medicine for Michael, Dana and me. We wish she were closer to us more of the time, but can report that she is doing well in Richmond, VA, and intends to stay there for the foreseeable future. We miss her though.

We still anticipate that Michael will be discharged in the middle of August. We are still evaluating continuing therapy options in Tucson and elsewhere. Appropriate neuro-services in Tucson are scarce, but we are hopeful to find the right combination of therapists to allow us to return home soon.

Our best to all of you, with love,
Dana and Ira

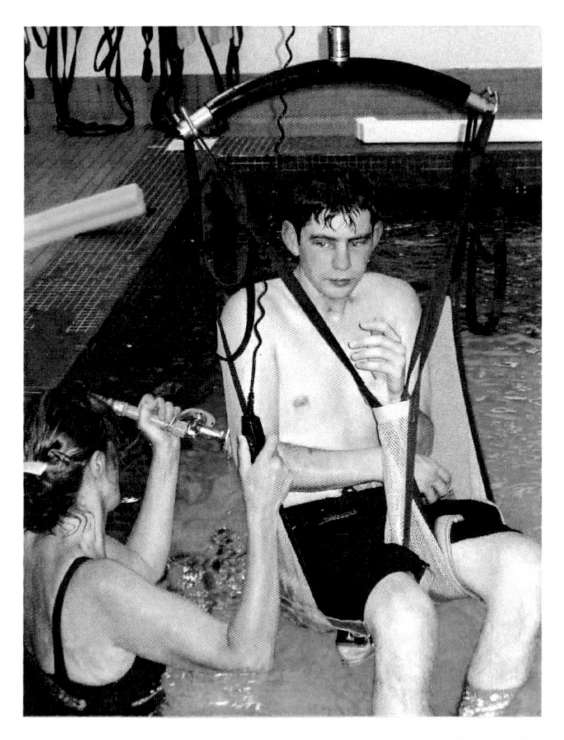

Pool Therapy: Cleared by the orthopedic surgeon, Michael, using a harness like the one used to transfer patients from bed to wheelchairs, gets an assist from the pool therapist as he begins to apply weight to his left leg.

I returned to Tucson for the last weekend in July. My purpose was to prepare for our return with Michael. I had pre-scheduled interviews at a new neuro-rehabilitation facility located on Grant Road. I also had come back to prepare our home for Michael's return.

It was necessary, we thought at the time, to clear out Dana's office and return it to bedroom status. I enlisted the help of a friend to assist me in moving Dana's desk and computer console into the master bedroom. After struggling with the weight of the desk and file cabinets, we shared a beer and laughed at how kids, like boomerangs, always seemed to come back. I cleaned out the clothing from the extra bedroom's closet to make room for Michael's clothing. I realized that the bedroom was no longer "extra." The master bedroom in our little nest was going to double as both bedroom and home office, just as our bedroom had in our last home. And we called this "moving forward?"

On Monday, July 31, it was raining in Tucson. Unusual during the summer months when passing monsoonal rains normally strike quickly and then disappear, the rain fell hard for hours and flooded many streets. Making my way through the temporary rivers streaming across Grant Street, I drove down to Aqua Neuro Rehabilitation Center (ANRC). Friends of ours knew the owners and had referred me to the facility, which was relatively new and virtually unknown in the local community.

ANRC was founded in 2005 by Lisa and Brian Sternberg. Their daughter, Marissa, then 19 years old, had suffered a severe traumatic brain injury in a car accident in Albuquerque while on her way to school in Denver. Marissa had spent a long rehabilitation period in Austin, Texas, until returning to Tucson. The Sternbergs had found that coordinated rehab services for TBI lacking in Tucson and decided to take control of the situation themselves rather than relying on the medical community to try to accommodate their daughter's special needs. They built a state of the art aquatic neurological rehabilitation facility in a sparsely tenanted strip mall and staffed it with physical, occupational, and speech therapists. In so doing, they had put together the only coordinated team approach to TBI rehab that I had been able to identify in Tucson.

I met with each of the therapists representing the three disciplines. First, I met Shelley, the PT. She immediately reminded me of Kim and Barb, Mike's therapists at Craig. She was young yet spoke to me of her education and experience in the field. I thought she would be someone Michael would relate well to. Then I interviewed Cara, the Occupational therapist, and another Shelley, the Speech therapist. Both had extensive resumes in their fields. In fact, Cara had interned at Craig Hospital years ago and worked at the same facility in Atlanta that Dr. Ripley had worked for prior to coming to Craig Hospital. Like many fields, TBI rehabilitation was a "small world."

The interviews concluded with a meeting with the director of ANRC. For the first time, I felt that there was indeed a solution which would fill the therapeutic void which we feared would be created when Mike left the well-coordinated therapeutic teams of Craig Hospital. The director took me around to tour the facility. It was small but well equipped. There were meeting rooms for Speech and Occupational therapies and a large room filled with state of the art physical therapy equipment and adaptive aids. I was impressed by the newness of all of the equipment and brightness of the facility. Finally, we entered the aquatic therapy room, which contained an above ground therapy pool with lifts and harnesses to support patients as they worked in its warm waters. The pool had air and water jets to provide resistance as the patients trained. The room was also equipped with video monitors above and below the water level to monitor patients during their exercises. The pool was state-of-the-art. While Mike no longer needed pool therapy, ANRC seemed like an ideal rehabilitation facility following his discharge from Craig Hospital.

Later that day, I met with Dr. James Allender, a neuropsychologist to whom I had been referred by another neuropsychologist who only did testing. I talked with him about Michael's injury and progress made while at Craig Hospital. He took a moment to consider what I had said and then explained that he could assist Michael both with recovery strategies as well as emotional issues during his return to Tucson. I found his manner reassuring, calming, and a sharp contrast to the sarcastic and edgy style of Dr. Schraa at Craig.

But to fully replicate the Craig-style team, I still needed to identify a physiatrist who could monitor Mike's physical condition and prescribe the necessary medications. Our primary physician referred me to Dr. Jonathan Ostrowski who agreed to see Michael upon his arrival in Tucson following discharge from Craig.

Upon my return to Denver, I reported to Dana with whom I had met and how greatly reassured I was that Michael would be able to get proper treatment in follow up to Craig Hospital. Both Dana and I felt growing excitement about the prospects of returning to Tucson with Michael. In wanting to share our good fortune in putting the team together, we buoyantly shared the information with everyone and anyone we could find at Craig.

In particular, we had become acquainted with the mother of a young gymnast who had experienced a training accident at a well known gymnastics training facility in Tucson. The young man, a teenager, was now a recovering quadriplegic on the third floor, the SCI floor, at Craig. I thought that a neurological rehabilitation facility like ANRC that had state-of-the-art equipment for physical therapy might serve his needs even better than Michael's need for cognitive therapies. His mother was grateful for the information and, as we were, was visibly relieved to have found some options back home for treatment.[6] For the first time, I felt that we could start to pay forward all the good deeds and kind wishes we had received as support from so many people over the two months we had just lived through.

---

6 As it turned out, the young gymnast did, in fact, attend ANRC when he returned to Tucson, just weeks after we had returned. Dana and I were there with Michael when he first arrived and our reunion in the lobby of ANRC was a happy one indeed.

Chapter 22
Cleared for Landing

By early August, Michael had progressed in his recovery to between Level 6 of the Rancho Los Amigos scale – Confused Appropriate and Level 7 – Automatic Appropriate. He showed little of the confusion he had exhibited just a few weeks before when he had been just emerging from PTA. He would, on occasion, mix up words or hesitate as he looked for just the right words to express his ideas, but he had little difficulty expressing himself.

Becoming more aware and more independent daily, Michael perceived himself as fully recovered. He continued to work with his therapists, but he was becoming more and more reluctant to cooperate. He was anosognosic, i.e., he still did not understand the extent of his injury and its effects. His cognitive deficits were becoming more and more subtle and difficult for untrained observers to see and Michael, himself, did not recognize these problems. Thus, he became completely disinterested in the routine of therapy. However, he finally was able to negotiate the hallways of Craig and stay on track with his schedule without direct or close supervision. It was becoming clearer to Dana and me that the end of our time at Craig was nearing. At the same time, we became more aware that Michael was becoming more challenging than the compliant patient he had been earlier in his recovery.

But make no mistake. Michael was strongly motivated to return to Tucson, to complete whatever therapies lay ahead of him and then (as he would often say) at the earliest possible time, to return to Denver! In fact, he had his mind set on a Thanksgiving deadline for his return. We knew that that was aggressive and not likely to be achieved, but we were happy with the fact that he had set a goal, any goal, for himself.

He began to ask over and over again when he would be able to drive. That, of course, raised a whole new set of issues. The physical and cognitive requirements of driving a car, the complexity of the task, which are second nature to those of us who are uninjured, are extremely challenging to persons recovering from a brain injury. Dana and I were frightened by the prospects of our son driving anytime soon. But Michael's reflexes and physical abilities were good so this became a real possibility in the near term. It was his lack of awareness of his surroundings (spatial cognition) and inability to make the quick judgments necessary to navigate traffic that continued to concern us. We told Mike that he would have to successfully complete physical therapy in Tucson and be cleared by an OT specialist before the auto insurance company would permit him to be behind the wheel again. Of course, his car, the RAV 4, had been destroyed by this time; and our cars were not the best for re-training him. Nevertheless, the idea of driving again would motivate and dominate Michael's thoughts for several months.

Having, at long last, been cleared by the orthopedic surgeon at DHMC to stand and walk, Michael used the first two weeks of August to strengthen his legs and regain his balance. He would walk long distances between therapies. At first, for support, he pushed a walker in front of him; then he graduated to a cane. Ambulatory once again, his newfound mobility and the fact that he no longer was confined to a wheelchair were clear evidence of how far he had come since early June.

OT Kim accompanied him on walks outside of Craig. They would walk around the entire block containing both Craig Hospital and Swedish Medical Center. As they made their way around on the sidewalks, Kim would stop and ask Michael to identify the street corner or the address they were standing by. Michael would search the scenery for street signs or numbers on buildings which he could identify. Where once he could not identify his own hospital room, now he was tasked with translating the sights and sounds of the environment outside of the hospital into an understanding of where he was. This proved to be a challenging cognitive task.

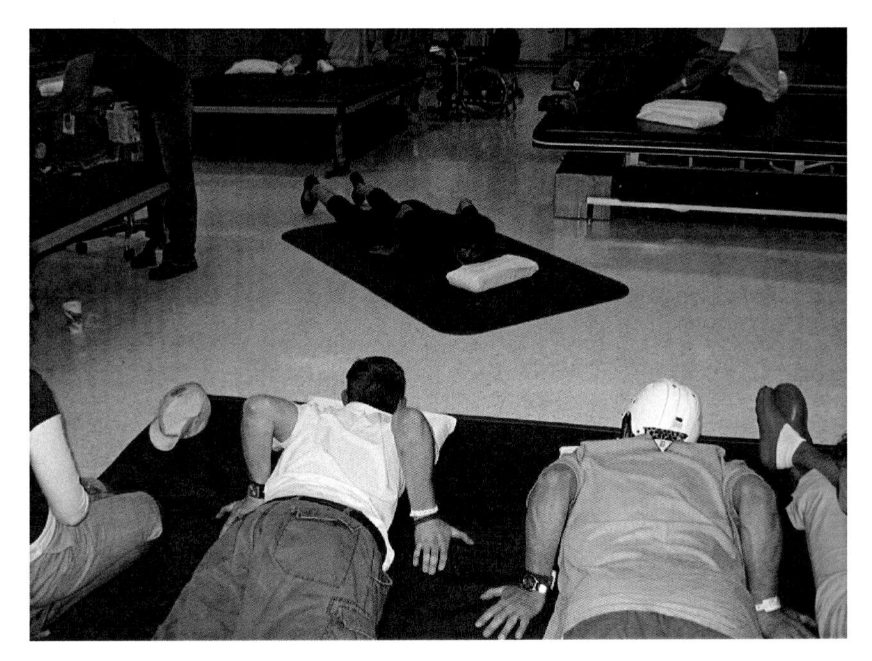

Michael (white tee shirt) participates along in a Mat Therapy session with other TBI patients in the Gym.

It was also in early August that Michael participated actively and often in a group therapy called Mat Therapy. Mat Therapy was held near the end of each afternoon in the Gym on 2 West. Mats were set out on the floor and TBI patients gathered around. If they were able, the patients would sit down on the floor on the mats. If not, they would sit either on the elevated mats or in their wheelchairs. One of the PTs would then lead the group through a series of calisthenics and muscle stretching exercises.

Mat Therapy was also a time for increased social interaction between the patients. Michael would talk freely with the other patients: Michel, the 60 year old French-born baker from Vail, CO, who had fallen from his horse; Mike, the Fortune 500 company general counsel from Omaha, recovering from an automobile accident in Denver; Jerry, the 40 year old car mechanic from Greeley, CO, and others. Throughout the stretching exercises, Michael would continuously attempt to joke around, pretending to be Superman (singing the theme song from the movie series) or a Denver Bronco. He appeared to be really having fun. Thus, Mat Therapy was often the highlight of his day.

In ways we didn't understand at the time, these happy times with the Mat Therapy group foreshadowed the emotional difficulties which Michael would have in the months spent in Tucson and later upon returning to Denver, when he would no longer be surrounded by like-minded people and caregivers.

Progress Report #12 - August 10, 2006

Cleared for landing! After 50 days at Craig Hospital, following 18 days at Denver Health Medical Center, Michael has been cleared for discharge. His last day at Craig will be August 16. We will be returning to Tucson on August 17, where Michael will be staying with us and attending outpatient therapy as he continues on his long journey to returning to full independence.

When we look back on our experience in Denver, we are grateful to so many for so much. From the heroic lifesaving measures of the paramedics and trauma teams in the hospital to the genuine kindness, wonderful care, and expertise of the caregivers and therapists at Craig to the thousands of acts of generosity and kindness from our family and friends, we will never look back on this as an "unfortunate" event because we are, indeed, very fortunate.

We include the many patients and family members in similar circumstances whom we have come to know here at Craig. We have a special bond with those who have "walked in our shoes" and we will remember each for their strength and love with special fondness. We came from all walks of life, social and geographic backgrounds, but we share a common realization... we are all human, we are all susceptible to life's risks, and we all have more strength than we ever knew we had to overcome what life throws in our path.

Michael's rehab team, made up of his doctors and therapists at Craig, met with Michael, Dana and me yesterday to review his progress and the prescription for ongoing recovery activities. In every area, Mike has shown excellent progress for such a short time out from the accident. His early recoveries, both physically and cognitively, are positive signs for continued improvement over the next months, and even years, ahead. But we are reminded that, while he will continue to improve his cognitive functioning, he will always be a survivor of a Traumatic Brain Injury. He will learn to deal with any continuing effects from this injury, working around problems when he can. His intelligence, youth and spirit all will work in his favor. And, as he assures us regularly, he is up to the task.

Over the last week, Michael has walked without the aid of a walker, relying only on the support of a cane. With another week of strengthening his left leg/pelvic muscles, he may need the cane only occasionally. He also visited the Cherry Creek Farmers Market, Dick's Sporting Goods Store at the Park Meadows Mall, and several fine restaurants. Tomorrow he will participate with other patients in Craig Hospital's Hobie Cat day at Cherry Creek Reservoir, where he will be boating on catamarans, sail boats, motor boats, paddle boats, etc.

When we return home to Tucson, Michael will need a period of adjustment to acclimate to his new surroundings, new schedule (hospitals are very regimented environments), new therapists and doctors. We too will need to adjust to our new situation, without the safety net of the hospital staff. And, while we would love to reconnect immediately with everyone there, we ask that you respect our need to "get our feet on the ground."

This will be our last progress report from Denver ... thankfully.

Love to all of you,
Dana and Ira

The summer of fun continued. Craig Hospital annually invites those patients, both SCI and TBI patients who are physically and mentally capable, to join the staff at Hobie Cat Day at the Cherry Creek Reservoir in Southeast Denver. Everyone who is able is transported by family members or by van from the hospital to the Cherry Creek Marina for a day of boating, barbequing, and games.

This year Hobie Cat Day fell on August 11. Dana, Michael and I drove in our car, loading his wheelchair in the back because the

July 2006 Family gathering at Craig Hospital: Standing (l. to r.): Joanne and Ira; Seated (l. to r.): Michael (belted in the wheelchair and wearing the Denver Police Department warm-ups given to him by Officer Henry Jones), Dana and Grandpa Bert.

beach would be too unstable for the use of a walker or cane only. As we pulled up to park in the marina's lot, we could see all along the shoreline Hobie Catamarans, other sailing boats and motor boats which were lined up and waiting to give Craig patients rides out on the reservoir's waters. The boats were provided by a local sailing club and manned by the club's members. Both the crews and the patients, especially the patients, were excited to get out on the water. On the street above the marina, SCI patients raced in recumbent wheelchairs. At the nearby picnic tables, patients, family members and staff sat under tents which provided shade from the mid-summer heat and sunshine. The atmosphere in the picnic area was like a 21st century version of the famous painting by Georges Seurat, ***Sunday Afternoon on La Grande Jatte…*** but with adaptive aids.

But, by the shoreline, there was a surreal feeling around the marina. It looked like a scene from some horrible movie where some disaster had just occurred on the shore and all the injured were being evacuated. As patients arrived, they were brought down to the shore where wood planks were set up as runways to help wheelchairs maneuver over the sand up to the boats. Each patient was accompanied by a tech who was assigned to assist the patients in their transfers from wheelchairs to catamaran trampolines, i.e., sitting on the boats' "floors."

Yet, for all the physical and mental difficulties of the patients, the air resounded with the sounds of joyous voices as boat after boat left the shore to sail out on the water. Being free from the confines of the hospital lifted everyone's spirits, patients', staff's and family caregivers', alike. Our sails filled with hope for a return to a more normal life.

When it was his turn, Mike hopped (literally) onto a Hobie Cat, accompanied for safety by his assigned tech, and rode out onto the lake in the intermittent soft breezes.

There was a stillness which kept the boats from accelerating to any speed which might even remotely be called exhilarating, but the peacefulness of being on the water was still refreshing.

The barbeque pit on the beach was manned by volunteers from the local electric and gas utility company. They cooked up hot dogs and hamburgers and set out potato salad and chips for all of the participants and their families. We thoroughly enjoyed this midsummer picnic by the lake.

By the time the sailing and dining were done, the patients were ready to return in their hospital rooms for rest. But all of us there will never forget the fun and joy of being swept around the lake, free from the daily reminders of what had brought us all together in the first place.

Dana, Michael and Ira at the Cherry Creek Reservoir for Hobie Cat Days.

Michael gets an assist from his tech on the Hobie Cat.

Chapter 23
The Return

Knowing that our time in Denver was soon coming to an end, Dana and I wanted to express our gratitude to the many people who had supported us in so many ways through this traumatic summer. We wanted, also, to provide Michael with a venue in which to say "goodbye" to his many friends. We invited as many as we could contact to join us at a "Movin' On" party for Michael. This would be victory celebration as well as his "going away" party.

The Craig Hospital Patient Family Residence Hall has a room for bringing friends, families and patients together. It is called the Digby Friendship Center, named after the generous family of a grateful patient who had provided the funds to furnish the room. Within this meeting place, there is a kitchen equipped with refrigerator/freezer, sink, microwave oven, dishes, silverware, and various appliances for food preparation and storage. The room has a dining table, large enough to sit 10 people, and an L-shaped sofa facing a big screen TV. Right outside of the Digby Friendship Center, in the patio between the Patient Family Residence and the East wing of Craig Hospital, is a built-in barbeque and sitting area, shaded by a redwood pergola. Together the patio and the meeting room are ideal for celebratory gatherings.

Dana planned the menu... punch, tea, cakes, fruits, etc.... and went shopping at the local Safeway for the party refreshments. Later, we drove to a nearby Wal-Mart on Hampden Avenue to purchase the party supplies and decorations.

On the morning of August 12, we placed homemade signs around the parking lots and Patient Family Residence. Like a well-marked trail, large arrows directed our guests to the Digby Friendship Center. As if entering the stage for curtain calls at the

Michael and friends say goodbye.

Karen, Ira and Gary at the farewell party in the Craig Family Residence.

Charla, Mike, Julia and friend at the farewell party.

end of a theatrical presentation, the various players in this summer's drama appeared to take their bows with their good wishes for Michael, Dana and me as we approached the day of departure. Bill and Anne, who were there for us at the first moment of crisis on June 2, attended this celebratory finale. Our Denver relatives were there: Bert, Jo, Adam, Mindy, and Sam. Our Congregation Emanuel friends attended, including Officer Jones, Michael's guardian angel from the Denver Police Department. The University of Denver support team was represented by our now dear friend, Dr. Schulten (and her two young sons). A cadre of Mike's friends and co-workers from the Washington Park Grille came to say their goodbyes including Dave, Helen and Julia. Michael's fraternity brother, Tim, and his fiancée Liz, came. Also, our friends from so long ago and now again in our present, Gary and Karen, came to celebrate our son's wonderful recovery. Everyone there expressed heartfelt wishes for a healthy and happy future for Michael.

There were hugs and smiles, and some tears, that afternoon. As I made my way around from visitor to visitor, from couple to couple, we talked about Denver Health Medical Center, Craig Hospital, the miracles of recovery we had witnessed, and how close we all had grown over that past three months. Michael, the star of this production, moved about, standing without the aid of a cane, talking to everyone there, clearly happy to be the center of attention on this day...a well deserved recognition of his efforts while at Craig. No smile was broader than his. He had come a long way, indeed, from his "low stim" environment.

Relatives talked to Mike's college friends, his co-workers conversed with our acquaintances from Congregation Emanuel and Bert and Jo talked to anyone within the reach of their voices. As we hugged our guests, we were embraced by good feelings, warm friendships and this community of love and support. We celebrated the strength of the human spirit and all that we, as a community, can achieve when motivated to pull together for a common cause. Looking at one friendly face to the next, I realized we were surrounded by a new family and recalled each person's impact on and contribution to Michael's recovery and to their support for both Dana and me. It was a very happy time.

Officer Jones, Dana and friends Mark and Janet.

Roommates: Dave and Michael.

When the party was over and the last of the guests had departed, I felt once again the weight of the responsibility for Michael's care shifting from Craig Hospital to Dana and me. The reality that our time in the safe cocoon of the hospital would be soon ending came into sharp focus. No longer would we be able to rely on nighttime nurses to watch over him. No longer would Kim and Barb be there to direct his energy and to make him smile. We would have to make the appointments to see doctors if we wanted to hear their insights into Michael's ever-changing condition rather than simply walk across the hall to ask to talk with the doctor. From now on, Michael himself would be responsible for his own progress, and Dana and I would be there only to guide and cheer him on.

Although we excitedly anticipated our return to Tucson, we were brought down to earth during those last few days in Denver. For despite the Craig Days, Hobie Days, and our farewell party, the middle of August was only an extension of the many prior weeks of hard work and effort. Once again, Michael was re-tested by his therapists, who wrote up their final comments in his file. He made his final visit to the orthopedic surgeon at DHMC, who cleared Michael to perform whatever physical activities Michael himself felt comfortable performing. There were no lingering restrictions...just a caution to continue follow up with visits to an orthopedic doctor in Tucson and to continue physical therapy.

Walking back to his room, following one of his last therapy sessions, Mike came upon a young blond college-aged girl who had been in a car accident. The accident had left her a paraplegic confined to a wheelchair, able to move her head, arms and her hands only. We had noticed her for some time now as her room was just down the hallway on 2 East. Michael stopped to tell her that he would be leaving in a day or two. With a broad smile, she said that she, too, would be leaving soon. She was going to return to college and finish her degree program. Michael said that he couldn't imagine having a spinal cord injury and having to be confined to a wheelchair as she was. To this, she replied, "I can't imagine having to live with a brain injury." There are no good injuries which bring people to Craig Hospital.

Whether SCI, TBI, or both, each person is challenged in ways they could never have conceived before their accidents. Each day, as a parent observing spinal injured patients co-mingling with brained injured patients, we were confronted by difficult questions: Is it better to have all of one's cognitive faculties while being physically confined for life to a wheelchair and needing physical assistance or is it better not to be physically limited but have limitations on one's consciousness and ability to reason? The answer to both questions is the same. Neither is better if you are the one with the injury. Because, whether injured or not, we are the sum total of the physical and cognitive faculties available to us. Our lives are as good as we choose to make them given those faculties, our individual talents and our shortcomings. In fact, at Craig Hospital, we had learned that this applied equally to the patients, the staff of caregivers, and the rest of us.

The goodbyes expressed genuine accomplishment. "Great work, Mike. You've really come a long way." "We're proud of all your hard work. Thanks for being such a good patient." "Thanks for making us laugh." What we never heard, however, was, "Mike, you're going to be okay."

August 14 was my last full day at Craig Hospital. I planned to leave the next day to drive back to Tucson; Michael and Dana would follow a few days later by air. There was a quiet, calm and peaceful feel to the day. However, the day before, the weather had been tumultuously changing, just as our lives had been throughout this summer. A cold front had arrived, announcing itself with thunder, lightning and torrential rains for about an hour. On this day, the air dried out and cooled to a perfect 75 degrees. Despite the excitement of leaving Craig, we calmly went about packing, making multiple trips from our apartment over the last two months down the parking lot to load up the car. I would be driving home to Tucson so that I could be there when Mike and Dana flew home in a couple of days.

After packing, I made my last walks through the hallways of Craig Hospital to attend what was for me final therapy visits and to bid my farewells to the staff, Mike's fellow patients and their families. But, after weeks of routinely crisscrossing the hallways from one session to the next, moving about the hospital now felt anything but routine. For the first time since the day we had first arrived at Craig, I felt like an outsider, someone who didn't belong. My son was about to graduate from this institution and was about to embark on his own journey. I felt a new phase of life beginning, as if I, too, was starting over again along with Michael.

There was a strong, unsettling undercurrent behind all the happy smiles and goodbyes. I thought about the changes we had witnessed in Michael since his arrival at Craig on June 20, and about all the changes we anticipated experiencing with him back in Tucson that leaving Craig Hospital was forcing us to confront. And, as with most change, I wished we could look into the future and know that everything would work out well. We anticipated that Michael would not only continue to improve and heal, but would actually thrive, enjoying his time with us at home. That's what we thought about and anticipated.

I made several final trips down to the car, loading up as much of Michael's, Dana's and my belongings as I could fit into it. Anything left over would have to be stored in Bert's and Jo's basement until Michael could return to Denver to reclaim them. Then, early on the morning of August 15, I drove away from Craig Hospital. I left hoping that we could provide Michael a safe and nurturing environment back in Tucson. But, strangely, I did not feel relieved to be leaving the hospital.

Michael departed his room on 2 East on August 16, 2006. He moved from his hospital room over to our family apartment in the Patient Family Residence. He spent the night with Dana in the apartment. That evening, Dana made her rounds to say her goodbyes. She requested a copy of Michael's medical records and received his discharge instructions and prescriptions. There was a brief ceremony that afternoon in the Gym at which patients and therapists gathered to say farewell to Michael. Cake and punch was served. Then, Michael and Dana left Craig Hospital to spend the evening with Bert and Joanne.

On Thursday, August 17, 2006, one day short of 11 weeks since the accident that had started him on his journey through DHMC and Craig Hospital, Michael left Denver and flew home to Tucson.

August 16, 2006: PT Barb, Michael and OT Kim at his farewell party at Craig Hospital.

Already back in Tucson after the two day drive through southern Colorado, New Mexico and southern Arizona, I had arrived at home, unpacked the car and made final preparations in our home. I drove to the airport to meet the plane. The loudspeaker announced the Frontier Airlines on-time arrival just as I sat down in the chair in the waiting area in front of the security check points. I was nervously excited to see both Dana and Michael so far from the hospital setting. Although I had been away from them for only two days, this reunion seemed more emotional than when I had returned to Denver from the quick trips to Tucson. This was Michael's homecoming, his triumphant return to his hometown after graduating college. He was embarking once again on his life's journey after detouring through DHMC and Craig.

In about five minutes' time, passengers from the flight began to descend the sloped hallway from the concourse, past the security station toward those of us waiting. The first few passengers who came into sight almost ran down the walkway. They seemed to be in a great hurry to get to their appointments, to meet their rides in front of the terminal or to get their cars out of the parking lots. The next few passengers walked briskly, chatting as they went... smiling, laughing, happy to be in Tucson on the ground, safe and sound. All around me, there were loud reunions of husbands and young families, grandmothers and grandchildren, business associates and bosses all around me.

I looked up the concourse past the screening devices and could make out Dana first and then Michael. Together, they stood out from the crowd. They walked more slowly, seemingly out of rhythm with the flow of the people traffic. Dana's attention was on Michael. Michael was just staring ahead down the concourse toward where I was standing but did not see me. Michael's posture was stiffly erect; his gait was uneven. He carried his cane in his hand, not leaning on it for the support it might provide him as he came down the ramped walkway. He had a wide-eyed look of someone taking in a bizarre scene and trying desperately to understand what was going on around him. Airports are places of hectic activity, but certainly were not foreign to Michael, who had travelled throughout the world. Tucson International Airport, in particular, was familiar to him. But his look conveyed, "What the heck is happening here?" He seemed unsure and somewhat agitated by all the noise and commotion on the concourse ramp down to the stairway leading to Baggage Claim.

I stood up and met them both, reaching out to offer a hug and a kiss to each of them. As we turned to leave, we stepped toward the "down" escalator to baggage claim. I said, "Watch your step, Mike," as we moved onto the escalator. He glared back at me. At the bottom of the escalator, we turned to walk to the Baggage Claim. "You should be leaning more on that cane, Mike," I said recognizing how long he had been sitting in the plane and now how far ahead we had to walk to the car. He was walking well for having been weight bearing on his left leg for only the past two weeks. But he was limping slightly and seemed uncomfortable.

"I don't need this cane, you know. Barb [his physical therapist at Craig Hospital] isn't here. You don't need to keep staring at me and trying to help me. I'm not a cripple, you know. I'm not as injured as you think." Mike's rapid stream of angry words directed at me seemed to come out of nowhere. Immediately my emotional excitement and anticipation were deflated by this diatribe, but I was not really surprised. TBI sometimes speaks loudly and angrily.

We drove up to our home in Tucson's foothills. Michael sat in the back seat and Dana along side of me in the front passenger's seat. As I drove, I glanced over my shoulder to see Michael staring down into his cell phone; he appeared to be texting his friends. He noticed my glance in the mirror. "What are you looking at?" he asked me in an accusatory tone of voice. "Stop staring at me." He seemed to notice everything but was absorbed by nothing, except his cell phone.

We pulled up to the house after about a half an hour. Unloading the bags from the car, we entered our home. "Welcome home, Mike," I offered. "I've been here before but I didn't grow up in this house, you know. It's not my home. My home is in Denver." (Ironically, he still didn't remember his condominium in Denver either, where he had lived for six months prior to the car accident.) *Oh, this is going well!* I thought to myself.

We unpacked a little before we sat down to our first meal back together in our home. It was good to have home cooked food on the table before us rather than the hospital or restaurant fare of the past three months. It was also nice to see Dana and Michael around our kitchen table, surrounded by comfortable, familiar surroundings, without the noise and distractions of the hospital... patients in wheelchairs and walkers, food servers preparing meals behind the counter and placing them on portable trays; nurses and techs shuttling the food back and forth to patients' rooms; the radio off to one side blaring some undecipherable rock and roll; bells and alarms going off as patients tripped RF wires or hit call buttons or were notified of the need to weight-shift in their wheelchairs.

As we ate, the conversation turned from all things hospital-related to insurance, and then, inevitably, to money. Mike surprised both Dana and me saying he wanted to open a new American Express credit card account. I replied that he might want to discuss this with his new Occupational Therapist who would help him with matters like checking accounts, charge accounts, and the like. He responded with an angry tirade.

Sometimes, TBI does not permit many rational conversations in a civil tone of voice, especially if the topic is personal to the patient. He chastised me. *Didn't I know that I was intruding on his life and that he was not injured as badly as the CT Scan indicated?* He had picked up on this idea during the final Family Conference with the Craig rehab team in the last week. He ranted at me. *Further, it was* **his** *money to do with as he pleased. Why could he not have a new credit card anyway*, he asked. His frustrations and emotions were raw and naked, without filter.

Dana sat there calmly and passively as Michael directed the brunt of the attack of this stream of inquiries and accusations at me. I took a deep breath, trying to remain calm, looking forward, perhaps naively, to the day when Mike would understand and accept the true extent of his injuries and his capabilities. *Greater understanding would come with more time and more healing* we had been told by almost everyone but, at that moment, his diatribe simply left me exhausted.

We had been told and we had read how to respond to TBI ravings like this. I tried to deflect the questions and said I would look into the credit card matter. I hoped this would defer this topic to another time. This seemed to satisfy Mike for the moment and, with that (un)resolved, we continued with the meal.

"When can I go back up to Denver?" Mike asked. "When can I go back to work and my condo?" He had been back in our home for less than an hour. "We don't know," Dana replied. "We'll have to wait and see how things develop." "I want to be back up there before my birthday [November 15]," Mike stated emphatically. "I don't need much more therapy. My hip is fine. My thinking is fine, too." Dana and I looked at each other with resignation, both of us internally doubting that Mike would be right about how quickly and completely he would recover his full faculties. But we also both realized that his longing to live normally back in Denver and to be free of therapy and therapists would stimulate his recovery; and time, itself, much patience, and good fortune would be needed before all Mike's objectives of independence would be achieved. Nevertheless, this exchange over our first dinner back in Tucson together was a precursor for the challenges Michael, Dana and I would need to come to grips with…the continuing impact of TBI.

Book Two
The Little Engine That Can

Chapter 24
Rodeo Days

Michael soon began his therapies at Aquatic Neuro Rehabilitation Center. For the next 10 weeks, twice weekly, he attended physical, occupational and speech therapies, continuing the work which had begun at Craig Hospital. Once a week, he saw Dr. Allender, his neuropsychologist. Once a month, Mike visited Dr. Ostrowski, his physiatrist.

At Craig, the emphasis of his therapies was on restoring basic activities of daily living (ADL's), e.g., eating, dressing, walking, personal hygiene, and basic cognitive functions, e.g., memory, comprehension, awareness. His therapies at ANRC were more directed at returning to independent living. The physical therapies were devoted to improving balance during dynamic exercises like running on a treadmill or jumping to the ground from a raised step. His speech therapies were focused on his ability to comprehend written materials with greater speed and retention. His occupational therapies tested his problem solving capabilities with real world "examples" of tasks requiring research, organization and mathematics. All together, his ANRC therapy sessions lasted 2-3 hours, three times per week. When not in therapy, Michael would spend most of his time in his room watching television. He rarely showed any interest in leaving the house.

By October, Michael expressed that he had had one therapy too many. While he had once been compliant to his Craig therapists, he now pushed back and questioned the necessity of therapy with each of his ANRC therapists. He often claimed to be cured. To Dana and me, his declarations showed just the opposite; he did not understand or accept that more time was required for healing. But, at 22, soon to be 23, despite having his whole life ahead of him, he felt that there was no more time… he wanted to be out on his own… NOW!

Michael also believed that he was ready to drive a car. I took him out on the road for practice a few times and, surprising me, he appeared to have no trouble behind the wheel. Maneuvering the vehicle was but one aspect of driving, but being alert to traffic was also critical. However, it seemed to me that he handled both reasonably well so long as nothing unexpected came in his path. He responded to traffic signals and signs. He did have some trouble picking routes to various destinations about town, reflecting some loss of familiarity with Tucson's streets and some difficulty comprehending informational signs. In late October, after more supervised practice, Michael was tested by an occupational therapist certified by the State of Arizona, specializing in disabilities related to driving. During the behind-the-wheel test, he was required to drive a specially adapted automobile where the therapist had the ability to wrest control of the vehicle from the driver if necessary. They drove all around the roads on the north side of Tucson and on Interstate 10 for an hour and a half. Upon returning home, the therapist told us that Mike had passed the test with no significant problems. Once cleared for re-licensing by that OT, he resumed driving using one of our two cars. We limited his travel to one location at a time and did not allow passengers. We felt it was important for him to be able to focus on the driving skills without any distractions.

In November, Dr. Allender and Michael reached agreement that, in order for Dana and me to be willing to allow Michael to return to Denver, his job and his condo, he would need to show us that he could live independently in an apartment. To that end, we rented an apartment just 3 miles from our home and Michael took up residence there for the months of November, December and January.

He was doing well, handling daily activities seemingly without any significant problems. He was able to shop for food, prepare his own meals and drive. In early November, he applied for and got a part-time job at a nearby Baskin-Robbins ice cream store where he had worked when he was in high school. This would help answer questions about his ability to function in a simple work environment. *Could he focus on customers, remember orders, handle money and, importantly, endure the fatigue of being on his feet for 4-8 hour shifts?* Indeed, Michael performed well. He seemed to be able to handle the busy times without any major problems and he showed enough stamina to endure the longer shifts. But when he was not at his job, he was exhausted and isolated in his apartment. He infrequently ventured out or sought the company of old or new friends.

After a month of working at the ice cream store, he moved on to a table-bussing job at Sullivan's Steak House, an upscale restaurant near to his apartment. There his work shifts were longer and later into the evening. The environment was noisier than the ice cream shop and the requirements of the job more demanding. Customer service was primary. Michael discovered that he had trouble in this job. He would come home agitated and sometimes very angry. He told us that he disliked the management of the restaurant and decided to quit after only two weeks. He, then, moved on to another job as a server at a newly opened Carrabas Italian restaurant on Oracle Road. He enjoyed the work atmosphere more than Sullivan's and worked there for several weeks.

Yet, Michael was lonely during this time in Tucson. He had been able to re-connect with only a few of his old friends from high school. They were attentive but had only limited availability as they worked and/or were attending school. Prior to having his own apartment, he often stayed home with Dana and me, usually staying in his bedroom watching TV and emailing friends up in Denver. He was noticeably constrained by fatigue, and, like any person recovering from a long hospital stay, he had limited physical and mental stamina. When he would get tired, he tended to become more vocal about his frustrations. He criticized his jobs here in Tucson and loudly and frequently declared his longing to move out of his Tucson apartment and back up to Denver. His emotions became more and more raw and exposed just as his awareness of how his life had been affected by the accident and TBI was becoming greater. Exhausted, he was like a weary bucking bronco, fighting to rid himself of his burden. Whenever he had time to rest and to enjoy quiet time by himself, his equanimity seemed to be restored.

Cognitively, he improved and had continued to show signs of improvement. He was discharged from ANRC therapies at the beginning of November; he had regained his ability to drive; he had shown the ability to live on his own without incident; and he had worked and showed us that he was employable. He had passed every test. He had overcome every obstacle or challenge to daily living. He appeared ready by the end of December to return to Denver and try to pick up where he had so abruptly left off seven months earlier.

In January, 2007, he returned to Denver.

Chapter 25
Better? Better Than What?

Thinking back on June 2, 2006, I remember how I felt when, having just travelled over 800 miles in the early morning to rush to Denver Health Medical Center to join Michael in the Surgical Intensive Care Unit, the doctors explained Michael's condition to Dana and me. They told us that Michael had suffered a severe brain injury, a Diffuse Axonal Injury, and that he was unconscious. They said that the next several hours or days would be critical to his recovery.

But they offered no hope, no comfort, and no prognosis. I asked, "What do you expect to happen?" They only said, "We'll have to watch and wait." Upon reflection, I think they only expressed opinions about his physical recovery from the bodily trauma suffered in the car accident. I don't believe the ICU doctors and nurses had ever been involved with TBI patients subsequent to their acute care and were, therefore, reluctant to opine on a prognosis.

I had never experienced anything like this before, i.e., where the doctors would not describe any future for the patient. The feeling, in addition to the terror, which began on hearing the news about the accident over the phone at 1:30 in the morning, was one of despair. While afraid to hear the worst, we were left bewildered by the lack of a prognosis. Not knowing, not able to anticipate with hope, is perhaps worse than having some certainty… even of a dire outcome. That feeling of bewilderment… wondering what the doctors weren't telling us, that sense of something important being missing… lingers with us still today. That "not knowing" has never completely been resolved by Michael's recovery and progress since that fateful day. Questions remain.

No one knows what tomorrow will bring. We plan, we imagine the future, we insure against various risks which can be anticipated, but we cannot foresee the unexpected, all of the eventualities, and the myriad of scenarios which may befall us. In our daily lives, we cannot predict the effect of a stock market meltdown, the impact of weather on our travel plans six months from now, or a tree colliding with an out-of-control car. So, while the doctors were unable to foretell Mike's level of recovery, whether he would or could return to life as he knew it, and whether he would have the ability to fulfill his own aspirations and dreams remained unclear. These uncertainties were not very different from the uncertainties every parent accepts for his/her offspring when the child is first conceived. In lieu of being able to see the future, we can only provide opportunity and then rely on hope.

Of course, I know now what transpired and all of the wonderful aspects of recovery Michael (and we) have been fortunate to experience. But I also know there are aspects of TBI which will never resolve. There are symptoms of injury which will always be present. Like scar tissue forming on one's skin, TBI never disappears completely and can never be cured.

Chapter 26
Bumps in the Road

Michael returned to Denver in January 2007, only eight months after the accident. Some people with TBI are still in the hospital at eight months out. Almost immediately he started back to work at his job at the Washington Park Grille. In order to become re-accustomed to the rhythm of the restaurant, he began as a busser, cleaning and setting tables, and a back waiter, delivering food from the kitchen to the customers. The pace was quick and the hours long, but the familiar surroundings, processes and menu items gave Mike the confidence to forge ahead, hoping to reclaim his server position. However, where once he thrived in that environment, now the hectic pace, noisy atmosphere of the restaurant, the long hours, and multi-tasking required to serve several tables of patrons at once while also following the orders of the restaurant manager, proved to be overwhelming.

One Sunday soon afterward, Mike called to tell us that he had had a very bad day at work. He had been working the Sunday brunch shift. Sundays are usually very busy at the Grille. Their brunches are filled with wonderful offerings of egg dishes, pastries, fish entries and wonderful desserts. As a result, they attract a lively crowd of families who come in after church and young professionals who live in the neighborhood. The patrons are the usual mix of neighborhood and extended area residents and visitors. Anniversaries and birthdays are also often celebrated there. With the large crowds and special weekend offerings comes a more hectic day at work for servers, bussers, back waiters and managers alike. Everyone is running around trying to keep up with the volume, assuring quick service to help with turnover rates at all of the tables. Often the systems which work well during the weekdays and weeknights are overwhelmed. Tensions grow between kitchen and serving staff, between the bar and the restaurant, and between management and servers... all trying to keep up.

Michael, who had always been something of a judgmental perfectionist when it comes to serving others and being aware of their needs, had gotten overwhelmed by the pace of service required on this particular Sunday. For the first time, he reported, he had lost his cool in front of customers and co-workers. He told us that he had yelled at others on the staff in public and treated customers more rudely than he should. His shift manager (and roommate) Dave had reported Mike's behavior to the restaurant's management who felt compelled to write him up. Being "written up" is designed to serve as a warning to the employee to shape up or face the consequences, i.e., demotion or termination. In Mike's case, the consequence of this incident was to indefinitely delay the resumption of night serving duties, and, therefore, his return to full earnings power.

Mike was contrite as he told us about this incident. He knew he had performed poorly, lost control and had brought this on himself. He was sorry that the incident had happened. He was also well aware that his TBI may have contributed to the incident. He didn't blame his momentary loss of control on his injury, although he did see it as a contributing factor. He told us that he didn't want to hide behind TBI as an excuse, but that he would have to be "more aware" in the future. Juxtaposing his contrition, Michael was furious at Dave for having reported the incident to the restaurant's management. He felt Dave had betrayed their friendship.

Although I was saddened by the restaurant incident and the delay in reaching the goal of nighttime serving, I was heartened to hear Michael talk about TBI and its effects. His level of awareness seemed to be increasing rapidly this month. Self-awareness is often impaired following a TBI. Nevertheless, his anger at Dave reflected a new level of emotional volatility which I feared would be difficult for Mike to control and might jeopardize his ability to hold on to employment and friends over time.

Several months later, in April, Michael came home to Tucson

to join the wedding celebration and reception for his sister, her husband and their family... consisting of two young boys and Darcy's mother-in-law. In addition, we had many of our own family members in town for the Passover holiday and to visit my parents, who were then in their middle 80's. In many ways, this was Michael's first real exposure to family since the accident. Everyone was delighted to see Mike so well recovered. They had not known what to expect from him. He did his best not to disappoint them, but he struggled to keep his innermost feelings, his anger and frustrations, from bubbling over into conversations.

He seemed to fully enjoy socializing. However, the joy he felt while socializing with the family only hid a deepening melancholy that belied his smile. That weekend Mike re-inhabited the extra bedroom in our home. This gave us a great opportunity to "check in" on how Michael was doing living on his own in Denver. Although happy to be back with us again, Mike expressed deep sadness and loneliness when talking about his life up in Denver. He continued to have little camaraderie or interaction with his roommate. Dave had been promoted to assistant manager at the Wash Park Grille while Mike was recovering in Tucson and had become romantically involved with Helen. Mike and Dave shared little in common these days other than the living space of the condo. They didn't go see movies together, couldn't hang together in the old bar scene, and had no time during the days to go out to play sports or workout together. These things were normal for the two of them before the accident. The things that made them friends before seemed to have been demolished in the accident along with the car.

Mike's other friends in Denver had, not surprisingly, either moved on to other locations following college or had become involved in their new jobs following graduation from DU. His best friends, Tim and Liz, were both working and in the evenings planning their wedding, which was scheduled for July in Breckenridge. Generously, they did make time to be with Mike; these visits were just not as often and not long enough to help Michael overcome his feelings of isolation. In fact, they seemed to highlight and exacerbate Mike's sadness at all his "alone" time.

Mike tried to reach out to others by going back to the Chi Phi house near the DU campus, where, as an alumnus, he thought he would be welcomed. Having missed out on Commencement and its ceremonial rite of passage, Mike was caught in limbo. He had received his diploma but had not experienced graduation; he had left school but had not had a chance to say "goodbye." The fraternity brothers were welcoming, but Mike sensed that he no longer fit into their drinking and partying lifestyle. Eventually, he stopped going down to campus.

Dana and I talked often about his reaching out and expanding his circle of acquaintances. We offered suggestions of part-time work elsewhere and volunteering. We suggested that he join Congregation Emanuel, which is close to his condominium, and might serve as a conduit to new people. We suggested leaving the Grille and applying for other work, a different kind of work. All of our suggestions were rebuffed by Michael with various challenges and hurdles, real or imagined. Working itself was difficult enough with its distractions, multi-tasking, changing schedules and long shifts. At this point, he would come home too exhausted, mentally and physically, to pursue other activities or opportunities. We failed to fully appreciate how difficult it was for Michael given the limits of energy and the role fatigue played in his inability to become involved in new activities.

Knowing what to do and initiating the action are two aspects of executive function. Michael struggled to initiate. Planning ahead as well as initiation of action can be problems for front left temporal lobe TBI survivors. Of course, planning, initiation, and direction can also be problems for normal 23 year olds with broadly based liberal arts degrees. The combination of age and TBI seemed to conspire against Michael.

Having exhausted ideas which Mike would eliminate from consideration even before they had a chance to be fully discussed, Dana and I felt helpless, we felt angry and we felt sad: Helpless to be able to get through to his young mind and excite him to all the possibilities we envisioned for him; angry that he seemed outwardly to be doing so well, but, in reality, was being blocked by his own cognitive and emotional obstacles. He was constantly running imaginary scenarios through his mind. If there were multiple paths and/or considerations, he would become easily overwhelmed. Unable to choose or to act, being confronted with choices seemed only to leave him with no rest and no peace of mind. His mental resources were taxed to their limits.

We, too, were feeling defeated. Our hearts ached for our son. We knew, from an intellectual standpoint, that he continued to be better and that he was thinking more clearly all the time. But, emotionally, it was withering to see so much promise blocked after Michael had expended so much effort during recovery therapy to just "be normal" again. It was at this point that Dana and I were just beginning to truly understand and accept that TBI does not ever return someone to his or her "normal," pre-injury status. TBI's survivors are forever changed, their paths are forever altered, and their lives are forever lived in its shadow.

The only option which Michael began to consider and, in some ways, perseverate on, was a re-return to living in Tucson. In his view, his difficulties at work, his lack of friendships, his derailed career all led him to now believe that a life in Tucson would be better than a life in Denver. After the months of yearning to return to Denver after his first return to Tucson following his discharge from Craig Hospital, he now began to speak only about how much he wanted to live "at home" in Tucson. He did not consider what he would be coming home to, only the loneliness he would be leaving behind. *What about our jointly owned condo? What would occupy his time in this much smaller community?* But he WAS thinking about moving forward despite having no idea where forward movement would lead… and, therein, in those thoughts, laid the smallest of victories!

In late May, back in Denver following the April reception for Darcy and James, Michael reported that the weekend's work at the Wash Park Grille went well. He had been very busy and made lots of money. He had served during a very busy lunch shift, handling 8 tables at one time. Mike reported that, other than the physical exertion of standing long hours and running back and forth to serve, he had had no trouble in keeping orders straight or handling the volume of work. However, Ann Marie, an assistant manager at the Grille, had contacted Dana on several occasions to discuss Michael's difficult relationships with his co-workers. She reported that Mike was often inappropriately condescending to them. She emphasized that he had a good response from customers...he could sell a bottle of wine to any diners, even if they had ordered ice tea! He was sociable and customers often asked to be seated in his station. Despite these positives, Michael continued to be disruptive of the staff at the Grille. In fact, he was on the verge of being fired.

From our distant vantage point in Tucson, Dana and I saw signs of cognitive weakness in these reports. Scheduling and planning ahead to next week, next month and next year were not well processed by Mike, but, perhaps, looking ahead to the future is not the focus of a 23 year old, we thought. Perhaps we were looking for signs of normality rather than symptoms of dysfunction. But as time wore on, we recognized the difference between an immature "live for today" attitude and an inability to process future events, to set meaningful goals and to define his future course of action. If we provided a plan, i.e., step-by-step directions, Michael was capable of executing the plan, although he rarely showed that he understood the urgency in any course of action which might actually help him. He knew he wanted to meet people, but he didn't want to join in new activities with others. He knew he wanted to find a different job, but he didn't spend any of his free time looking for employment opportunities or networking.

In fact, Dana and I were in our own state of denial. We thought: *If Michael moved back to Denver, he would get better; when Michael was able to drive again, he would get better; when he got a better job, he would get better.* But we slowly came to accept that Michael might never "get better" in the sense of living without any cognitive deficits which resulted from the TBI.

Ironically, Michael was eagerly looking forward to the first anniversary of his automobile accident. Dana and I, on the other hand, were anticipating this milestone with anxiety and sadness. For almost twelve months, or at least the 10 months since Michael emerged from post-traumatic amnesia and became aware of the June 2 accident, he had been looking forward to shedding some of the restrictions which the doctors and therapists imposed during the first year of recovery. Primary among those taboos were smoking tobacco or other substances and drinking alcoholic beverages. The doctors explained that smoking tobacco products increases the amount of CO_2 and other harmful gases, which can reduce the oxygen flowing to the brain. These substances in the bloodstream can impede the neural functions, and, therefore, slow the healing processes for a person recovering from TBI. Further, nicotine is an addictive drug, which, like other addictive drugs, stimulates an increase in the amount of dopamine and other neuro-transmittors in the brain, reinforcing the addictive behavior. Drinking alcoholic beverages similarly introduces alcohol into the bloodstream. As we all know, until the alcohol is metabolized, it has an anxiolytic effect, i.e., it acts to reduce anxiety. Reducing the feeling of anxiety may feel good, but alcohol also increases dopamine and thus, the habit of drinking to reduce stress is reinforced. Brain functions such as reasoning, inhibition and coordination of motor skills can also be impaired as other parts of the brain are affected. We had been warned by Dr. Ripley that patients who have not ingested alcoholic beverages for a year, and then have an alcoholic drink, sometimes, if only rarely, experience their first seizures.

For obvious health reasons, Michael had abstained from smoking throughout the past year. Being hospitalized for three months made nicotine withdrawal a non-issue. He wasn't allowed to smoke, and didn't, while in the hospital, and, we believe, he had not smoked since he left Craig Hospital in August 2006. He claimed that he had become a committed non-smoker. However, he took up smoking cigarettes again sometime later, perhaps as a response to peer pressure around the restaurant-service worker population, much to our chagrin and disapproval.

Michael had been careful not to violate the prohibition against drinking alcoholic beverages in this first year of recovery. But, instead of swearing this off permanently, he looked forward to the one year anniversary with great anticipation of taking his first sips of wine. Despite the risks to his continued recovery, despite the underlying contribution of alcohol to the accident which had got him in this pickle in the first place, he was determined to celebrate the anniversary with a small sample of wine.

Why would someone who has just endured a year of personal hell jeopardize the progress made and the progress yet to be made for just a drink? Was he so addicted that he needed to drink? To comprehend this, one has to understand the psyche of a 23 year old male. The pressure among young adults to drink is enormous. It is a social addiction rather than a physical one. It's not that his peers wished Michael ill or that they were demanding his participation in the rites of their passage to adulthood by attending bars or drinking parties. No, the pressure came from within. Mike believed he needed to drink alcoholic beverages to be successful socially with people of his generation. He was adamant that he would not overindulge and drink to excess or drive while intoxicated. *Who knowingly does any of those things?* To a 23 year old, the logic is clear... to be accepted by their peers, they must drink. To not drink is to accept the notion, rightly or wrongly, that he would be ostracized by the people closest to him each day, his friends and co-workers.

His perseveration on this one prohibition, and the nearness of the finish line which the one year anniversary represented, showed us that Michael was still blinded to certain reasoning. We had urged Michael to abstain permanently believing that nothing was to be gained by drinking alcoholic beverages although much could be lost. But we would not win this battle.

Letter to Michael, June 1, 2007

To Michael:

Today marks an anniversary. Not the kind that one would choose to celebrate, but the kind that one would be remiss to ignore and let go unrecognized. It marks an important event to be remembered, respected and noted.

For this is a day which is notable for what occurred one year ago has meant to all of us. Before that fateful day twelve months ago today, life and its course were going in one direction; now, its direction is changed because of what has transpired in the year since that day.

We are, of course, speaking of your automobile accident, an event which almost took you from us. Gratefully, you can only know about the accident from what you have been told about it. Some memories are best left unremembered. We hope that you never recall the impact of that terrible event other than through hearsay. And it's also well and good that you do not recall the first weeks following the accident during which you were confined to the hospital.

For us, on one hand, that was a very dark time which was filled with fear and uncertainty. We were unable to know what the future would hold, but we were keenly aware of how terrible the present was. On the other hand, we experienced life as we had never had before. We felt the full force of our love for you, our son. We learned this through the depth of the strength of our own internal energy to help you overcome this adversity, of our own ability to learn about areas of medicine and science we had never been exposed to before, and of our feelings for the support from family and friends. We learned these things also through the unexpected but overwhelming support and kindnesses of people we had never known before including your friends, your teachers, and the strangers who took care of you with such dedication. People like Officer Jones, Dr. Schulten, Janet and Mark, Tim and Liz, Adam and Mindy.

But to commemorate this day with you is to acknowledge how great a sacrifice you have made over the past twelve months. This was not a path you would have chosen but nevertheless a journey you have so successfully travelled. We know that no one more than you keenly feels the differences these past twelve months have made in your life. But the differences are wonderful for us to behold. With grace and spirit, you endured the physical trauma of those first weeks in the hospital. You gave your best efforts at Craig Hospital as you became more and more aware of the challenges before you. You emerged from your coma with intelligence, humor and a warm sensitivity which could have easily been lost to despair and anger. Despite your urgent desire to be your own person, independent and free once again, you worked through your time in Tucson and back in Denver, recognizing not that time heals all wounds, but that some things take time to heal. Your patience has been well rewarded.

You have heard us say many times that your recovery is remarkable. People are continuously reminding us that you and we are extremely fortunate for how well you are today. But, in truth, we feel more than just fortunate that we now can better appreciate what the events of one year ago have meant to all of us. Today, we look forward with great anticipation for seeing our son moving forward, living a life of happiness and fulfillment, in whatever paths your new future will take you.

You have always been a precious gift in our lives. We feel that as much today as at any time previously. For all of your strength, perseverance and dedication to getting better, we congratulate you. For all of your hopes and dreams today and in the future to be fulfilled, we encourage and support you. We hope that on this day, this anniversary, you know you have fully graduated and are ready to move ahead. You make us proud to be your parents. We love you for who you are, for who you have become and for the person you will become in the years ahead.

Mom and Dad

Chapter 27
The Wedding – A Promise Fulfilled

Tim and Liz were married on July 28, 2007, in Breckenridge, Colorado. The ceremony went off without a hitch (except to say that Tim and Liz got "hitched.")

We had gotten to know Tim and Liz during our summer in Denver the year before. Tim, one of Mike's fraternity brothers, was fondly nicknamed Tabasco Tim due to his affinity for hot, spicy foods. His fiancée Liz had been one of Mike's dorm mates during his freshman year at DU. They stood by Mike through his hospitalizations at both Denver Health Medical Center and Craig Hospital, visiting him often and long after other friends had stopped coming by. Then, upon Mike's return to Denver, they reached out to Mike when others had become more and more distant. They were, and are, true friends.

When Michael was laying unconscious and bruised in the SICU at Denver Health Medical Center, Tim would come to visit and often reassured Dana and me that Mike was going to be in their wedding the following July. And, then, when Mike had awakened from his coma and emerged from PTA at Craig Hospital, he, too, had vowed to make it to the wedding in full health.

Dana and I were delighted to receive an invitation to the wedding. We enthusiastically drove the 900 miles from Tucson to Breckenridge to attend the wedding. When we left Tucson on July 25, 2007, the temperatures were in the mid- 90s and thunderstorms were threatening once again after a week of afternoon monsoon rains. We drove through Southern Arizona and up along I-25 up to Santa Fe, NM. We continued the next day to drive up to Denver for an evening at Bert and Jo's and yet another night in the infamous basement bedroom. The day before the wedding, we drove on up to Genessee, Colorado, to have lunch visiting with our Tucson neighbors at their summer home. Then we continued on to Breckenridge to join the wedding festivities.

The rehearsal dinner was a casual, Western themed barbecue, complete with ribs and beans, bandanas and straw cowboy hats, and entertainment by a husband and wife team who sang the music of John Denver. Being outsiders to both family and friends, Dana and I introduced ourselves to the wedding party's family and guests as Michael's parents. When they learned who we were and why we were attending the wedding, they eagerly told us that Mike had been the life of the party the night before at a dinner held for just the wedding party's participants. "How engaging he was," we were told, "The life of the party!" Some who didn't know the events of the past year just shared how funny Mike was, telling stories and jokes. Others who had been aware of his accident and the trials of the last year spoke with great admiration for his strength of personality and lively attitude. We just smiled reflecting on our pride in Michael.

The next day, the wedding ceremony was held in the afternoon under threatening skies, by the side of a lovely little pond near the south side of Breckenridge. The groomsmen, decked out in their formal attire, marched down the aisle in single file led by the groom. Mike strutted in third position just behind Tim's best man. Mike was dressed in a black tuxedo with royal blue vest and tie. He had combed his hair up into his signature spiked style. His pants were a bit too long in this rented tux. As he marched down the aisle, he smiled broadly. The bride's attendants wore royal blue gowns and carried bouquets of yellow daisies and blue ribbons. The parents of the groom followed next. Then, the mother of the bride was escorted down the aisle by her son, Liz's red haired brother. Finally, with the congregants standing, the father of the bride and Liz walked proudly down the aisle.

Tim and Liz held hands as they spoke their vows and made their promises to each other to fulfill a life of love, devotion, and caring. About 100 guests from places as far away as Washington D.C., Wichita, KS, Los Angeles, CA and New York City and as close by as Denver, CO, were in attendance. None, however, had travelled any farther than Michael Adler, who stood up on this day for Tabasco Tim and Liz, a promise fulfilled.

Chapter 28
Another Call – Another Detour

Michael started to drive again in late October, 2006, and passed his road re-test with the State of Arizona nine months later in July 2007. In September 2007, back up in Denver, he accidentally damaged his car, a brand new Volvo sports wagon which we purchased for him for its safety features, by running over a road hazard. His engine warning light came on as the engine's fluids were leaking badly. Unaware of the severity of the damage, Mike thought that the warning light was merely a reminder to change the oil. Instead of pulling over and calling a mechanic for help, he continued to drive the car. As a result, his car's engine was "totaled." The engine needed to be replaced. A month or two later, he drove across two traffic lanes in an attempt to enter a gas station and was hit by a driver coming up the turning lane on Monaco Blvd. The damage to the car was relatively minor although it would require some body work.

Then, on Sunday, March 2, 2008, at midday, the phone in our Tucson home rang. I walked over to where the phone sat on the counter and checked the Caller ID. Looking down at the handset display, I saw the words "Inmate phone line."

What the heck is "Inmate phone line?" I wondered. *Could this be a solicitation?* The number shown on the display had the area code 303. *Denver, Colorado*. With this sudden realization, my breath caught in my chest. Picking up the phone, I heard a recorded message: "This is the Denver City Detention Inmate phone line. You are receiving a collect call from: "Mike," I heard my son's voice speak his name. "This call will cost $4.00 for the first minute and $1.00 per minute thereafter. To accept this call, hit '0' or hang up now." I pressed '0'.

"Hello," I said somewhat cautiously into the phone. Already my heart was pounding, my heart racing. Mike answered, "Dad, I'm in jail. I was arrested last night at 2:30 for DUI. I ran my car into the median after I left a farewell party for a friend who is leaving Starbucks. [Michael now worked at Starbucks having lost his job at the Wash Park Grille two months earlier.] I have been in jail all night and haven't slept."

"Oh my God, Mike, I can't believe this. How badly is the car damaged?" I asked. My first thoughts were not for his physical safety. I could hear from his voice that he was physically all right. But this was the third time in just over a year that the new Volvo sports wagon which we had purchased for Mike so he could be "safe" had been damaged in a road incident/accident. Mike replied, "I couldn't get it started after I hit the median. The right side is badly damaged, but I don't know how much. Dad, I have to post a $1,500 bond to get out. I am trying to use my credit card, but it hasn't gone through yet. I don't know if it will." "Mike, I don't know what to say or what to do. When you get out, you have no way to get home, do you?" "No," Mike said quietly. "Okay, I'll call Grandpa Bert and get him to come down to pick you up. I'll call him right now to see if he can come." "Okay, Dad. I'm so sorry. This is terrible."

"I'm not going to fix the car this time. You'll have to do that." I said angrily. But more than angry, I was in shock.

Next to *that other* phone call we had received 21 months earlier, this was the worst call I had ever received. Mike had just started to regain his confidence in himself working a new job at the Starbucks in the Cherry Creek Mall and occasionally substitute teaching at two Denver Public Schools. He had come back from and survived that earlier accident. He had just been retested for cognitive abilities and had performed fairly well, his neuropsychologist had reported to us. But there were lingering dangers. The residuals of TBI and the normal challenges of being 24 years old continued to conspire against him. *Would we ever be able to sleep without wondering if our children were safe? Would Michael ever get fully back on track to being the great kid with the great future he had been just two years ago?* My heart was sickened by this newest turn of events. I ached for my son; also, I ached for our lost aspirations for him.

"I don't know what else to say, Mike. I will do what I can to get you out of there, but I have to call your grandfather right now." "Okay, Dad," was all the response that he could muster. I could hear in his voice how frightened he was.

Hanging up the phone, I stared down at it in disbelief. *Was this really happening...again?* I called my wife who was at a women's group luncheon somewhere in town. I told her the news and suggested that she might want to come home right away. She was, of course, stunned by the news and our conversation was short.

I dialed my father-in-law's number and in a few seconds he answered. "Bert, this is Ira. I've got some bad news. Mike has been arrested for DUI and is in jail. He's at the Detention Center at 14th and Cherokee." "Oh my," Bert replied, "that kid gets into more hot water. I know where that is and Jo and I will go right down to get him." "You might have to wait a few hours until he is released. He has to post a $1,500 bond. If his credit card doesn't work, you might have to use yours, Ok?" I asked. "Yes, we'll take care of it, if need be." "Take your cell phone so I can call you if I get any more information and call me when you get down there." "Will do," he replied. I set the phone down. My mind raced with thoughts about my son's predicament. Then, I started to make emergency travel plans to fly up to Denver.

The arrest had come at 1:00 a.m. on the morning of March 2, 2008, <u>exactly</u> 21 months following the first automobile accident which had left Mike in a coma for 8 days and a TBI survivor for life. Michael had been tested for sobriety right there on Colorado Boulevard and then handcuffed. He was taken by police cruiser to the DPD station near University Avenue and I-25 and held there for a short time. Then he was transferred by police van to the DPD holding facility located near downtown Denver. He was put into the drunk tank with others for several hours, during which time he was taken out to be tested for his blood alcohol levels. He was then removed into another cell which had one metal cot and a mattress on the floor. He told us that he had shared the cell with an overweight inebriated Hispanic man, who slept on the mattress, while Michael curled up without covers on the metal slab. He was offered a shower by his jailors, which he had refused, and was given one meal of prepackaged meat and stale bread. He was interviewed by a prison psychologist after he had reported the medications he took regularly for the effects of TBI: an antidepressant and an attention sharpening drug. He was finally released to his grandfather at 3:00 p.m. Sunday afternoon.

On Monday, March 3, I flew up to Denver. Again, I made some notes during the flight:

> Another flight to Denver under less than ideal circumstances. I sit here angry, upset, deeply saddened, emboldened and, by necessity, fired up – knowing that I will need to take action once I land and that it will be six days of effort and heavy lifting.
>
> Once again, there are children sitting in the rows in front and behind me- young children, innocence in their faces, wide eyed wonder at the airplane experience. Yet I look at them and wonder: *Will they be safe? What trauma or trouble awaits them as they maneuver their way to adulthood? Enjoy their youth!* I thought, silently exhorting their parents.
>
> I once felt safe and comfortable in the world, confident of my own and my family's future. Now, after two years of constant worry and near continuous sadness, interrupted only by brief periods when I could suppress these feelings, a profound melancholy was taking over again.
>
> My in-laws suggest that I chant Buddhist chants. My wife tells me to "stay in the moment – the future will take care of itself." My father asks: "Do you think it's the other accident that caused this?" *What do you think?* I silently reply, exasperated. My friends say, "Ouch!" "What a shame." But I know they are first and foremost glad they are not in my shoes. They will call their children, hug them, dine with them – all embracing their good fortune..."At least we're not having to face DUI, like the Adlers."
>
> According to the pilot, the ride to Denver was predicted

to be bumpy. Of course, he was referring only to air turbulence. The air turbulence was nothing compared to the bumps and hurdles, which were challenging Michael. I feel swept along in the wake of Michael's life challenges. Dana and I, too, were being dragged from the safety of the shore out to sea by the undertow, as it were. It will be another exhilarating ride and a nauseating one, much like a roller coaster. We have lost control of our facticity, that is, the circumstances in which our lives are being presented to us. Our ability to influence our own destiny seems limited to dealing with these unwelcome events.

In front of my face – embedded in the headrest of the seat directly ahead of me is a screen, a video monitor. It flashes an advertisement for a law firm, "Holland & Hart – the Law Out West," which reminds me to call my nephew Adam, a partner in that very firm. It also shows a Mapquest screen of our flight's progress toward Denver. Our altitude and airspeed is displayed as well. I think to myself – *what if the data on my screen differed from that of my seat mates? Perhaps we have entered the Twilight Zone yet again.*

Once on the ground, I made my way through the airport to the baggage claim. While waiting for my duffel bag to appear, I called Mike to let him know I was in town. My bag appeared and I hustled out to the car rental shuttle bus which would take me to the Enterprise Car Rental lot. Without delay, I picked out a small SUV and headed over to Mike's condominium.

As I approached the Lowry Town Centre, I called Mike again and asked him to meet me downstairs to assist with the luggage. I pulled into his parking spot, where the Volvo used to be parked, and I exited the car. Mike was standing there on the sidewalk. We approached and hugged each other. He actually looked good... healthy and fit. But I could see that he was frightened. I squeezed him hard to let him know that things would work out. This was not the time for harsh parental judgment. He needed to know that I still loved him...unconditionally.

We quickly dropped off my bags and turned our conversation past the usual greeting chit-chat to the pressing legal matters. I asked to see the paper work from the arrest and quickly read through the citations, bail bond information and court appearance papers. I asked Mike if he had the number of the Denver Impound lot and suggested we go look at the car.

We wound our way around Commerce City looking for the Impound lot, which, while I had been there only two years prior, was still hidden away in a maze of streets, industrial warehouses and distribution centers. In this part of town, Denver's road grid is not very easy to navigate. Instead, we were confronted by a series of dead ends or winding two way streets filled with industrial truck traffic. But, after a few minor detours and one stop at a convenience mart to ask directions (luckily, Mike speaks some Spanish), we arrived at the Impound.

We entered the same waiting room I had not wanted to sit in the first time I had been escorted there by Officer Jones two years earlier. Without Officer Jones to clear the way this time, we had to take a number and a seat to wait our turn. We sat in silence. In about 20 minutes, we were called to the window where I asked to see the car, handing over some of the papers. The woman behind the window looked into the file cabinet, withdrew other papers related to Mike's vehicle, and told us we would be called to go look at the car. In another five minutes, the door opened and the yard man announced, "2006 Volvo." Mike and I got up and walked toward him. "Only one of you can go see the car," the yard man said. I turned and told Michael to take a seat, then I followed the man to his pickup truck. We drove a few aisles over, past the place where Mike's crumpled RAV 4 had been sitting almost two years earlier, and found the Volvo.

As I got out of truck, the yard man informed me I had 15 minutes to inspect the vehicle. The car was in bad shape. The front fender, the right quarter panel and the right front wheel were badly damaged. The right front tire was flat, explaining why the car was "disabled" when Mike was arrested.

Remembering my cell phone's capabilities, I took several pictures of the damage to the car. *This would be expensive to fix*. I knew I would have to arrange for a tow to the body shop. I looked inside of the vehicle and saw a few personal items of Michael's left in the car two nights before. His golf clubs were lying in the back in the trunk space. The yard man said I could take whatever I could carry that was not tied down or part of the car itself, so I entered the car and gathered up a book bag, the Garman GPS device, a coat and a few other small items. I left the golf clubs for a later date.

I found the car key sitting on the dashboard, so I placed it in the keyhole and turned it to start the car. Mike had earlier said to me that the car had not started after he hit the median the night of his arrest and accident. However, the car's engine immediately turned over and sounded good. *At least the car works!* I shut the engine off and left the vehicle to climb back into the pickup. "Let's get out of here," I said to the yard man.

Back in the rental car, I showed Michael the pictures taken on my cell phone. He became very still and could not look at me directly. Dinner that night was difficult. Mike cooked. We sat down at the table in the living room of the condominium facing each other. We talked frankly and emotionally about the events of the last two days and the last two years. I told him how deeply I loved my son. I told him he was as important to me as anyone in my life. I felt the need to let him know that I wanted to help and that I did not intend to pile on to his difficulties with my own judgments or anger. But I said that I expected him to take responsibility.

Then, Michael opened up. His emotions flooded out of his mouth. He said that he had the worst luck of anybody in the world; that his problems felt insurmountable and, while he was not suicidal, he wondered how he was going to overcome this latest difficulty, "...now that my life is shit." He said he had found Denver not to be the place he thought it would be when he had returned last January, when he wanted to get back there so quickly after his return to Tucson. He thought it would be like college life... but it had not turned out that way. He wondered aloud why he hadn't had a girlfriend since high school. Again, my heart ached for my son.

We talked about his anger, his sadness, his sarcasm as well as his intelligence and sensitivity. I told him that this latest incident marked the "...end of his childhood." He had to face up to life as an adult. I told him that, while people, places and events affect our lives, only we can give our lives meaning by the things we do and the way we act. He needed to overcome his problems... not for me, his father, and not for Dana, his mother, but just for himself. He needed to find for himself a place of happiness and to do those things which make him happy. I knew that only Michael could make this happen for Michael. By the end of the evening, we both were emotionally spent but feeling closer than we had been for some time. We hugged and then went to bed.

The next morning Mike and I woke up early, ate some breakfast and then headed down to meet with Dr. Davidson, Michael's neuropsychologist. I had anticipated that this latest incident would be disturbing to Mike and asked him to make the appointment while I was up in Denver. Mike had been seeing Dr. Davidson about once or twice a month, so that this visit would be out of sequence.

We entered the doctor's office and sat down...Mike in a chair and me on the sofa. Mike began by recounting to Dr. Davidson the experience of being arrested following the party with his Starbucks co-workers and a few other friends. When describing his excessive drinking, he simply said he used poor judgment in drinking too much and would not drink again... ever (a promise, I am reminded once again, he would not keep).

After Michael related the weekend's events, I tried to describe Mike's emotional state for Dr. Davidson. I mentioned Mike's reference to suicide the night before, emphasizing that he did not seem to have any intent or want to end his life. He had simply mentioned it. Mike expressed, as he had the night before, that he "can't imagine not battling through, not overcoming..." but that he felt he faced more problems in the last two years than others would face in their lifetimes. He said, "I feel like God's punching bag." Dr. Davidson responded, "Like Bobo, the clown? You know, it keeps on being punched and springs back up?" Mike said, "Yes, exactly, but I don't know that I can spring back up every time. I'm scared and I might lose control."

Dr. Davidson asked, "What are you in control of?" Mike replied, "I made a poor decision, I didn't pull over when I realized I was driving drunk and I drank too much in the first place. That's all." Davidson turned to me and said, "When Michael minimizes issues, that's the TBI talking." Then he reminded both Mike and me that TBI makes the brain twice more sensitive to the effects of alcohol than a normal brain. We talked more about the consequences and Dr. Davidson summarized their prior talks: "What feels like incursions to your autonomy are just reminders for you to self-monitor your responses. It's even more important than before."

In describing his neuropsychological testing, Dr. Davidson reported that Mike's overall cognitive functioning, the way the entire brain works together as a unit, tested at a normal level. However, there are some deficits which rank in the "low-average" range, related to right frontal lobe lesions. These injuries affect his ability to recognize situations and adjust flexibly to external signals and/or feedback. There is a mental "stickiness" to first responses and less of an ability to modify responses based on additional feedback from the environment or other people. He said that Michael exhibited some difficulty in generating new non-verbal solutions and reactions to non-verbal information. Despite rating very high on verbal fluency, his figural fluency as determined by the Ruff Figural Fluency Test was slightly below normal.

Dr. Davidson's observations were important to an understanding of TBI. Michael is an extremely intelligent, social and sensitive person, one who has, and will always have, some symptoms of TBI. These symptoms of TBI are areas which might improve, but will likely always cause problems for Michael as he tries to monitor his own reactions and behavioral responses to the world about him. Dr. Davidson referred to this in a later report as social prosopagnosia, i.e., blindness to social cues from others.

After meeting with Dr. Davidson, we drove over to meet with a DUI attorney referred to us by friends. At the meeting with the attorney, we learned about the standard legal processes and ramifications surrounding a DUI citation. We were told that the law does not differentiate between TBI survivors and other citizens. Suffice it to say that there are licensing as well as criminal implications to DUI arrest. At the end of the meeting, the attorney announced that he would be unavailable for Mike's first court date since he had a death penalty murder trial starting that week. He told us his partner would assume the case if his firm were to be retained. My response to this late revelation: *I think not*.

Nevertheless, after hearing of Michael's history with drinking, driving and TBI, the attorney shared a profound insight. "You [Michael] may not have an alcohol problem, but you have a problem with alcohol." This was his way of saying that Mike was not necessarily an alcoholic or substance abuser but that he should avoid all opportunities to drink or take drugs. "Good advice," I thought to myself.

The next day, March 5, I woke up at 4:25 a.m. My mind immediately turned on and I could not go back to sleep. I tried to plot the day ahead:

1) Get Mike off to work on time and prepared for his bus ride.
2) Pack for my move to Bert and Jo's house.
3) Get in touch with Curtis Ramsay, another attorney we were referred to whose office is in Boulder.
4) Call the Volvo dealer for instructions as to where and when to tow the car from the Denver Impound Facility.
5) Drive to Bert and Jo's to pick up the Volvo's car title which had been sent to Denver by Dana.
6) Call the towing service.
7) Go to the Impound to pay the towing and impound fees in order to release the car.
8) Deliver remaining personal items from the car to Mike's condominium.
9) Pick up Mike at Starbucks at the Cherry Creek Mall.
10) Go to dinner with Bert, Jo and Mike.
11) Return Michael home to his condo.
12) Return to Bert and Jo's for the rest of the evening.

Other than crisscrossing the city several times that day, the tasks ahead laid out pretty well in my mind. I recognized that this type of planning was something that Michael himself would have difficulty with now and, perhaps, for the rest of his life.

It was cold (25°) and snowing lightly. Michael woke up about 7:00 and showered, dressed, ate some cereal and left to walk to the bus stop. With his license suspended and his car undrivable and sitting in the Impound, he would be riding public transportation for the foreseeable future. In the weeks that followed, Michael learned to look up the bus schedules, ride the bus and get around using public transportation, including the new train system in Denver.

He called me from the bus stop at 8:05 and again from the Mall at 8:25. Work was scheduled to start at 9:15. In the meantime, I showered and dressed, packed up my clothing, computer and backpack. I left the condo about 9:00 to head to Bert and Jo's. Just before noon, I left the Dendingers' home for the Impound lot. Just as I turned onto Quincy, my cell phone rang. Curtis Ramsay, the Boulder attorney, was returning my call. I pulled over onto a side street to speak with her with undivided attention. We arranged a meeting for the next day, March 6, at 3:00 p.m.

As I continued up to the Impound, I called the Volvo dealer to get instructions on where to deliver the car. I was instructed by the Service Department representative to deliver the car to the body shop on 4th and Kalamath. "See Ernie, he'll take care of you." I did not get lost in the maze which is Commerce City on this now routine trip. When I arrived at the Impound lot, I called the Volvo Roadside Assistance hotline to arrange for the pickup and towing of the car. Wednesday at the Impound must be a slow day because I waited just 10 minutes before being called to the window. Speaking with the same woman as two days before, I paid the fees and fines ($160) then waited for Metro Towing to appear. Jose from the towing company arrived in less than a half hour and we waited to be called by the yard man to enter the yard. I hopped into his truck's cab and we drove out to Mike's car in his flat bed tow truck. He attached the winch to the car and dragged it up the bed. It could not roll up the bed of the truck as the front right wheel was turned perpendicular to the body of the car. We cleaned out the remaining personal items from the car and Jose left to deliver the car. In all, the Impound had been a non-event, a nuisance errand. I was finished there by 1:00 p.m.

I left the Impound lot and headed over to Michael's condominium to return his personal items from the car. I called over there to see if Dave, Mike's roommate, would be there to let me in. Luckily, I caught Dave before he had to leave for work. When I arrived, I unloaded the car, two trips up the three flights of stairs to their third floor apartment. Then I visited with Dave for a few minutes. I shared the ramifications of Michael's legal dilemma and thanked Dave for his extension of friendship to Mike at this difficult time. For all of the friction between Dave and Mike while Mike worked at the Wash Park Grille following the accident, there did not seem to be any lingering animosity, at least not on Dave's part. On the other hand, Dave expressed little sympathy for Michael's predicament. Perhaps he was uncomfortable speaking with Michael's father. Dave had never sought any counseling after the accident occurred and perhaps he had never dealt with his part in the events leading up to it.

I left to go to the Cherry Creek Mall to pick up Mike following his work shift. I knew I would be early and found time to wander about the mall and sit in the public areas set aside in the mall. I felt the need to de-compress for a few minutes. As I sat there, Mike came over and delivered a very well made Coffee Light Frappucino. As I sat there, observing the passers-by and sipping my drink, I felt optimistic for the first time that Michael would survive this latest incident.

After his shift at Starbucks, I drove Michael over to Bert and Jo's to go out to dinner. They had selected a little neighborhood Chinese food restaurant. During the meal, Mike was animated, listening to our conversation and yet distracted, picking up on each song playing over the noise of the restaurant. He would quote various pearls of literary wisdom, repeat lyrics and change subjects regularly. I felt that he was trying to divert attention away from the worst parts of his own thoughts. Perhaps he was just fatigued from working all day and, therefore, unable to stay focused on one thought at a time. Or perhaps he just felt comfortable to be himself, without fear of social rejection, in the presence of family. He was, in any case, stripped bare of any pretensions as he jumped from topic to topic.

On the way back to his condominium that night, we talked more about drinking or, to be more exact, not drinking. How might he cope with social situations when others were drinking alcoholic beverages? Who did he think would require that he drink to be socially accepted? I raised the suggestion that being the "designated driver" might be a perfectly acceptable response to the offer of alcohol or finding oneself in groups where virtually everyone else had imbibed and some had had too much. He found this suggestion reassuring, despite his adamancy that he would abstain forevermore. I pulled up into his building's driveway and we shook hands. We had agreement on these points. Of course, I wondered if he would remember this conversation in the days and months that would follow.

I drove back to Bert and Jo's, went downstairs and, exhausted from the day, fell asleep around 9:30 p.m. Unfortunately, I woke up at 4:15 a.m. Once again, I couldn't go back to sleep as thoughts crowded out the sleep. I began a new list of activities for the day:

1) Find an AA meeting for Friday and/or Saturday
2) Find Level 1/Level 2 state-certified DUI classes near Mike's condominium…sign up for classes on Friday.
3) Go to Volvo – see Ernie
4) Go to meet Curtis Ramsay, attorney in Boulder

I sat in bed and considered giving Mike a bracelet or necklace with the following inscribed on it: "Michael Adler – TBI 6/2/06; DUI 3/2/08" as a constant reminder not to drink. I thought it would act like a medical alert bracelet. Would this be too heavy handed? Emotionally debilitating to Michael? Or would it be received in the spirit with which it was intended: a reminder and a touchstone whenever he felt himself drawn to take a drink of an alcoholic beverage?

Some ideas which come to us in the early morning are good ideas; some are not. On balance, the bracelet seemed a good idea. But, I did not act upon my return to Tucson. The direction that events of the last part of the week took us seemed to negate the need for such things. Later, Michael would get his chest tattooed with two expressions: *Carpe Diem* (Seize the Day) and *Felix Culpa* (Fortunate Fall). These, he claimed, would serve as a constant reminder not to drink and to feel fortunate for having survived so much. The bracelet would have served the same purpose, but without marring (decorating) his skin permanently.

Like most best laid plans, not every item of my early morning list worked out that day. We could not find a reasonably proximate AA meeting, given Michael's limited transportation modes. But, by searching through the internet to the Colorado State Human Services department website and its links, we found a listing of providers of DUI classes. Several were close by to either Michael's home or his workplace at the Cherry Creek Mall. We found that not all listed agencies served the adult population; several were, in fact, designed for minors only (like the one at George Washington High School, a mile from Mike's condo). But Michael located a class near to his place of work and available at a convenient time of day, i.e., evenings. He took down the contact information as the location was closed and committed to me to call on the following Monday.

Having taken care of these business items, we drove the rented car to the Volvo body shop to obtain an estimate for the repairs. It was there that Michael first saw, and came to an appreciation of, the extent of the damage to the car and the seriousness of his actions the prior weekend. He got the sobering news that the car would cost approximately $4,200 to repair. Of course, the cost would fall to the insurance company and the deductible to Dana and me.

Later that morning we headed up to Boulder, Colorado, hoping to learn more about the legal consequences of his arrest from our second attorney interview. After lunch at a Mexican bistro on the Pearl Street Mall, we drove over to the law office of Ms. Curtis Ramsay, attorney at law, which was located in a grand old brick building on Arapaho Street. We waited a few minutes in a conference room on the first floor. When she arrived, Ms. Ramsay greeted us and speaking directly to Michael asked how he was feeling and if he was all right. Surprisingly, yet happily, she did not have an officious tone, much unlike the attorney we had met the day before. She was more concerned with Michael, the young person, than Michael, the newly minted criminal.

As they went over the details of the arrest, we discussed Mike's previous accident which left him with TBI. Since it, too, had been alcohol related she was concerned about the arrest record. I explained that his prior record had been expunged. We talked about Mike's TBI medical history. Ms. Ramsay immediately said that she understood the implications and that she would guide Michael very carefully through the legal processes, both in court and throughout his probation, which she felt confident she could achieve. She explained that she would go over the procedures and outcomes carefully by first speaking with Michael and then following up with written communications to reinforce the information. She offered that Michael could call her anytime he had any questions about his case or its consequences. We left her office feeling reassured. Over the next few months, Ms. Ramsay would extend herself beyond her role as an attorney and would become a friend and resource to Michael, Dana and me.

His preliminary hearing before the court was waived as Ms. Ramsay filed a motion for a pretrial conference to determine an acceptable plea bargain. Prior to that conference, Michael began attending DUI classes which, Ms. Ramsay advised, would likely be required by the State of Colorado as part of his probation. The strategy was to show the District Attorney that Michael was sincerely contrite and not taking the arrest lightly. Every Wednesday for several months, Michael went down to the certified DUI class located near the Cherry Creek Mall and spent one to two hours learning about the consequences of substance and alcohol abuse. Mike actually found the classes to be a social outlet and interesting. He would often quote newly learned statistics to me over the phone.

The pretrial conference took place without Mike's presence and the results were excellent. The District Attorney agreed that he would accept a plea from Mike to a reduced charge of Driving While Ability Impaired, a misdemeanor, which would require 24 hours of DUI classes, DUI therapy sessions, if required by his probation officer, 24 hours of community service, attendance at a Mothers Against Drunk Driving panel and, last but not least, payment of court costs and fines totaling about $1,500. His driver's license was suspended for 90 days from the date of the arrest, yet it would only be reinstated after Michael applied for and could provide evidence that he was covered by non-cancellable driver's insurance. His attorney's costs were approximately $4,000.

Considering the alternative was a DUI guilty plea, which would result in a lengthier and more expensive probationary period and a permanent felony conviction on his record, Mike got off pretty well. Between airfare, car rentals, automobile repairs, DUI class fees, court costs and penalties, and legal fees, this incident cost over $6,000!

Chapter 29
Road Work Ahead

After two years of recovery from the first traffic accident which resulted in his prolonged hospitalization and recovery from TBI, Mike had lived on his own for 18 months during which time he had four car related incidents, three requiring extensive body and/or engine repairs and one alcohol-related; he had worked at the Wash Park Grille, been let go from that job and had successfully found minimum wage work at Starbucks; he had learned to maneuver about Denver using its public transportation and had diligently attended to all of his probationary requirements. He had continued to see a neuropsychologist and made a few contacts with the Craig Hospital vocational rehabilitation department. And, although he had lost contact with many of his friends... including Dave, his roommate, who moved out to his own apartment shortly after the two year anniversary of the accident they had experienced together, Mike had begun to make new friends and explore new life experiences. He had fought through many of the obstacles life had thrown in his path.

During the next three years, Michael moved back to Tucson, where he transferred to a very busy Starbucks at Swan and Grant. He lost that job following a minor violation of a Starbucks' company policy but found work at a nearby Safeway grocery store as a personal shopper for Safeway.com, their internet ordering/ home delivery service. He asked to get trained in cashiering, failed the cashiering test the first time, but passed on the second try. He requested transfer to another department within the store...to no avail. He worked on his feet for whole 7-8 hour shifts and worked highly variable hours requiring waking up most days at 4:30 a.m. He continued to struggle with fatigue as a result. Having to retire early in the evening prior to his early start the next morning, he lived alone and in great social isolation in a nearby apartment. He was unhappy with his life and his work. If asked about his work schedule, which was constantly changing, he could not recall his assigned times which were posted once a week, and learned to refer to his smart phone's calendar for his schedule. This type of compensating strategy, which helps him work around one of his cognitive deficits (difficulty with working memory and short term memory), is a common strategy employed by TBI survivors.

During this period in Tucson, he contacted the Arizona Department of Employment Security (DES), Vocational Rehabilitation (VR) department hoping to receive help in obtaining a better job. First, he was placed on a six month waiting list due to state budget problems. Then, he met with a counselor who arranged for neuropsychological testing to determine his recovery status. The tests were administered one month later by a neuropsychologist. Three months after that Mike met with the counselor and neuropsychologist to learn the test results. In the meantime, of course, he continued working at minimum wage for Safeway and had not received any assistance in locating a better work situation, one more suited to his abilities-both cognitive and physical. Following up on the test results, his VocRehab counselor suggested that he search the internet for jobs, without providing any guidance as to the type of job which best fit his capabilities and avoided his cognitive deficits. After nine months of waiting and testing, Mike had received nothing of value from the Arizona DES-VR.

Frustrated once more with his living situation in Tucson, Michael decided to move back to Denver yet again. This time, however, he had to wait until our renters' lease on the Denver condo had expired in the middle of 2012. So with no incentive to seek another job prior to moving again, now 28 years old, he continued to work as a personal shopper at Safeway.

While he waited in Tucson, he sought a break from the routine of Safeway and headed to Denver for a short vacation over the 2011 Memorial Day weekend. He posted a note on Facebook that he would be at the Wash Park Grille at 7:00 p.m. that Friday and invited any and all friends to meet him there. Serendipitously, a woman who knew Mike at the University of Denver during his time at Chi Phi fraternity saw the posting and came to the restaurant to see him. They immediately "hit it off" and Mike and Meredith spent the remainder of the weekend getting reacquainted.

Following the weekend, he arrived back in Tucson with a changed attitude. No longer depressed, he was energized by his new relationship. He and Meredith promised to stay in close touch with each other, even planning to visit one another monthly from that point forward. They spoke by phone daily. Despite the distance, Mike went back to Denver and Meredith came to Tucson with some regularity. Both were anxious for his return to Denver to live full-time the following June. Dana and I liked Meredith from the first meeting. Her energy, wit and vivacious manner are infectious... just the right medicine for Michael. We were happy for them both, but especially for our son, whose positivity and optimism had been re-kindled.

In May, 2012, Michael, Meredith, Dana and I packed up Mike's belongings in a rented truck, attached his car to a trailer and caravanned the 900 miles back to Denver. There Mike moved into the condominium he had lived in for six months prior to his accident in 2006 and for 18 months in 2007-2009. He rejoined Safeway, ironically employed in the Starbucks kiosk for the next 12 months. During that time, still seeking a job better suited to his capabilities and financial needs, and egged on by Dana and me, he contacted the State of Colorado's Vocational Rehabilitation department. He was immediately assigned to a vocational counselor whose job was to assist him with finding a new job. He updated his resume...a college education and six years working in minimum wage employment...and practiced his interview skills.

After a year making coffee drinks as a Safeway employee, he decided to study for the Colorado State Life Insurance Exam. With great effort and focus, he learned the different forms of life insurance and the arcane laws of the State of Colorado related to insurance sales. In only two weeks, he passed the exam and was licensed. I was happy that he had passed the exam, but, at the same time, I was skeptical about a career in life insurance sales being a proper fit and suitable career. The typical insurance salesman spends long days on the road travelling to appointments or making cold calls. Mike did not have a network of friends and acquaintances with whom to initiate contact and build referrals. Nevertheless, Mike signed on to train with a national agency. But, after two weeks of exhausting travel, long meetings and frustrating efforts at marketing, Mike came to the realization that this career was not for him. Twelve to 18 hour days were not sustainable and he found trying to identify viable client leads to be frustrating and unprofitable.

He knew, also, that he could not pursue insurance sales while looking for yet another position, so he quit the agency. With new insight into his abilities and his constraints (both physical and mental), but with a clear understanding that he needed to find a way to make a living, he threw himself into the job market once again. This time he was assisted by an employment counselor provided by Colorado's VocRehab. Together, they searched the internet for employment opportunities apropos of his abilities.

Throughout the summer of 2013, Michael proved to be an energetic job seeker, working the on-line application sites for hours each day. He identified sales jobs, warehouse jobs, merchandising jobs, courier jobs, and administrative jobs. He applied to schools, both public and private, local companies and national chains. Through the summer of 2013 he showed new initiative and perseverance. Having worked in the service industry on and off for six years, at 29 years of age, his resume was weak. Employers were hesitant to take a chance on Michael. By the end of the summer, he had interviewed or applied to over 20 companies, with no offers of employment. Yet he continued on (like the Little Engine that Could..."I think I can, I think I can, I know I can!"). In October, he found a call center which serviced customers for companies like Netflix. He interviewed, took their aptitude tests, and was rejected yet again. But, within the organization, he was referred to another section of customer servicing. This time he was offered a job on the spot.

As of this writing, Michael and Meredith are living together in the condo. He successfully completed the call center's training program and is working a stable daily schedule answering calls from customers who have questions regarding a children's digital notebook product.

Were the other jobs to which he had applied overreaching for Michael, post-TBI? Was his resume a barrier to employment despite his intellect and personality? Was he just too inexperienced in job search, interviewing, or office environments? Are there jobs for TBI survivors that can provide enough income to live on without government support? These are questions which confronted Mike and which confront all persons who have survived a TBI and are trying to enter the workforce.

Epilogue

As for me, I was motivated by my son's and our family's journey through TBI to go back to college in 2010. I decided to pursue a Bachelor's Degree in Psychology at the University of Arizona. Learning about brain function, personality, cognition and psychological disorders has positioned me better to assist Michael going forward and to assist other caregivers of TBI survivors. Having firsthand observed the social isolation experienced by a survivor of TBI and also the frustrations of the caregiver, I believe there is a clear need for support groups and peer mentoring for those family members and friends faced with caring for a loved one who has suffered a traumatic brain injury. The requirements of medical privacy, the inadequate resources available to most families affected by TBI, and the limited availability of public funding sources conspire so that the need for assistance is rarely satisfied.

As parents, we continue to support our son in any way that we can. Dana and I have continued to subsidize Mike's income because no one can live on minimum wage and only 30-35 hours of work per week. We provide for his share of rent of the condominium, his insurance (home, auto and medical), homeowners' association fees, property taxes, phone bills and the limited purchases made on credit cards. But more critical than financial support, we are always there to listen to him, to be his sounding board when he becomes frustrated with his co-workers, potential employers, friends, and anyone else who triggers his post-TBI emotional volatility. We are always there to help him solve problems.

Michael is still a sensitive and strong willed individual who does not want to be singled out for his TBI. Yet his understanding that TBI has long term consequences continues to grow. As he put it, "I have lived more life than people twice my age!"

His journey through recovery and the many years ahead will be ***his*** journey to travel. He will decide whether to seek the assistance of therapists to overcome any shortcomings. He will determine when and where to work, to study, to learn, to live. And, it is up to Michael alone to find people to be with who care, who understand, who laugh and love, as he does.

Earlier, I wrote that Michael was precious to me for the legacy I thought he represented, the hope for the future, and for the sense of immortality that I felt with his birth. His life represented the potential renewal of my own spirit. Following his accident, hospitalizations, therapies and life challenges, he is as precious to me as ever. Indeed, over the last six years, I have been imbued with a new sense of my own life and its purpose. I may not have the same hopes and dreams for him as before, but I still have hopes and dreams. Like my son Michael, I have not been defeated by the changes in our lives which have occurred since that phone call in the early morning hours of June 2, 2006; rather I have been re-directed – to helping when I can, to learning more about our human condition and what makes the Self unique to each one of us, to appreciate what we have and not to regret what we do not.

For Dana and me, we have come to accept the new young man now before us. However, our experience with TBI is like a shadowy cloud which follows us wherever we are. Michael was a great source of pride before the 2006 accident. While he was in a coma at Denver Health, we felt we might lose Mike forever. We are fortunate that we did not. As he works through the challenges which living with TBI presents every day, Michael has shown courage, an ability to persevere, brilliant intellect and a caring heart. He has a depth of character which few people will ever exhibit. He is once again, and always will be, our son. We love him.

The Adler Family – December 2012: (l. to r.) Darcy Warren, Ira, Dana and Michael

Not The End

Glossary

Acetabulum the curved part of the hipbone which holds the top of the femur or thigh bone

Activities of daily living (ADLs) self-care activities usually performed in the home or outside of the home such as washing, eating, and dressing

Angiogram an X-ray photograph of a blood vessel

Anosognosia a common effect of TBI is a lack of patient awareness of the cognitive difficulties which may exist. According to Kihlstom and Tobias (1991, p. 199), "The patient appears unaware of any problems in memory, language, perception, voluntary movement, or whatever. Evidence bearing on the claim of unawareness may come in various forms: (1) the person may simply not acknowledge that there is anything wrong; (2) the person may acknowledge some difficulty but attribute it to some source other than disease; or (3) the person may actively deny any difficulty at all."

Anoxia total deprivation of oxygen to the body or an organ causing the death of tissue

Arachnoid membrane the middle of the three membranes that envelop the brain and spinal cord

Axon the part of a neuronal cell that transmits electro-chemical impulses to one or more neurons

Bolt a hollow screw inserted through a hole drilled in the skull through the dura mater, the membrane which protects the brain, into which a sensor is placed to measure intracranial pressure

Brain stem the lower part of the rear of the brain next to the cerebellum

Carotid artery the artery on each side of the head which supplies blood to the head and brain

Cerebellum the part of the brain which helps to control and sequence motor movement

Cerebral cortex the outermost layer of the brain's neuronal cells which controls cognition and movement

Cerebrospinal fluid (CSF) a clear fluid which bathes brain tissue, carries nutrients to brain cells and protects brain tissue

Cerebrum the cerebral cortex in which cognitive activities such as reasoning, learning, perception and emotional responses occur

Coma a state of unconsciousness characterized by a lack of awareness of one's surroundings and condition

Computerized Tomography (CT) a medical test which produces a two-dimensional image using data produced by a stream of X-rays directed at the body

Concussion a mild traumatic brain injury caused by a blow to the head or shaking of the head and neck; effects may usually temporary such as loss of consciousness, confusion, lack of concentration and impairment of memory; successive concussions may cause more permanent injury and symptoms

Confabulation the unintentional reporting of memories of events which did not take place or are not related to one another

Consciousness awareness of one's condition, location and self; also, awareness of one's thoughts, perceptions, memories and feelings

Contusion injury evidenced by bleeding under the skin or membrane

Coup/contrecoup the injury to one side of the brain caused by a traumatic impact and then to the opposing side of the brain resulting from the swing of the brain inside the skull cavity

Dendrites the part of a neuronal cell that receives electro-chemical impulses from one or more transmitting neurons

Diencephalon part of the forebrain which includes the thalamus and hypothalamus

Diffuse axonal injury (DAI) shearing and stretching of axons widely dispersed throughout the brain due to traumatic brain injury

Dura mater the leathery membrane which surrounds and protects the brain within the skull

Edema swelling of an organ resulting from an accumulation of fluid within the tissues

Emergency medical technician (EMT) a healthcare provider in emergency situations

Executive functions the umbrella term for the management of cognitive processes such as working memory, reasoning, planning, problem solving and initiating/execution

Femur thigh bone

Frontal lobe the area of the cerebral cortex where executive functions are thought to take place, including emotional responses, forming our personalities

Grand mal seizure more currently known as a tonic-clonic seizure, which is a generalized seizure resulting in convulsions (a rapid contracting and relaxing of muscles), caused by an electric disturbance in the brain

Hypothalamus the part of the diencephalon structure which helps in the regulation of autonomic body functions

Hypoxia lack of adequate oxygen supply to the body or organ causing damage

Intracranial pressure (ICP) the pressure which the brain tissue and cerebrospinal fluid combine to exert within and against the skull

Jaws-of-Life hydraulic rescue tools used to extricate victims from vehicles following automobile and other accidents

Limbic system the system of brain structures which are thought to control motivation and emotion

Magnetic Resonance Imaging (MRI) a medical test which utilizes radio waves and magnetic fields to produce images of areas of the body in which blood flow, and therefore, activity, is occurring

Myelin the protective sheaf which surrounds axons providing insulation from other axons, thus regulating the direction of impulses along axons rather than between axons

Nasogastric (N-G) Tube a plastic tube inserted through the nasal passage down the esophagus into the stomach to allow for direct delivery of food to the stomach

Neurologist a medical specialist who diagnoses and treats diseases of the nervous system

Neuron a cell body which receives and transmits electro-chemical signals; the fundamental cell structure which comprises the nervous system; sensory neurons transmit information gathered from the environment, motor neurons transmit information to and from the body's muscles and interneurons relay information from one neuron to another throughout the body and within the brain

Neuropsychologist a specialist in the behavioral effects of cognitive functions, including, for example, attention, memory and language

Neurosurgeon a medical specialist in surgical procedures to treat injuries or diseases of the nervous system, spine and brain

Occipital lobe the part of the cerebral cortex located at the back of the brain which performs functions related to visual processes and perception

Orbit the bone socket in the skull which surrounds and protects each eye and the optic connections to the cerebral cortex

Osgood-Schlatter Syndrome (Disease) usually associated with growth spurts in children and adolescents, an irritation to the ligaments in and around the patella, causing knee and leg pain

Parietal lobe the part of the brain located on the upper sides of the cerebral cortex involved in sensory processing including taste, touch, temperature, spatial relationships and movement

Perseveration difficulty switching from one task to another, from one thought to another, or from one topic to another

Persistent vegetative state (PVS) a state of consciousness characterized as partial arousal rather than full awareness lasting more than four weeks. If lasting longer than a year, it may be classified as "permanent."

Petit mal seizure a brief loss of consciousness resulting from a electrical disturbance within the brain

Physiatrist a medical specialist who is trained in medicine and rehabilitation

Pons part of the brainstem which transmits information from the forebrain to the cerebellum

Post traumatic amnesia (PTA) a dysfunction of memory following a traumatic brain injury involving confusion, disoriented working memory and the inability to remember events following the traumatic event

Prosopagnosia inability to recognize another's face or the information they transmit about the other person's cognitive or emotional response

Ruff Figural Fluency Test a neuropsychological test developed to provide clinical information regarding nonverbal capacity for fluid and divergent thinking, ability to flexibly shift cognitive set, planning strategies, and executive ability to coordinate this process (http://www.ronruff.com/tests/ruff-figural-fluency-test-rfft/)

Seizure a period of sudden excessive electrical activity of cerebral neurons

Spinal cord the structure of neurons and sheaths which distributes motor and sensory information between the body and the brain, located within the vertebral column (spine)

Step Down Unit (SDU) a hospital unit which provides care following the most acute phase of recovery in the SICU from life-threatening disease or injury, while still providing more monitoring of patients than in a normally-staffed in-patient division

Stroke a cerebrovascular accident involving either a blockage of a blood vessel (ischemic stroke) or a leakage of blood from a blood vessel (hemorrhagic stroke), either depriving the brain of the flow of blood or putting pressure on and damaging brain tissue

Subdural the area beneath the dura mater or between the dura mater and the arachnoid mater, i.e., within the brain itself

Surgical Intensive Care Unit (SICU) the hospital nursing unit which provides the most close monitoring and treatment of life-threatening diseases or injuries following general surgery or emergency trauma

Temporal lobe the part of the brain located below the parietal lobe, behind the frontal lobe and in front of the occipital lobe where visual, auditory, speech and language functions are thought to be centered

Thalamus a key brain structure which receives and distributes information from various parts of the cerebral cortex

Thorax the chest cavity

Tracheotomy a surgical procedure in which an incision is made to the front of the patient's throat and a tube (a tracheostomy) is inserted through the incision into the air pipe to permit more direct respiration to the lungs

Traumatic brain injury (TBI) an intracranial injury which occurs when an external force traumatically injures the brain

Vail Bed a canopy bed with nylon netting on all four sides that is zipped into place, the purpose of which is to protect patients who are confused, agitated, or suffering from other cognitive impairment(s) which may put them at high risk for wandering, or for injuring themselves or others

Videofluoroscope Swallow Test a X-ray procedure to monitor the flow of food and/or liquid from the mouth to the esophagus using radioactive foods to highlight the reflexes within the esophagus

APPENDIX A

Levels of Cognitive Function
Adapted from the Rancho Los Amigos scale

Level 1 – No Response

- Appears to be in a deep sleep (coma)
- Does not respond when the person is touched, moved, talked to, or when medical procedures are done
- Does not open eyes, speak, or move body parts on purpose.

What you can do:

- Give small amounts of varied stimulation; talking, TV or radio, etc. Ask therapists for guidelines on how to organize stimulation for best response.
- Talk as if person understands; tell the person where he/she is, why, and talk about things that interested the person before.
- Use soothing, calm voice. Touch person. Talking loudly won't help.
- Don't talk about medical information in front of the person.

Level 2 – Generalized Response

- May open eyes or respond to medical procedures by moving arms and legs.
- May move around in bed.
- Responses are slow and usually the same no matter what the cause.
- Responses are involuntary or unconscious.

What you can do:

- Short periods of TV or radio.
- Talk to person, assuming he/she understands. Do not talk about medical information.
- Use soothing, calm voice. Touch person. Don't talk loudly.

Level 3 – Localized Response

- Starts doing what you ask inconsistently, such as raising a hand, opening eyes.
- May begin pulling at tubes and need restraints for own protection.
- Can look at people and follow movement in room. Attention is often momentary.
- May respond better to familiar faces and voices.
- Response more directed at specific stimulation.

What you can do:

- Tell person what happened, where he/she is, why he/she is there.
- If you question person, keep questions short and simple.
- Should have visitors, but a limited number and for brief periods of time.

Level 4 – Confused, Agitated

- Increasing awareness, activity and responsiveness.
- Memory better for past events than most recent events.
- Easily agitated. May become aggressive and yell, hit, etc.
- Attention better, but still limited (minutes)
- May not be cooperative due to confusion.
- Confabulation is noted at this level – patient may fill in gaps in his/her memory by giving detailed accounts of fictional events.

What you can do:

- Don't try to reason or bargain with person.

- When person is agitated, try to change the subject. If this doesn't work, leave the person alone to calm down.
- Visitors still limited and for brief times.
- Frequently repeat where person is, what happened, what date it is, etc. Bring in familiar pictures, posters, favorite things.

Level 5 – Confused, Inappropriate/Non-agitated

- Agitation less except when tired.
- Can pay attention longer and follow simple commands.
- Becomes distracted if instructions are too long.
- Day-to-day memory is poor.
- Makes more sense, but some responses still inappropriate.
- May be able to follow through on routine activities, but not initiate them.
- Doesn't realize he /she can't be left alone.

What you can do:

- If person's responses are incorrect, correct gently. Don't argue.
- Though conversation may seem normal, you can't reason with him/her. Change the subject instead.
- May ask same questions (especially about going home) over and over. Explain once or twice, then change the subject.
- May need attendants for the person's own safety.

Level 6 – Confused Appropriate

- Can initiate some activities and follow through.
- Attention span good for social conversation, but has trouble with lengthy complex information.
- Memory worse when information is given too quickly.
- Begins longer therapy sessions.
- Begins to retain information longer from one session to the next.
- May have unrealistic goals for the future.

What you can do:

- Give guidance and structure for planning.
- Give emotional support.
- Help and encourage person to write things down for memory.
- Encourage and help the person to participate in activities he/she enjoyed before injury when safe.
- Give guidance in problem-solving and decision making.
- Give feedback and help with social situations.

Level 7 – Automatic Appropriate

- Little or no confusion.
- Has impaired ability to solve problems and plan ahead.
- Requires little supervision for learning or safety purposes.
- Has some understanding of problems, but unable to relate them to work or educational situations.
- Can learn new information, but at a slower rate.
- May appear bored, depressed or irritable due to supervision and restriction.

What you can do:

- Still needs some assistance in planning and organizing time day-to-day.
- Can reason with the person to some extent.
- May still need counseling for return to school or work.
- Encourage the person to be responsible for routine household tasks.
- Encourage involvement in local support group.

Level 8 – Purposeful Appropriate

- Able to plan realistically for the future.
- Processing still slow.
- May have permanent memory problems.

- Less emotional control and tolerance for frustration than before.
- Able to formulate more realistic goals.
- May be unable to respond quickly in an emergency or other stressful situation.
- May have difficulty planning/managing time.

What you can do:

- Encourage the person to compensate for memory problems with memory notebook, etc.
- Needs no supervision at home or in community once activities are learned.
- Needs understanding and support in emotional situations.
- Encourage return to school or work in a graded fashion, not all at once.
- Encourage continued counseling and involvement with community support group.
- The speech pathologist uses pictures, workbooks and other tools to help the patient attend and improve his/her cognitive skills.
- Could be candidate for vocational rehabilitation program to determine current vocational abilities.

APPENDIX B

Post Traumatic Amnesia

An individual coming out of a coma doesn't just wake up but will go through a gradual process of regaining consciousness. This stage of recovery is called Post Traumatic Amnesia (PTA) and may last for hours, days or weeks.

When fully conscious, the brain is constantly active... perceiving, processing and remembering information. Following emergence from coma individuals may go through a period of Post Traumatic Amnesia (PTA), which is a higher level of consciousness and awareness than coma, but less than full-consciousness. A mild concussion may also cause a brief period of Post Traumatic Amnesia. During PTA, individuals may be disoriented... confused about where they are, who those are around them and the time, date or year; highly distractible; have difficulty with thinking, memory and concentration; and be afraid, disinhibited, agitated and emotionally labile. They will not be able to store continuous or recent memory, such as what happened just a few hours or even minutes ago. If physically able, they may wander, so it is important to make sure their surroundings are free of any hazards.

Behavioral changes can occur during this phase, where the patient may be quiet and passive, or aggressive, abusive and agitated. Some individuals during this stage may give inappropriate comments and actions. Patients usually have little or no awareness of these cognitive and behavioral impairments and will usually remember nothing of what happened during PTA, even though they appear fully awake. Any challenging behavior by the person suffering PTA is likely due to the effects of the injury and therefore should not be taken personally. In most cases a person will usually not remember most, if any, of what has happened during this time. Also, too much stimulation during this time can increase the person's level of confusion and distress. During PTA, patients may not be able to cope with too much noise or activity, so it's important to keep activity around the individual to a minimum (low stimulation). The same rule applies when someone is trying to communicate with the person; they should avoid overloading the person with too much information at once and keep sentences short.

When does post-traumatic amnesia finish? PTA is usually seen as ending when the patient begins to retain information, such as where they are, why they are in hospital, and the month and year; in other words, continuous memory returns. However, individuals during PTA may show brief periods of orientation and ability to recall information; these are known as "'memory islands." Therefore, assessment should take place at regular intervals to get a clearer picture of the degree of PTA. The good news is that signs of orientation and "memory islands" are indicators that the person may be emerging from PTA.

Following PTA, more assessments are conducted to gain further insight into the nature and extent of injury, along with the commencement of rehabilitation. ***Behavioral issues sometimes worsen at this point as the patient becomes aware of what has happened to them and may have difficulty coping with the various emotions that arise.*** Along with Glasgow Coma Score, length of PTA is commonly held to be one of the best measures of severity of brain injury. This also means it can give a rough indication as to the degree of recovery that can be expected. General indication of injury severity as a function of PTA duration:

- PTA less than 5 minutes = "very mild injury"
- PTA between 5-60 minutes = "mild injury"
- PTA between 1-24 hours = "moderate injury"
- PTA between 1-7 days = "severe injury"
- PTA greater than 7 days = "very severe injury"

Source: Craig Hospital *(1999), Traumatic Brain Injury Manual for Patients and Families*

APPENDIX C

Neuroanatomy and Cognitive Function

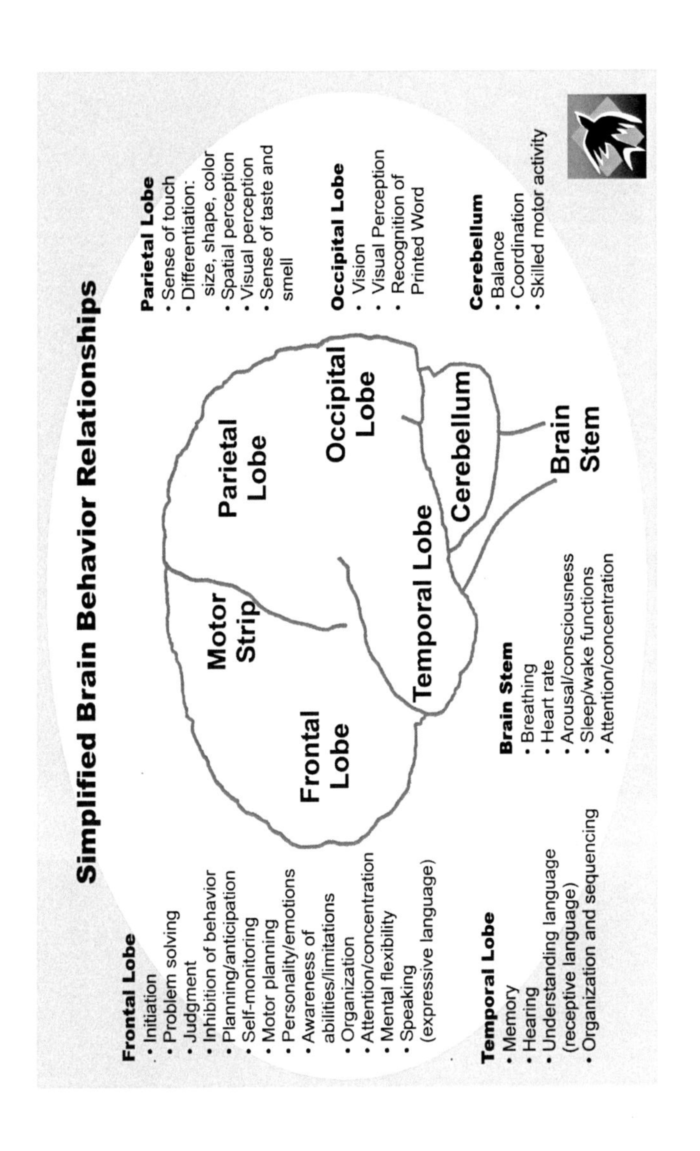

Source: Cummins, M. (2013), Understanding Brain Injury, Family Resource presentation, Brain Injury Alliance of Arizona.

References

Carlson, N.R. (2011), *Foundations of Behavioral Neuroscience, Eighth Edition*, Allyn &Bacon, Boston MA

Craig Hospital *(1999), Traumatic Brain Injury Manual for Patients and Families*, Englewood CO

Hagen, C., Malkmus, D., Durham, P. (1979). Levels of Cognitive Functioning, *Rehabilitation of the Head Injured Adult; Comprehensive Physical Management*, Downey CA: Professional Staff Association of Rancho Los Amigos National Rehabilitation Center.

Kihlstom, J.F. and Tobias, B.A. (1991), Anosognosia, Consciousness, and the Self, in *Awareness of Deficit After Brain Injury, Clinical and Theoretical Issues*, edited by Prigatano, G. P. and Schacter, D. L., (1991: 198-222).

Klonoff, P.S. (2010), *Psychotherapy after Brain Injury*, The Guilford Press, New York.

Senelick, R. and Dougherty, K. (2001), *Living with Brain Injury: A Guide for Families*, HealthSouth Press, (70-71).